A complete list of books available
in the *Vintage RUSSIAN Library*
can be found
on the last page of this volume

THE YEAR OF PROTEST, 1956

An Anthology of Soviet Literary Materials

TRANSLATED AND EDITED, WITH AN INTRODUCTION BY

Hugh McLean and *Walter N. Vickery*

VINTAGE BOOKS

A Division of Random House

NEW YORK

FIRST VINTAGE EDITION, OCTOBER 1961

VINTAGE BOOKS

are published by Alfred A. Knopf, Inc.,

and Random House, Inc.

Library of Congress Catalog Card Number: 61–14895

Manufactured in the United States of America

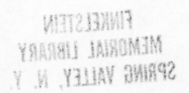

ACKNOWLEDGMENTS

In the preparation of the English versions of all the short stories and of Kron's "A Writer's Notes" we made use of draft translations made by the United States Joint Publications Research Service of New York, to which organization we express our gratitude for making them available to us. However, these draft translations have been extensively checked and revised by us, and all other translations are entirely ours; we must therefore assume responsibility for all of them, as, of course, for all editorial matter. We are grateful to the editors of *L'Express,* Paris, for allowing us to publish our English translation of the Paustovsky speech, to which they hold copyright.

H. McL.—W. N. V.

Contents

Contents

INTRODUCTION

I. A WORD OF EXPLANATION

Until the appearance of *Doctor Zhivago* and the international drama that followed, it had been a long time since the Western world paid much attention to Russian literary developments. By a curious paradox, the more immediate and pressing our concern with Russia as a political phenomenon, the more our interest in Russian literature has declined, at least that literature produced currently, in the days of cold war and sputniks. Twenty or thirty years ago some people, hoping to discover twentieth-century Tolstoys or Dostoevskys, may have acquainted themselves with the writings of Mayakovsky, Babel, Leonov, Pilnyak, Fadeev, Olesha, Sholokhov, and others. But since the Second World War, Soviet literature has tended to become the exclusive province of that peculiar product of the postwar world, the "Russian expert," who scans it for clues into the workings of that enigmatic society he seeks to interpret.

Occasionally the ordinary citizen, tempted to engage in this same puzzle-solving pursuit, may have ventured to read such books as Ehrenburg's *The Thaw* or Dudintsev's *Not by Bread Alone,* especially when such books are hopefully believed to illustrate "subversive" tendencies in Soviet society. But the only contemporary Russian novel that can be said to have appealed to Western readers on literary grounds is Pasternak's *Doctor Zhivago*—a book that cannot even be published in the U.S.S.R. and in some sense cannot be regarded as a product of *Soviet* literature at all.

Official Soviet spokesmen have an easy explanation for our neglect of their literary production—bourgeois hostility to the Communist ideology embodied in this "most advanced and progressive of world literatures." But this explanation explains little, for, if true, it would have been even truer in the days, thirty or forty years ago, when communism was still a revolutionary international movement and represented a genuine subversive (as distinct from a military and imperialist) threat to Western capitalist society. Yet this was precisely the time when Soviet literature achieved its greatest popularity among Western "bourgeois" readers. No, the real trouble with contemporary Soviet literature is its peculiar quality: it simply does not offer the ordinary reader enough of the kinds of gratification, esthetic or otherwise, that he expects from *belles lettres*.

If the Western reader has any notion at all of Soviet literary developments over the past ten years, it is probably not derived from a reading of that literature itself or even from reading literary articles about it. It has rather come from the newspapers. Careful readers of *The New York Times,* particularly in the past seven or eight years, may recall a number of stories with a Moscow dateline dealing with events in the sphere of Soviet letters. The death of Stalin in 1953 led to a new era of "thaw"—the title of Ehrenburg's novel (1954) has become a general appellative of the period—and Western reporters have recorded various recurrent stirrings of "thaw" spirit during subsequent years, and the equally recurrent signs of the authorities' uneasiness in the face of this spirit and their efforts to counteract it. In fact, almost since its inception Soviet literature has moved in cycles whose limits are marked by the authorities' indulgence or their apprehension; some details of these cycles are charted on the following pages.

The year 1956 marked one of the widest swings of the Soviet literary pendulum in the direction of liberalization. The "Geneva spirit" of 1955 began to pervade Soviet internal affairs; the "collegium" of Khrushchev, Malenkov, Molotov, *et al.* was still functioning in apparent harmony, appearing *en masse* at cocktail parties in Western embassies; Bulganin and Khrushchev displayed their beaming countenances and short-lived camaraderie all the way from London to Rangoon. Most important of all, the Twentieth Congress of the Communist Party, held in Moscow in February 1956, ended with the celebrated "secret speech" by Khrushchev (carefully leaked to Russia and the world), in which the validity of the whole Stalinist heritage was opened to question.

Soviet writers, timid and tentative after their long existence in a frozen state, began gropingly exploring the new possibilities for self-expression, particularly critical self-examination. An era of muckraking set in, very restrained, to be sure—an era when literature undertook to expose to the public gaze some of the social and psychological ulcers that had long been festering behind the Stalinist official façade.

There were two major outlets for this new "protest"

literature: the magazine *Novy Mir* (*New World*), edited by Konstantin Simonov, and two large anthologies entitled *Literaturnaya Moskva* (*Literary Moscow*). It was on the pages of the former that Dudintsev's famous novel appeared—artistically a mediocre book, but one that caught the spirit of the times with its openly hostile, though understanding, portrayal of high-ranking Soviet officialdom. Perhaps even more revealing than Dudintsev's book itself was a public meeting held to discuss it, one of those rare occasions in Soviet life when a cut-and-dried official discussion panel turned into a genuine popular demonstration of real, and not official, feelings—in this case the pent-up resentment, excitement, and idealistic fervor that stirred Soviet intellectuals at the thought that a new day might really be dawning. An extremely forthright and vigorous speech delivered at that meeting by the veteran novelist Konstantin Paustovsky (and never published in the Soviet Union) is included in this book.

The high point of the "reformist" trend in Soviet literature came with the publication, late in 1956, of the second volume of *Literaturnaya Moskva*. By careful planning, masking their responsibility with the "collegiate" principle of editorship and camouflaging the "subversive" pieces beneath a large bulk of orthodox respectability, a sizable group of Moscow writers, including many of the best-known names in Soviet literature, managed to get this sensational volume published. But they had evidently gone too far. The official watchdogs became alarmed, and before long the erring writers were called sharply to order. To make matters worse, the Hungarian uprising, which broke out in October 1956, seemed a kind of translation into direct action of the same kind of protest the Soviet writers had expressed. Actually there are vast differences, both emotional and ideological, between these two "protests." But, nevertheless, the identification between them was made and firmly lodged in the minds of the Soviet authorities, as Khrushchev himself testified. The formula the authorities arrived at was clear: too much freedom for intellectuals leads to "Hungaries." Official attacks on the errant writers multiplied and culminated in a statement or series of statements issued by Khrushchev himself in the summer of 1957. The thaw was over.

Our object in this anthology has been to let the English-speaking reader see for himself what this Soviet "literary protest" of 1956 amounted to. We have presented translations of some of the works which evoked the angriest buzzing in official quarters, partly from *Novy Mir,* partly from the second volume of *Literaturnaya Moskva,* together with what explanatory material we thought would be helpful, including an introductory essay on the historical and ideological background of this year of literary protest.

All the major literary genres are represented here except full-length novels: short stories, poetry, drama, criticism, and even oratory. These selections are probably a reasonably fair sampling of Soviet literature of better-than-average quality. From these samples the reader can, by an effort of the imagination, form some conception of how a modern Soviet writer writes, how he manages to bring his work through the filtering process of official truth and official prohibition and still retain something of his own. Despite their artistic shortcomings, these works can give the reader some notion of the "feel" of Soviet art, and of Soviet life as well.

II. THE SOVIET LITERARY PROTEST
OF 1956

1.

There is in the world today a bitter struggle between two ideologies, socialist and bourgeois, and in this struggle there can be no neutrals. . . . We would not be Marxists-Leninists if we were to stand to one side and adopt a passive attitude of indifference toward attempts to drag into our literature and art bourgeois views which are alien to the spirit of the Soviet people.

These words, which sounded so much like so many other minacious official sermons that have appeared in the U.S.S.R. in the past, are actually quoted from the "crackdown" article by which, in the summer of 1957, Khrushchev brought the short-lived literary thaw to an end. The article is entitled "For Close Ties between Literature and Art and the Life of the People." Like all Soviet pronouncements from the summit of power on whatever subject, it has become a Scriptural authority of guaranteed truth, endlessly reprinted and endlessly quoted. The article itself purports to be a summary of oral statements made by Khrushchev at three separate meetings with Moscow writers and artists held in May and July 1957.

Khrushchev is a man of great energy. It may nevertheless seem surprising that a man who has to assume the responsibility for every major decision in Soviet domestic affairs and foreign policy, and who, furthermore, obviously has no personal interest in literature or art, should nevertheless deem it necessary to intervene personally in the world of letters. Why did he do it? To answer this question, one needs to know something of the background of Soviet literature and its relations with political authority.

2.

Writers in the Soviet Union are supposed to be "engineers of human souls." This definition, which is attributed to Stalin, means in practice that literature must serve as one of the instruments for working on people's minds and emotions and inducing them to carry out voluntarily the political program of the Communist Party. Literature is called upon to devote itself to "the task of the ideological reforming and education of the workers in the spirit of socialism," as one official prescription puts it. Writers are not, as in czarist days, merely subjected to negative censorship to prevent them from disseminating pernicious ideas or stirring up subversive feelings. They must now play a positive part in shaping the citizens' hearts according to Party directives. Any work of art is necessarily a political act, and in politics, as in war, "there can be no neutrals." Soviet artists, as Max Eastman once said, are in uniform.

Once upon a time there had been something resembling normal civilian life in the Soviet literary world. The leaders of the Revolution, Lenin and Trotsky, despite all their ruthlessness and their contempt for the vacillating intelligentsia, were nevertheless themselves products of that intelligentsia and imbued with some of its characteristic respect for culture. Lenin, preoccupied with other matters, paid little attention to artistic affairs and had the humility to acknowledge his ignorance in this sphere. Trotsky was himself a natural-born literary artist who somehow found time, even while still in power, to write a brilliant work of literary criticism, however prejudiced and violent: *Literature and Revolution*. Believing that art developed according to laws of its own with which it was dangerous to interfere, he advocated a "hands off art" policy for the Communist Party. Though the Party never wholly accepted Trotsky's literary libertarianism, during the 1920's literature was more or less allowed to take its own course, as long as writers did not openly attack the regime. Most of the leading writers (the so-called "fellow travelers") were avowedly non- though not anti-Communist. The critics and literary theoreticians, divided into rival schools and groupings, were engaged in a running debate about how art was to be fitted into the Marxist theory of the class struggle and what its place was in a state that claimed to be a dictatorship of the proletariat. Party leaders like Trotsky and Bukharin took part in these debates, but there were no voices loud enough to settle all arguments.

After 1928, however, the vise began to tighten. The oppositions in the Party, Left and Right, were successively liquidated, and the country embarked on the first Five Year Plan. Literary power, editorial and critical, became concentrated in the hands of the leaders of the R.A.P.P. (the Russian Association of Proletarian Writers), an organization that occupied itself with issuing "social commands" and assigning writers "production quotas" under the Five Year Plan. This sort of nonsense did a great deal to demoralize Soviet writers, even though, as recent research has shown,[1] the R.A.P.P. leadership occasionally made efforts to defend the autonomy of literature against the Party bureaucracy.

A further step in the subordination of literature occurred in 1932 with the abolition of the R.A.P.P. and the formation of the Union of Soviet Writers. This move, carried out by decree suddenly issued from on high, was represented as a step in the direction of liberalism, and the R.A.P.P. was reprimanded for its sectarian stridency. But in practice it meant that writers were brought still tighter within the grip of Party control. All other group affiliations of writers and critics were outlawed, and the men of letters lumped helplessly together in a union totally dominated by its Party *apparat*.

Two years later a solemn conclave, the First Congress of Soviet Writers, was held to celebrate this event. Here, with great fanfare, the ill-starred Andrey Zhdanov and others proclaimed the newly discovered "method" that was to guide Soviet writers in the future: *socialist realism*—a term supposedly invented by the great and wise Leader himself. The term is a slippery one, and the reams of verbiage latter-day Soviet theoreticians have turned out discussing it have added little to its intellectual substance or conceptual clarity. In the Charter of 1934 it was defined as follows:

> Socialist realism, which is the basic method of Soviet artistic literature and literary criticism, demands of the artist a truthful, historically concrete portrayal of reality in its revolutionary development. Whereby truthfulness and historical concreteness must be combined with the task of the ideological reforming and education of the toilers in the spirit of socialism.

One needs experience with Soviet gobbledegook to be able to decipher what this formula means. The key phrases are "revolutionary development" and "ideological reforming and education." To portray reality in its revolutionary development means that the writer should view the world according to the Soviet Marxist timetable. This approved schedule for the course of history maintains that mankind in the twentieth century is undergoing a necessary, good, and inevitable transition from capitalism to socialism; this stage has already been accomplished in the Soviet Union and its satellites, which are now marching forward toward the paradise of "communism," deterred only by the efforts of world capitalism, writhing in its death agonies, to turn history's clock backward. But these attempts are doomed to failure, and eventually socialism (communism) will triumph throughout the whole world. In the meantime the Soviet Union has by definition (if not by experience) the most humane, progressive, and freest socio-political regime in the world. To show "reality in its revolutionary development" means fundamentally to demonstrate the above as a true picture of the course of history. According to the "method" of socialist realism, any "reality" that does not fit this picture is not fit for portrayal in Soviet literature. Furthermore, as the march of history is necessarily progressive, the message of any work of art pro-

duced according to the method of socialist realism must
necessarily be one of progress and optimism. Soviet art
must affirm and affirm again that theirs is the best of all
possible systems, steadily progressing from better to best
and led by the best of all possible parties (or, rather, by
the best, only possible Party).

As for the "ideological reforming and education of the
toilers," this is education in a very special Soviet sense.
Soviet literature is not called upon to stimulate the specu-
lative or contemplative capacities of its readers, to arouse
them to a questioning search for meaning in the world
around them. In the Soviet Union the quest for meaning
and truth has long since been declared officially ended.
Except, perhaps, in the sphere of science, the Party is already in possession of "all we know and all we need to
know," and the educative function of literature is therefore simply to purvey this truth to people who need to
know it, and in such a form that they can grasp it. Above
all, the Soviet writer must teach his readers a clear-cut,
unambiguous moral lesson: he must show them that their
personal happiness and fulfillment lie exclusively in whole-
hearted striving for the goals laid down by the Party.

To return to the Writers' Congress of 1934: after this
resounding send-off, Soviet literature, equipped with its
new "method," continued to deteriorate. The terror that
gripped the country during the great purges inevitably
had a depressing effect on literature. Some leading writers
and critics fell victim to the "sword of the Revolution":
Boris Pilnyak, Isaac Babel, Osip Mandelstam, Ivan Kataev,
D. S. Mirsky, and many others disappeared forever, and
their names were erased from history. Others were sent
into exile in the provinces or Siberia for many years. Some
of these last have since returned, and some, though by no
means all, of the dead have been posthumously rehabilitated
since Khrushchev's de-Stalinization speech of 1956. The
majority of Soviet writers, of course, were not physically
purged. Out of conviction, fear, or a combination of both,
most writers complied and learned to do the regime's
bidding, with a greater or lesser amount of inner evasion.
But for the most part the quality of their writing sank into
that sterile conformism which has marked it ever since.

During the war years there took place a certain relaxation of controls. Just as greater freedom was permitted in

the sphere of religion, so too in literature the stress of
war and the need to bolster morale led to a lessening of
the ideological pressures on the Soviet writer. But even
during the war the iron fist still occasionally showed from
beneath the velvet glove. In 1943 the noted humorist
Mikhail Zoshchenko was given a severe dressing-down
for his serious novel *Before Sunrise*—a foreshadowing of
the still harsher fate that awaited him after the war. But
the general atmosphere of reconciliation under the banner
of patriotism gave rise to widespread hopes that the relative liberalism of the war period would be still further extended in the aftermath of a victorious peace. But such
hopes were quickly smashed.

3.

The end of the war was naturally a time for exultation. A
magnificent victory had been won, and won by the whole
nation; Russia had been delivered from the cruelest and
most dangerous enemy she had ever faced. It was also a
time for stocktaking and contemplation: what kind of
society, what kind of world would be built on the ruins?
Russia was now one of the two super powers on whose
policies the fate of the postwar world would largely depend; what would be her relations with the rest of the
world, especially with her former allies?

Russian intellectuals naturally began to think about
such things as the war drew to its end. As far as their
loyalty was concerned, they felt that they had proved it on
the battlefield. They had no desire to make any fundamental
changes in their society or its leadership. They simply
wanted latitude to think, to speculate, to wonder, and to
contribute their ideas to the shape of things to come. They
wanted to be free from suspicion and terror. The war
had brought many of them into contact with foreigners;
they wanted these contacts maintained and extended. They
wanted Russia to rejoin world culture. And, like everyone
else in Russia, they were tired. They wanted rest and relaxation.

But the bosses at the top had other ideas. They saw the
postwar world as the arena for an intense power conflict
with Russia's former allies, especially America. Russia
must grab what advantages victory had provided and prepare for the "final struggle" with the capitalist world. The

cold war was begun before the hot one had ended. And on
the domestic front there was no time to lose. Certainly
it was no time to let intellectuals indulge in free specula-
tions or musings. If for tactical reasons the ideological
reins had been loosened during the war, they must now
be yanked tight again. If the country was weary of war
and tension, it must be galvanized once more against a new
enemy. The people must be spurred on to repair the
devastation as quickly as possible and prepare for a new
conflict. And all the wartime nonsense about friendship
and co-operation with the capitalist nations must be erased
from people's minds as quickly as possible. A big crackdown was inevitable.

It began, as far as literature was concerned, on August
14, 1946, in the form of a decree issued by the Central
Committee of the Communist Party. Two Leningrad magazines, *Zvezda* and *Leningrad,* were selected as scapegoats.
The editors were accused of printing works "devoid of
ideas, ideologically harmful," works "permeated with longing, pessimism, and disillusionment in life." Such attitudes
were not allowed.

> The Soviet system cannot tolerate [the decree went on]
> the education of youth in a spirit of indifference to Soviet
> politics, to Soviet ideology, the inculcation of a couldn't-
> care-less attitude. The strength of Soviet literature, the
> most advanced literature in the world, lies in the fact that
> it is a literature in which there are not and cannot be
> interests other than the interests of the people, the inter-
> ests of the state. The task of Soviet literature is to help
> the state to educate the youth correctly, to answer its
> requirements, to bring up the new generation to be strong,
> believing in its cause, not fearing obstacles, ready to over-
> come any obstacles.

The Central Committee ordered that *Leningrad* cease publication. *Zvezda* was admonished to mend its ways, and to
supervise the mending process the Deputy Chief of the
Propaganda Administration of the Central Committee was
appointed its editor-in-chief with full responsibility for the
magazine's ideological orientation.

Two individual culprits were singled out for special
opprobrium. One of them was Zoshchenko, who was

accused of maliciously seeking to expose the seamy sides of Soviet life in order to ridicule the Soviet people and the Soviet regime. The other was Anna Akhmatova, one of the leading poets of the "Acmeist" school before the Revolution. She had published little since the early twenties except for a few lyrics, mostly patriotic, issued during the war; but she was dangerous as a symbol of the "decadent" past—a past endlessly repudiated but still morbidly attractive. Soviet youth must look forward, not back; and it should mind its job and not concern itself too much with emotional subtleties. Like Pasternak a decade later, Zoshchenko and Akhmatova were expelled from the Writers' Union to the accompaniment of choruses of indignation sung by "the whole Soviet public."

It is likely that the peculiar personal viciousness of these attacks was motivated partly by the desire to remind writers that the Party still carried a sword, that those rebellious could still be relegated to outer darkness. It was important to sow fear and mistrust and thus prevent the growth of any feeling of solidarity among writers. The Soviet regime could not tolerate anything remotely resembling an oppositionist intelligentsia; this was a lesson it had learned from its own revolutionary past.

The August 14 decree was reinforced by the personal intervention of Zhdanov, the "culture specialist" on the Politburo. Zhdanov's attacks on Zoshchenko and Akhmatova were even more virulent and grotesque than those contained in the decree. Further, lest anyone think that the August 14 decree applied to literature alone, it was followed up by similar pronouncements dealing with the theater repertory, the motion pictures, and, two years later, the opera.[2]

"Zhdanovism," as this program of extreme cultural regimentation came to be called, effectively transformed postwar Soviet literature into a barren waste. Writers had been given a stern warning: no further ideological waverings would be tolerated. They were to laud all things Soviet and traduce anything that smacked in the slightest degree of Western bourgeois culture. They were to stress the fact that all Soviet progress was the work of the Party. Soviet people were not to be depicted as in any way pessimistic, weary, or sorrowing; Soviet man was made of superhuman heroism and devotion to duty. He had no need to pause for relaxation. The Soviet soldier returning from the front longed only to plunge enthusiastically into his peacetime production work. Optimism was mandatory.

Zhdanovism effectively emasculated Soviet literature. Any signs discernible during the war of renascent virility were obliterated. Writers were obliged not only to paint a highly unrealistic picture of Soviet life but to depict something that bore little resemblance to human life of any kind. Taboos were laid down against the representation of whole areas of human life and feeling. Human emotions, which are the real stuff of literature, had to be grossly oversimplified or simply falsified. Production themes dominated over human relations to such an extent that some novels read like engineering handbooks. Soviet literature was reduced to an endlessly tedious series of factory or collective-farm moralities.

This catastrophic deterioration in quality confronted the Party leadership with a new dilemma. How could Soviet authors serve the Party as its "engineers of human souls" if the possessors of those souls found their works too boring to read? Reading is a much more popular pastime in Russia, among all classes of society, than it is elsewhere in the world. But even book-hungry Russians balked at the contemporary fare that was offered them in the postwar era. Huge editions of nineteenth-century classics were rapidly sold out while smallish editions of contemporary works languished on bookstore shelves. "The most advanced literature in the world" was falling on deaf ears. Ideological rigidity had defeated its own ends. What were the Kremlin culture bosses to do? Their ideological vise had effectively squeezed the life out of literature, and the corpse could not perform the "educative role" they assigned to it. But, on the other hand, to loosen the screws meant to run the danger of a revival of a spirit of intellectual independence, of a striving for greater creative and critical freedom and a desire for expanded cultural contacts with the West. Equally repelled by both these unpleasant alternatives, the bosses could only storm and rage. Someone else must be responsible: the writers had not taken the decree sufficiently to heart; there were erroneous critical theories in circulation, perhaps invented by "cosmopolite" agents from the West.

The "anti-cosmopolitan" campaign is the most celebrated

example of the government's hunt for a scapegoat that could be blamed for the cultural decline brought on by its own policies. The poor quality of contemporary literature was especially apparent in the field of drama, partly because the indifference of the public to contemporary Soviet plays was so graphically displayed in the form of half-empty houses. By 1948 this problem had been officially recognized and a discussion launched to discover the "causes."

Certain drama critics took this discussion too seriously and began speaking caustically about the terrible sameness of Soviet plays. Here was the "treasonable plot" the literary policemen had been looking for. By early 1949 what had begun as a discussion of the shortcomings of the Soviet drama had been transformed into a full-scale campaign against the "seditious" critics. They were accused of forming an "anti-patriotic clique" with the express purpose of undermining Soviet morale through corruption of its literature. A *Pravda* article (January 28, 1949) states that "the top-priority task of Party criticism is the ideological crushing of this anti-patriotic group of theater critics." This "task" was speedily carried out, and before long the hapless critics were confessing that they had indeed fomented a plot to undermine Soviet literature.[3]

In this atmosphere the plight of the Soviet writer was a sorry one indeed. It was not only his fears of "mistakes" and subsequent reprisals that he had to contend with. The system of collective responsibility meant that editor, publisher, and any organization that had sponsored the work, perhaps even the Writers' Union itself, would come in for their share of the blame should a book be found "ideologically harmful." Everyone became his brother's censor. Sins of omission were as bad as sins of commission; you could be reprimanded as severely for what you had not written as for what you had. Not only that: *ex post facto* indictments for crimes of the past could be issued at any time. Fadeev's *Young Guard,* for instance, which had actually received the Stalin Prize for 1946, was subsequently discovered to be guilty of a disastrous omission: Fadeev had failed to show that the Party had been responsible for all the successes of the underground fighters in German-occupied territory. He obligingly rewrote the book, incorporating these new discoveries of socialist "realism." It has since been admitted that this sudden revolution in the critical estimate of *Young Guard* and the order to rewrite it came from Stalin himself. Thus the vanity and caprice of the dictator provided an additional hazard, and an unpredictable one, with which the writer might have to contend.[4]

As a result of all these pressures and threats, the product turned out under the name of literature during the dark period of 1946–53 is a misshapen and often ludicrous thing. One of the characteristics (even of the pieces included in this book) which may strike the Western reader is the extraordinary preoccupation of Soviet characters with problems connected with their work, and especially with technical problems of industrial production. But the examples given here are as nothing compared to the average novel of the Zhdanov period. Writers got so absurdly entangled in the assembly line that finally even stony-faced Soviet critics began to laugh at them. In one play[5] the young hero makes a rendezvous with his girl in the woods. She arrives there ahead of the appointed time and begins to wonder why in the world he could have wanted to meet her. After long thought she hits on the solution: there is a new production process he wants to discuss with her! In the same play there is a wedding feast at which the central topic of the guests' conversation is again—improvements in the assembly line. In another play[6] the hero and heroine confess their love for one another while collating analyses of a metal, "without taking time off from work, so to speak," as one Soviet critic caustically remarked. To show characters only at the work bench was to fail, it was now discovered, to do justice to the many-sided nature of Soviet man.

Up until Stalin's death in March 1953, though a few extremists were occasionally called to heel, no serious attempt to rectify this hopeless situation could be made. It remained to be seen what would happen now that the Leader was gone.

4.

The immediate response to Stalin's death was a flood of fulsome lamentations and panegyrics in the familiar style of bombastic sycophancy that had become customary in the later years of the Dictator's life. But this was only the result of a time lag—the effect of historical momentum, so to speak. Writers were doing their old tricks while they waited to see what new winds might blow.

Before more than a few months had passed, the amnesty granted to some political prisoners, the promise of higher living standards, and the dramatic fall of Beria and with him the almighty power of the secret police were indications that a basic change had taken place.

It was not long before the intellectuals began to test out the limits of their freedom. Olga Berggolts, herself a poet, voiced a plea that lyric poets be allowed to express their private individuality, their loves and sorrows, without being accused of narrow subjectivism. That was in April. In June, Tvardovsky, one of the most gifted Soviet poets, published six chapters of a long poem called "Horizon Beyond Horizon." The fifth and sixth chapters contained a strong protest against regimentation in literature. In October, Ilya Ehrenburg, always a bit of a daredevil, published an article entitled "On the Writer's Work." He called for greater psychological depth and portrayal of more varied emotions. His article implied that certain controls, once necessary, had now outlived their usefulness. And most heretical of all, he expressed the view that the inner world of man was a sphere about which writers knew more than anybody else. Finally, he stressed that no critic or criticism could be infallible.

This trial balloon was followed by another, an article by a hitherto unknown author named V. Pomerantsev entitled "On Sincerity in Literature." The title was itself an indictment: sincerity had been a scarce commodity in Soviet literature. The article's forceful tone and impatient outspokenness made it a literary sensation. Pomerantsev had said in print what everyone must have felt for a long time: how wonderful it would be if we could only write as we really feel!

Ehrenburg made his second contribution to the move for freedom when, in May 1954, he published the first part of his famous novel which provided a name for the whole era, *The Thaw*. Like so much of Ehrenburg's work, it is sloppy and lifeless as a novel and devious and ambiguous as an ideological manifesto. But in its presentation of the predicament of the Soviet artist, the novel could only be taken as a cry for freedom. Two of its characters are painters. One of them is a successful "Soviet" painter (apparently a socialist realist) who knowingly, to please the authorities, prostitutes his talent and produces the advertising posters that pass for painting in the Soviet Union. He wins prizes and has articles written about him. The other artist is wretchedly poor. Supported by his wife, he paints for himself pictures that he can neither sell nor exhibit but that are, nevertheless, great works of art. (Unfortunately, these underground masterpieces are not adequately described, but even they appear to bear little resemblance to the contemporary art of the West. They are some sort of lyrical landscapes, but lacking any socialist moral.) This contrast between the idealistic and the cynical artist is, of course, hackneyed enough, but it nevertheless created a sensation in the Russia of 1954. It had been a long time since Russians had been allowed to entertain in print the idea that there might be such a thing as a cynical time-server who actually won Soviet prizes.

Besides this somewhat ambiguous plea for a more vigorous art, Ehrenburg also drops many remarks and treats many subjects in the course of the novel which he would hardly have dared to do a few years before. He refers ironically to the anti-cosmopolitan campaign and the doctors' plot, guardedly alluding to their anti-Semitic character, praises Shostakovich's outlawed Tenth Symphony, and—most "advanced" of all—involves one of his heroes (very chastely, to be sure) in a love affair with a married woman. It was indeed a thaw.

Other works and other articles attested to the same tendency. The Party sensed the enormous force of the pent-up longing for freedom. It began to fear that the tide of liberalism was approaching a point at which it could no longer have been stemmed without drastic repressions.

Orthodox attacks on the liberals multiplied. On May 25, 1954, Surkov, the Secretary of the Writers' Union, carried the attack on Pomerantsev and the others to the columns of *Pravda*. So far there had been no official intervention. But the fact that Surkov's authoritative article was printed in the Party newspaper was a clear indication that the Party could be expected to intervene more directly if this should become necessary. It did not. The Writers' Union was able to do its own housecleaning. On June 3 *Literaturnaya Gazeta* reported a decree of the Writers' Union dismissing the editor of *Oktyabr,* one of the leading literary magazines, from his post. On August 11 Tvardovsky was relieved of his duties as editor of *Novy Mir. Novy Mir,* which had published Pomerantsev's article and other questionable materials, was accused of fostering "idealistic" and "nihilistic" views. (In 1956, under another editor, it encountered similar charges.) The liberals had "sought under today's conditions to revive the principle of 'intuitivism,' divorcing art and literature from their part in the creative and constructive life of the people—a principle maintained at the end of the twenties and at the beginning of the thirties by literary groups that derived their inspiration from sources hostile to the Party program for building socialism."

A halt had been called. The first "thaw" was over. But the new frost was not to be quite as severe as it had been in Stalin's time. There was less open threatening and intimidation, less extravagant vilification. Though literary articles continued to criticize the same works with typically Soviet repetitive monotony, no real hounding campaigns were organized. Clearly there was a widespread desire in both literary and official circles to avoid the excesses of a darker age. A sort of uneasy compromise had been reached. It was to be an era of Stalinism purged of the particularly sadistic and paranoid elements contributed by the old dictator himself, a calmer, saner, and just perceptibly more tolerant Stalinism.

This compromise was the leitmotif at the Second Writers' Congress, held in December 1954. The reprimands issued to Ehrenburg, Pomerantsev, and others were repeated. But there was also strong criticism of the bureaucratic methods of the top leaders in the Writers' Union. The time-honored practice of hounding writers who had "erred" was also deplored. The demand was voiced that greater attention be paid to questions of artistic technique and more allowance made for the peculiarities of the individual artist.

The basic trend of the Congress and of Soviet literature as a whole in the following year was away from politics. Ehrenburg and others had used fiction as a vehicle for veiled criticisms of the political and social situation. Pomerantsev had in the last analysis maintained that esthetic merit was more important than ideological orthodoxy in a work of art. At this the Party had spoken: they

had overstepped the mark. The dismissal of two leading
editors left no doubt that the Party meant business. The
lesson of 1954 was therefore to avoid the political hetero-
doxy of *The Thaw* by playing down politics and in general
paying more attention to people's private lives. This shift
away from the political in the literature of 1955 may not
be immediately apparent, since political ideology always
looms so large in Soviet literature at any time. But it seems
to be the prevailing tendency of that year.

5.

This period of relative quiescence was dramatically broken
off by the Twentieth Party Congress, held in February
1956. For nearly three years the *epigonoi* had wavered in
their attitude toward the Stalin legacy. How strong a hold
did the ghost of the Leader have on the hearts of their
subjects? Engaged as they were in a bittter struggle for
supremacy among themselves, they could not decide
whether the Stalinist mantle was an asset or a liability.
Would they win more support, not only among the people
at large, but especially among the managerial class, the
rank and file of the Party, by posing as Stalin's loyal heirs
and spiritual successors, or by representing themselves as
long-awaited liberators from the oppressive and arbitrary
tyranny of the past? True, the latter solution was a bit
awkward, as they themselves had been active instruments
of that tyranny and were closely identified with it. But
this was nevertheless the course finally chosen, by a decision apparently taken while the Congress was already in
progress. Khrushchev delivered himself of his famous
secret speech, and the idols of Stalin came crashing down
from their pedestals.

Khrushchev's exposure of the "cult of personality" was
not intended merely to set the record straight on one man.
He and his colleagues wanted to make this ideological revolution the signal for a general moral stocktaking throughout the Party and the country. They hoped to reinfuse the
Party with its erstwhile militant and idealistic spirit. The
evils of Stalinist rule had penetrated deep and wide into
the life of the country. As Khrushchev put it, the cult
of Stalin "became at a certain stage the source of a whole
series of exceedingly serious and grave perversions of
Party principles, Party democracy, and revolutionary le-

gality." All this must now be put right. There must be
a regeneration of the Party, represented as a return to the
untarnished sources of communism embodied in the theory
and practice of Marx, Engels, and Lenin. The "Leninist"
principles of Party management, as Khrushchev saw them,
embodied collective leadership, "observance of the norms
of Party life set forth in the Statutes of our Party," and,
above all, "a wide practice of criticism and self-criticism."
The Communist Party of the Soviet Union was by its own
admission cleaning house. And Soviet literature was quick
to seize the opportunity to lend a hand.

Writers had for years been obliged to paint a rosier picture of Soviet life than they knew to be true. They had
been obliged to keep silent about abuses they knew to exist.
They had knowingly falsified the role played by Stalin in
many important events. They had treated the Party as the
deus ex machina which irons out all problems. They had
depicted man more as a political and production unit than
as a sentient human being. Now with the Twentieth Congress they could speak the truth. Falsehood would be cast
aside. Evil and corruption would be exposed. The Party
no longer demanded hypocrisy of the writer. Now he
could write the truth, knowing not merely that this would
not cause offense, but that he was thus serving the Party's
cause. The idealism of the writer seemed wedded to the
rediscovered idealism of the Party.

For a time the Party seemed to accept this view of things
and to encourage, or at least allow, writers to raise issues
and voice criticisms that would have been unheard of a
few years before. The new literature of 1956 was essentially a literature of protest—of moral protest, especially
against hypocrisy and falsehood. Truth must not be com-
promised in the name of any high-sounding objective.
There must be no concealment, no covering-up. Truth must
cast its merciless light into every nook and cranny of
Soviet life.

If we take the demand for truth and sincerity as the
cornerstone of the 1956 protest, it is not surprising that
one of the principal targets for attack was the hypocritical
manipulation of Party slogans and Party goals. Many
writers sincerely desired to revitalize Party idealism and
enthusiasm, feeling that in Stalin's day Party ideology had
all too often been concocted entirely of empty phrases

and dead letters. The vital spark of Communist zeal had faded and given way to opportunism, manipulation, and cynical calculation. For this reason the literature of 1956 repeatedly draws a distinction between the "true" Party as something vital, inspiring, endowed with lofty ideals, and the "other" Party of lifeless dogma, meaningless propaganda, and unscrupulous careerism. The crude but spirited poem by Konstantin Murzidi (p. 151) is an excellent illustration of this feeling. But the sentiment crops up elsewhere and often. The bewilderment of an idealistic youth at the discovery of the cynical underside of Communist rule is the burden of Evgeny Evtushenko's "Stantsia Zima" (p. 122).

One of the major moral stumbling blocks encountered by an idealistic Communist in contemporary Russia is the existence of an entrenched and privileged bureaucracy. It is almost invariably members of this class who are guilty of the vices of careerism and cynicism so frequently deplored. Therefore, to attack this evil was at the same time to attack a particular class. It was not so much economic inequality that bothered the writers; they seem to accept the fact that some people are always richer and more comfortable than others. What angers them in the bureaucrats is their lack of sincerity, of idealism, of desire to do anything more in life than sit tight in a comfortable spot. They have lost their human shape, become calculating, egotistical, indifferent to others. Though they are not necessarily large-scale malefactors themselves, they acquiesce in and use to their own advantage a system of which they can see the injustices. These injustices they dismiss as inevitable, fearing in any way to disturb a system in which they have learned to maneuver skillfully and to which they owe their privileged position and the accompanying material advantages. Examples of this type of evil bureaucrat may be found in this volume in "One's Own Opinion" and "A Trip Home." Equally open to condemnation are the corrupt cynic who uses the system to crush others and advance himself and the timid and careful time-server who lacks the courage to speak his mind and correct abuses.

This attack on a privileged class, the bureaucracy, amounts in essence to the repudiation by intellectual idealists of the Soviet version of the "bourgeois" stuffed shirt, with all his bourgeois characteristics—his apathy, his philistine indifference to things of the spirit, his worldliness, his corruptness, egotism, and readiness to compromise ideals. It is an attack with which Western society has been familiar for a long time.

In much of the literature of 1956 there is an inescapable implication that these bad qualities of the Soviet bureaucrat are not idiosyncratic aberrations of isolated individuals, but rather general attributes of the entire class, itself a product of the Soviet system. This implication was more than the most liberal in the reformed neo-Stalinist leadership could tolerate, for it called into question one of their most sacred dogmas, that the Soviet Union was a classless society in which all evil was owing to the remnants of capitalism. When Paustovsky, in his speech at the meeting held in October 1956, to discuss Dudintsev's novel (p. 155), spoke of the obtuseness and vulgarity of "the Drozdovs," pluralizing the name of a character in the novel, he was implying that Dudintsev had successfully described the attributes of a whole species. For this heresy Paustovsky was bitterly reproached.

The Soviet literary protest of 1956 has sometimes been represented in the West as something in the nature of a revolt against the Party and the regime. This it certainly was not. It is, of course, impossible at this distance to define exactly the different attitudes of individual writers toward the Party. But the main stream of writing criticizing various aspects of Soviet life seems to have been motivated by the desire to improve what already exists. If hypocrisy, careerism, and corruption are exposed, they can be corrected. If weaknesses are laid bare instead of being covered up, they can be remedied. The Party can become stronger, the bureaucracy less corrupt, and the Soviet Union will be a better place to live in. This seems to have been the line of thought of the most outspoken of the writers.

But despite all its protestations about the need for "merciless Bolshevik criticism and self-criticism," the Communist Party of the Soviet Union has not in fact reached that degree of political maturity where it can tolerate anything that smacks of opposition, even the most loyal. For to do so would be to surrender another of its most cherished myths, the myth of its omniscience, its infallibility, its unique possession of the secret laws of history.

The Party must reign supreme above all things. It, and it alone, must possess the keys to its subjects' souls.

The literature of 1956 shows that the most responsible and idealistic Soviet intellectuals, though perfectly ready to accept Party leadership in the political, economic, and even ideological spheres, are nevertheless seeking to work out an ethos that would leave some areas independent of Party doctrines. In Alyoshin's play *Alone,* the right of the Party to interfere in a man's private life, in his love affairs, is questioned. And Evtushenko's "Stantsia Zima" is the story of a young poet's independent search for answers to many "eternal questions." He does not find the answers, but he does not turn for help to the Party:

> . . . suddenly I somehow found that I
> must answer all these questions on my own . . .

Nor was the Party prepared to surrender one iota of its control over literature and art. The article ("A Writer's Notes") by Aleksandr Kron (p. 164) will hardly strike the Western reader as a clarion call for the liberation of Soviet literature from Party shackles; it is a rambling, vague, and often incoherent lament over the condition of the contemporary Soviet theater, in the course of which an attempt is made to link the worst features of the bureaucratization of literature with the "cult of personality," i.e., Stalinism. Kron specifically denies any advocacy of complete artistic freedom, trying to build himself a halfway house on the foundation of a somewhat sophistical semantic distinction. After enumerating some of the (Stalinist) "mistakes made in the supervision of the theaters," Kron observes: "These mistakes are grave. But this does not imply that art should not be supervised at all. It is not guidance, but tutelage that is harmful." Instead of "tutelage" (*opeka,* a legal word implying something like "guardianship" or "trusteeship"), Kron is willing to settle for "guidance" (*rukovodstvo,* a word varyingly translated as "guidance," "leadership," or "management," but still implying a high degree of supervisory powers). But the Party was not ready to make any such semantic bargain, and in the later attacks on Kron these very sentences were quoted as exemplifying his rejection of the doctrine of Party supervision of literature.

No Russians of 1956, Kron included, ever dared to go so far in their published criticisms or revisionism as those Polish intellectuals who, encouraged by the signs of faltering and ideological hesitation at the Muscovite Center of the Communist world, went on to pooh-pooh the entire theory of socialist realism and openly attack the whole system of ideological supervision of art.[7]

6.

The year 1957 was to witness the partial crushing of the liberalizing movement. Various pressures were brought to bear on recalcitrant writers. Meeting after meeting was called to denounce either their works or their policy as editors. But the pendulum had not swung all the way back to Zhdanovism. The "culprits" behaved in a very novel way. They neither repented nor recanted nor fell to accusing one another of ever more heinous heresies, as they would certainly have done in the old days. At a March meeting of the Moscow Writers' Union (the center of the disturbance being among Moscow writers) they defended themselves vigorously and courageously. In May a plenum of the Board of the Writers' Union of the whole Soviet Union was held. This enlargement of the arena meant that they were now under fire from writers and critics from all parts of the country. Though they knew that the attack on them had Khrushchev's personal backing, at this meeting they nevertheless simply sat with their hands folded and their mouths shut. This "heroic silence," as one of their bitterest critics, L. Sobolev, labeled it with disgust (see p. 163), was taken, no doubt correctly, as a mute act of defiance, a refusal to knuckle under.

Twice before the May plenum and once more after it, Khrushchev summoned groups of writers and artists to what he described as "comradely meetings." He told the writers that "bourgeois" tendencies among Hungarian intellectuals had played no small part in bringing about the Hungarian uprising. He warned them that their writings were being used as weapons by the capitalist world. He told them that they had been misled by Shepilov, a former culture boss then in disgrace, whose interpretation of the ideological requirements of Soviet art had been (comparatively) liberal and sophisticated. Also, in a manner that defied even Soviet logic, they were ominously linked with the main Party "opposition" over which he had just triumphed, the "anti-Party" group of Malenkov, Molotov, and Kaganovich. By this time, probably, sympathetic fellow writers were also urging the recalcitrants to capitulate; for there must have been a fear that the rashness of a few could endanger the many.

Hence it is not surprising that "admissions of error" eventually began to be heard. It seems almost certain that many of these admissions were made grudgingly and without conviction. It would also seem probable that this led to widespread bitterness and disillusionment in literary circles. Not only had literary freedoms once more been curtailed, but the Party, which at the Twentieth Congress had seemed desirous of purifying itself so that it might lead the country toward a new, cleaner, truer, and more idealistic future, had once more displayed the old paranoia, the old authoritarianism. Once again the old clichés were trotted out, the old suspicions voiced, the old repressions resorted to. Thaw No. 2 was over.

It would, of course, be unjust to suggest that there had been a complete return to Stalinism or Zhdanovism. In spite of the 1957 repressions the writer's situation is still considerably better than it was in 1953. But the improvement can be seen only in this comparative light. Literature remains the handmaiden of the politician; it has not been granted the right to independent existence. And as the fate of Pasternak and *Doctor Zhivago* have shown, when a really independent and personal work is produced, even of the highest artistic quality, the Soviet public is denied the right to read it and decide upon its merits; and the author, after being awarded the most coveted of all international literary prizes, is subjected to a vulgar campaign of vilification organized by his own government. But Pasternak is a case apart. The run-of-the-mill Soviet writer has neither the international reputation nor, very likely, the conviction or even the courage that would enable him to detach himself so profoundly from the pressures of the world he lives in. The most he can hope for, like the writers included in this book, is to maneuver as best he can within the narrow limits set by Party dictates.

If we imagine these limits as a series of fences hemming the Soviet writer in on all sides, we can perhaps better conceive of the conditions under which he writes. First, as to his selection of materials. Although he may to some extent touch on what Khrushchev called the "darker sides" of life, he must remember what the same Khrushchev said in his secret speech at the Twentieth Congress: "We should not give ammunition to the enemy; we should not wash our dirty linen before their eyes." The duty of a socialist writer is still to portray all Soviet darkness as rapidly fleeing before the light of progress. Optimism is mandatory. On another side, if the writer seeks to look more closely at people's private lives and at their, or his own, inner world, he must remember not only the prudishly Victorian Soviet taboos against the slightest frankness in sexual matters, but also that the doubts, the conflicts, the stupidities, even the stubborn, selfish pursuit of personal happiness regardless of its collective consequences—these universal human attributes are officially "not typical" of Soviet man and therefore not appropriate for representation in art. One of the foundation stones of the regime is a mythical conception of human nature, and the writer's function is to perpetuate, not destroy, this myth. On a third side, the Soviet writer finds barred the road of philosophical speculation. All Soviet writers necessarily and by definition have the same *Weltanschauung,* and there can be no question of any further discussions about the "meaning of life," as all such questions have been settled long ago in the Marxist scriptures. Finally, even in matters of form, the Soviet artist must bear in mind that he is writing for a mass, and not an elite, audience, and that attempts to experiment with new formal means may not be immediately intelligible to the average reader; the Party has wisely decreed all such experiments to be "bourgeois formalism," and therefore evil. The Party has supplied the Soviet writer with an infallible method: socialist realism.

If we try to imagine what territory is left for art when all these vast spaces have been fenced off, we can perhaps better understand why Soviet literature is so pathetically narrow and lifeless.

7.

Discussions of latter-day Soviet literature, even those written outside the reach of Comrade Zhdanov and his successors, seem willy-nilly to conform to the principle of "Party-ness" he laid down for Soviet art: they tend to become discussions of literature-as-politics rather than of literature itself. In the West we are apt to discuss Soviet writers in terms of their allegiances, their deviations, their social aspirations, their muted notes of dissent, rather than of their esthetic worth, their psychology, or their style. Our histories and interpretations of Soviet literature have tended to become extended chronicles of essentially non-literary events—denunciatory attacks on writers issued from on high, their occasional protests and attempts at self-defense, their frequent abject capitulations. The actual literary works, both of Party stalwarts and of deviants, we have treated more as sociological source material than as literature properly so called. We have hoped that through literature we could learn something of the human reality of Soviet life behind the official façade. Furthermore, the search for this reality, by a natural psychological process, tends to become politicized in another way: it tends to become a search for "oppositionist" leanings. The staleness and monotony of the incessant choruses of everlasting yeas make us catch at every discordant note as at least a sign of some individuality and life. This anthology of discord, of course, conforms precisely to this pattern, and this introductory essay has become the usual chronicle of political woes rather than a literary discussion.

Is any really literary discussion feasible? It would not be impossible, to be sure, to apply to current Soviet literary works those techniques of purely literary ("formalistic") evaluation and analysis which are now so stridently condemned in the Soviet Union. We might dissect the versification of "Stantsia Zima," trace the dramatic structure of *Alone,* or scrutinize the use of epithet in "The Khazar Ornament." But such an undertaking would doubtless seem a bit ludicrous, something like Theodore Spencer's famous critical dissection of "Thirty Days Hath September." A work must have some ballast of literary quality before it can stand such buffeting.

As for the works included in this book, we are well aware of their esthetic inadequacies. Alyoshin's *Alone,* though a competent piece of stagecraft (it was given an excellent production at the Vakhtangov Theater in Moscow), is a tissue of well-worn psychological and literary clichés from beginning to end. Evtushenko's "Stantsia Zima," though it shows some youthful sincerity and verve, is derivative, sentimental, and occasionally sloppy in technique. The stories of Nagibin, though they show signs of talent, are nevertheless very slovenly in execution and frequently resort to the most banal clichés of character and plot (e.g., the true-blue Communist who emerges from behind the stove to bring on the happy ending in "The Khazar Ornament"). The critical piece by Aleksandr Kron on the contemporary theater is impressive for its sincerity and courage, but is neither well reasoned nor lucidly expressed.

The reasons why Soviet writers should exhibit such a low level of technical competence are many. It is not only the badgerings and bullyings of Zhdanov and his sort that have forced them to take refuge in literary conformism, to seek the safety of the cliché. The whole system of editing and censorship, the very organization of the Writers' Union and its apparatus of supervision, the tight grip maintained by the Party over the distribution of material rewards and glory—all this inevitably serves, not to stimulate writers to produce original works of quality, but to turn out the kind of smoothly machined, well-grooved article that will pass easily down the assembly line and slip past the inspector's eye. The Party regards literature as an important instrument for molding and shaping the emotions of its subjects. These emotions are far too important a matter for any kind of *laissez faire* to be admissible. A writer who carries out the Party's assignment, whether from conviction, self-interest, or the two combined, is handsomely rewarded with the good things of life; he who bucks the system is not so rewarded and may get hurt. The vast majority "adapt"; they try to give Caesar his due and at the same time preserve some modicum of artistic integrity for themselves.

As mentioned above, the Party wants its sermon to reach as large an audience as possible. It therefore disapproves of that tendency toward abstruseness and esotericism so characteristic of much contemporary Western art and literature, which has restricted audiences of intellectual initiates. Two of the greatest and most original masters of fiction in the twentieth century, Proust and Joyce, have been forbidden names in Soviet Russia since the mid-thirties, read only surreptitiously by a few *cognoscenti* and certainly not to be used as models by any Soviet writer.

It is not only that a complex art cannot be used to convey propaganda messages to mass audiences, or even that it might contain hidden subversive messages addressed to an intellectual elite which it would require highly literate censors to detect. Nor is it even the obtuse and intolerant philistinism—the desire to destroy what one does not readily understand—so characteristic of the parvenu mentality of the Soviet bosses. Besides all this there is something intrinsically subversive in any genuine work of art: it has its own laws, its own system, its own values, independent of the world from which it sprang. Regardless of its "ideology," it represents a self-sufficient value outside the "system."

Furthermore, the Proustian and Joycean tendency toward psychological as well as stylistic complexity which has characterized so much modern fiction in the West (and in which development it owes a profound debt to both Dostoevsky and Tolstoy) is fundamentally abhorrent to the Soviet ideological manipulators. Detailed, uninhibited, penetrating scrutiny of the hidden processes of human feeling and thought is also intrinsically subversive, in that it elevates individual experience to the status of a value in itself, in part independent of the social experience around it. Moreover, it tends to puncture official myths about human motivation. In general, Soviet art seeks no new truths about human experience; nor, despite periodic genuflections in the direction of the "true," as distinct from "spurious," innovation allegedly encouraged in Soviet artists, is it permitted to engage in any serious formal experimentation. Socialist realism is not a temporary school eventually to be superseded; it is an infallible method laid down for eternity.

One of the most insidious results of the mode of existence imposed on Soviet writers is a certain deterioration of the critical faculty that seems to take place even in those who try to preserve their artistic self-respect. Even an absurd *status quo* has a way of seeming to acquire reasonableness simply by virtue of its prolonged existence. Writers write, books and magazines are published, reviews are turned out, prizes awarded, royalties received, and comfortable lives led. The vast machine of Soviet literary production keeps lumbering on, turning out works labeled novels, short stories, poetry, and plays; reputations rise and fall.

All this in time appears to be in the nature of things. Most writers always, and some officials occasionally, realize that all is not well with the problem of quality. But few probably realize just how bad the situation really is; few recognize the extent to which Russia has simply dropped out of world literature. A Soviet literary magazine of the 1920's looked pretty much like a literary magazine anywhere, except for a greater preponderance of articles on Marxism and the class struggle. The quality of fiction, verse, and criticism is equal to anything then appearing in any Western country, and in many cases better, as it often possesses a liveliness, excitement, and lack of commercialism missing in Western magazines. But a present-day Soviet literary magazine, except for a few brief intervals like 1956, is something quite different: gray, dreary, and monotonous; utterly lacking in zest or controversy, it hardly seems an effective instrument for engineering anyone's soul. And it is not; it has simply become an official institution, operating on a government subsidy, which exists by historical inertia and because the regime cannot think of any way to make literature lively and safe at the same time. Hampered and hemmed in as they are, the writers no doubt tend to ascribe their artistic shortcomings to the external pressures under which they must write. But one suspects that even if these pressures were to be removed, they would need a long period of education and experiment before a vital and living literary tradition could be re-established.

One feels this esthetic complacency, this lack of real striving for quality, in many of the pieces included in this book. A writer like Nagibin, for instance, has a talent that has never been "pushed," forced to concentrate its best. This is probably a general characteristic of Soviet writers today. A really good book is infinitely hard to write. It would inevitably have a lot of its goodness ironed out by editorial boards and discussion panels; it might not be properly understood by the masses anyway (assuming they would read it). And, besides, who would know it was good? No, it is much easier, safer, and except, perhaps, *sub specie aeternitatis,* more rewarding to do what others do—turn out works that may be passably good or passably bad, but are most of all safely ordinary.

Perhaps we should not, in the West, be too self-righteous

or superior in our condemnation of this degenerative process, for there is a certain curious but striking parallel between the deterioration of Soviet writers under the kinds of political, economic, and psychological pressures described above, and the deterioration of some of those Western writers, artists, and composers who choose to work for the so-called "mass media." Perhaps the whole phenomenon of Soviet literature can be better understood and better visualized by Western readers if it is compared, not with Russian literature of the past or with the best Western literature of the present, but rather with that part of the Western cultural product which is really addressed to mass audiences and which is, by and large, on a comparable level of quality: the average movie, the average TV drama, the radio "soap opera," the novels serialized in mass-circulation magazines.

The comparison, of course, by no means implies that the two comparables are in balance. First of all, it should not be forgotten that alongside the mass culture, there exists in the West a "high" culture that can address itself with any message it likes in any form it likes to any public it can reach, and that there are no international limits set to the circulation of this culture. In Russia, on the other hand, contemporary "high" culture (except music) has been virtually liquidated by bureaucratic decree, and the individuals who would have produced it are forced (and richly rewarded for compliance) to turn out products that are supposed to convey an approved propaganda message in a form acceptable to the mass taste. Furthermore, the popular arts in the West are to some extent sustained and no doubt improved in quality by borrowings and downward percolations from the high culture; and the comparison, always possible in the West, between genuine and spurious contemporary art makes it possible to recognize the meretricious or second-rate for what it is—something not always so easy in Russia. However, after these qualifications are made, the juxtaposition of Western mass culture with Soviet culture-at-large is revealing.

In both spheres there are two governing principles, the cliché and the taboo, which are closely intertwined. Originality amounting to anything more than superficial novelty is frowned upon; it is likely to be disturbing, unsettling, a stimulus to fresh thoughts or feelings; whereas

one of the functions of this type of cultur[e]
reassuring effect of endless repetition o[f]
other words, the perpetuation of popula[r]
of these cultures large areas of artisti[c]
barred off by taboo. The Soviet taboos [are]
outlined, and some Western ones can be identified with
little thought. Hollywood will serve as a convenient example. Try to imagine, for instance, a Hollywood film in
which a sympathetic character argues plausibly against
the existence of God, advocates sexual freedom for
adolescents, or suggests that the U. S. Government was
guilty of a "crime against humanity" when it caused an
atomic bomb to be dropped on Hiroshima. These might
be classed as "ideological taboos," summed up by the
general rule that it is unwise to make a film intensely
partisan or polemical on any subject. You might offend
some large block of customers. It is in fact unwise to make
a film expressive of any ironic, bitter, or tragic view of life;
people do not go to the movies to be upset. There are also
artistic, formal taboos, probably more a matter of inertia
and lack of artistic initiative than of rigid prohibitions.
"Experimental" films are seldom box-office hits.

The refuge from the taboo is the cliché: a well-tried
formula proved by experience which will produce results
guaranteed to offend nobody and supposedly satisfy the
consumers. There is both a Soviet and an American brand
of mass-market myth. Esthetically speaking, it is not such
a great distance from the American cliché film about the
rich boy who meets the poor girl and marries her in defiance of his family's snobbery to the Soviet novel about
the young engineer who discovers a new production
process (or an American spy), is made a Hero of Socialist
Labor, and marries Manya, a pretty engineeress from next
door who has invented an epoch-making gadget of her own.

NOTES

1. See Edward J. Brown: *The Proletarian Episode in Russian Literature, 1928–1932* (New York: Columbia University Press; 1953).

Introduction

..e of the curiosities of 1958 was the Central Committee's decree of May 28, in which it repudiated its own "operatic" decree of ten years before (February 10, 1948), when several Soviet composers had been called to task for writing undemocratic, formalistic, and decadent operas. In 1958 the Central Committee reaffirmed the general socialist-realist principles of its 1948 decree, but discovered that all the specific applications of these principles to particular operas and composers had been quite erroneous, as they had been based on "a subjective approach to individual works of art and creativity on the part of J. V. Stalin." Apparently, after seeing an opera he did not like, Stalin used to order it attacked in the newspapers on the grounds that it had violated principles of socialist realism.

3. For a fuller discussion of the anti-cosmopolitan campaign, see p. 187, note 27.
4. Fadeev was a highly placed victim indeed: he was then First Secretary of the Writers' Union. He was an old Communist who had always hewed closely to the Party line (except for an unfortunate identification with the R.A.P.P. leadership, which caused him some difficult moments after the R.A.P.P. was axed). Fadeev committed suicide in 1956, an inveterate alcoholic.
5. Dmitry Shcheglov's *Gde sosny shumyat* (*Where the Pine Trees Rustle*).
6. A. Bek's *Novy profil'* (*The New Profile*).
7. There is evidence, however, that such heretical ideas are by no means unknown (though they must remain unpublished) even in Russia. Besides the reports of various Russian-speaking travelers on highly "subversive" literary conversations with Soviet intellectuals, there exists a most illuminating and keen-witted article written by a Soviet Russian, in which the infallible "method" is subjected to a relentless barrage of logic and irony. Entitled "Socialist Realism," it originally appeared in *L'Esprit* (No. 2, 1959); an English version was published in *Dissent* (Winter 1959). Naturally it cannot be published in Russia.

DRAMA

[Samuil Alyoshin's play *Alone* was the sensation of the theatrical season of 1956. It was produced in Moscow at the Vakhtangov Theater and played to packed houses at every performance. Soviet audiences—predominantly female, according to reports —came away profoundly moved by the action and passionately partisan in their judgments of the play's moral dilemma.

Western readers may find it difficult to grasp just what could have made this play so overwhelming a success. It impresses one as a competent, but hardly brilliant handling of an unusually hackneyed theme—the emotional ramifications of an adulterous love affair. But, first of all, for Soviet audiences this ever-fascinating theme was by no means hackneyed: it had been virtually outlawed for many years. And, more important—something even rarer than adultery in Soviet literature—this theme is presented as a genuine moral problem. For once the Party line is unclear. No ready-made solution is offered. Instead of being presented, as he almost always is in a Soviet play, with a clear, straightforward lesson to be learned, the Soviet spectator or reader of *Alone* is left to decide the moral question for himself. Who is right? What should the characters do?

A middle-aged, successful Communist engineer, an ideal hero (granted his age), upright, dedicated, vigorous, creative, likable, after seventeen years of happy married life falls in love with a younger woman. She too is a "good" Soviet figure: intelligent, courageous, persevering, also an engineer, but a feminine and attractive woman. She too is married. Her husband, though something of a weakling, is certainly not a villain. Finally, the lonely heroine, the engineer's wife, is also "good"—a devoted and beloved schoolteacher and a loving wife and mother. The engineer and his wife have a vivacious and affectionate teen-age daughter, and there is a good, kind old grandmother around too. In fact, everybody is "good," but still there is this troublesome love affair. It exists; it refuses to be stifled, despite more than usual efforts on the part of the principals. What are you going to do about it?

The author does not answer the question; nor, for once, does he allow the Communist authority figures in the play to straighten things out by wise decree. The problem was left open. This was the novelty. Here was plenty of private, unofficial human feeling; and here was a real moral problem. Soviet audiences were not used to such plays about their own kind, but they responded with enthusiasm.

Alone (*Odna*) was first published in *Teatr*, No. 8, 1956, from which text this translation was made. It has since been reprinted in a volume of five of the author's plays—his first published volume: *P'esy* (Moscow; 1958).]

ALONE

A PLAY IN FOUR ACTS AND EIGHT SCENES

S. Alyoshin

Cast of Characters

MARIA MIKHAYLOVNA PLATONOVA.

VARVARA VASILEVNA NEFEDOVA (VARYA).

VERA ALEKSANDROVNA (GRANDMA VERA).

NINA.

LIDA.

MARGARITA.

SERGEY PETROVICH PLATONOV.

PAVEL NIKOLAEVICH NEFEDOV.

ANDREY VIKTOROVICH KRAVTSOV.

VASILY FEDOROVICH.

IGOR ALEKSANDROVICH GOLOVIN.

KOLYA KRASNUSHKIN.

IGNATYUK.

BELLBOY.

ACT I

SCENE I

The PLATONOV *home. December. Evening. A room in the* PLATONOV *apartment. Two doors, one leading into the hall, the other into the dining room. Near the window a drawing board and a desk. A telephone. A couch. Armchairs. A bookcase and a clock with a pendulum. The clock has stopped.* MARIA MIKHAYLOVNA, *a woman of about forty, is asleep on the couch. Her mother,* VERA ALEKSANDROVNA (GRANDMA VERA), *about sixty-five years old, is reading the newspaper.* NINA, MARIA'S *fifteen-year-old daughter, is sitting at the desk reading a book.*

GRANDMA VERA: I don't feel well. I never felt this bad.

NINA [*without looking up from her book*]: Oh, Grandma Vera, you say that every day. Really you do.

GRANDMA VERA: It's true, I do. Good Lord. Look at the way this French ex-minister talks. How he does jabber! Did you read it?

NINA: No, I haven't.

GRANDMA VERA: You should have. You ought to take an interest in such things. What time did your mother ask to be wakened?

NINA: Oh dear! [*She turns around.*]

GRANDMA VERA: It's no use looking. The clock's stopped.

NINA: I'll look in the dining room. [*She looks through the door on the left.*] Mama! It's ten past seven! Oh dear! How terrible. Come on, Mama! Don't pretend. I know you're not asleep. You a teacher, lazing around like this. [*She pokes her mother.*]

MARIA MIKHAYLOVNA [*She makes waking-up noises.*]

NINA: Come on. When Papa comes, I'll tell him that you've been asleep the whole time.

MARIA MIKHAYLOVNA: Tell-tale. [*She sits up.*] Pass me the exercise books, tell-tale. And my red pencil.

NINA: Here's your dreadful red pencil and the poor little exercise books.

MARIA MIKHAYLOVNA: Exercise books, exercise books. Why are there so many of you? I am giving up my profession as a teacher to become—

GRANDMA VERA: Stop talking nonsense.

MARIA MIKHAYLOVNA: I don't have the right to talk nonsense? That's bad.

NINA: What will you become? Tell us.

MARIA MIKHAYLOVNA: I'm joking. I was born to be a teacher. [*She makes marks in the exercise books.*] One . . . One . . . [*She writes a two.*] and two! I'm a bloodthirsty person. Only I don't want to be the sort of teacher that our principal likes.

NINA: What sort does she like?

MARIA MIKHAYLOVNA: She doesn't want a woman teacher to be like a woman or a man teacher like a man. That's the snag. And I'm the most ordinary woman among women. I like to dress up. [*She goes on marking as she talks.*] I don't like cooking. I like doing my hair. I like having bare arms in summer. And I like to be attractive. Do you understand?

GRANDMA VERA: Masha!

MARIA MIKHAYLOVNA: And I don't like it when I get a reprimand for wearing a low neck or a slit skirt. To hell with it!

GRANDMA VERA: Maria!

MARIA MIKHAYLOVNA: To hell with it!

GRANDMA VERA: Come now, Masha.

MARIA MIKHAYLOVNA: You see what a bad, evil person I am. And anyone who doesn't like me can give me his exercise book, and I'll give him a two.[1]

NINA: Mama, you're marvelous!

MARIA MIKHAYLOVNA: Quite right. Give me your exercise book and I'll give you a five.

[*The phone rings.*]

Hello? Ah, Pavel Nikolaevich. We're expecting a telegram. Please do, we'll be at home all evening. [*Bowing to her mother*] I've already done so. [*She puts down the receiver.*] Nefedov wishes to be remembered to you. At last we'll get to see his wife. She's going off on a trip somewhere. They want to bring round some papers. [*To* NINA] What are you doing? Reading?

NINA: Just a teeny half a page more.

MARIA MIKHAYLOVNA: I know what your half-pages are. You've got five minutes more with that book. And then to work on your lessons.

GRANDMA VERA: Just the same, we ought to wind the clock.

MARIA MIKHAYLOVNA: Not under any circumstances.

NINA: Grandma Vera, surely you know that winding the clock is a man's job.

GRANDMA VERA: Copy-cat.

NINA: Who is?

GRANDMA VERA: You are, of course. You're copying your father.

NINA: I'm not copying him. I just think that way too.

MARIA MIKHAYLOVNA: It doesn't matter. We've waited three months. We can wait a day or two more. He'll wind the clock when he comes home.

[*A knock on the door.*]

GRANDMA VERA: Come in. [*No one enters.*] That must be Petya. [*To* NINA] Go and see what he wants.

[NINA *goes out.*]

Petya's got to sit in the kitchen again.

MARIA MIKHAYLOVNA: Is Lida having a party?

GRANDMA VERA: Guests.

[NINA *returns.*]

NINA: Petya brought back *Spartacus.*[2]

MARIA MIKHAYLOVNA: And, as usual, he doesn't want to come in?

NINA: You know him. He wants another book. But it has to be an interesting one.

MARIA MIKHAYLOVNA: I'll pick something out for him right away. [*Rummages in the bookshelf*] I'll give him Kaverin's *Two Captains.* [*She goes out.*]

GRANDMA VERA: How old is he?

NINA: About thirteen.

GRANDMA VERA: He doesn't look more than nine.

NINA: I can find out exactly. [*She goes out.*]

GRANDMA VERA [*to herself*]: Guests. A fine sort of guests.

[NINA *comes in.*]

NINA: He'll be thirteen . . . January, February, March . . . in three months. His birthday's on March fourteenth—the same day as Papa's.

[MARIA MIKHAYLOVNA *comes in.*]

GRANDMA VERA: How did he like *Spartacus?*

MARIA MIKHAYLOVNA: Fine. He's going to be a gladiator.

[*She sits down on the couch and starts in again on her exercise books.*]

GRANDMA VERA: That child never looks you straight in the eye. He always keeps his eyes down.

NINA: He's ashamed. He has no father. And his mother's no good.

GRANDMA VERA: You're still too young to be passing judgment on grown-ups.

NINA: But surely it's not good the way she makes him stay in the kitchen? He does his lessons there, reads there, and sometimes he goes to sleep in his chair. Mama, you really ought to have a talk with her.

MARIA MIKHAYLOVNA. How's that half-page of yours?

NINA: I've finished. [*She slams her book shut and goes into the other room.*]

GRANDMA VERA: It's true enough, Masha. I'm sorry for the boy. She'll ruin him.

MARIA MIKHAYLOVNA: No, she's a kind mother. But I did talk to her. And she says nothing.

[*There is a knock at the door.*]

That's her. Come in.

[PETYA's *mother,* LIDA, *comes in. She is about thirty-two. She has had a drop to drink. She wears slippers, no stockings.*]

LIDA: Hello.

GRANDMA VERA: Good evening. [*She leaves the room.*]

MARIA MIKHAYLOVNA: Sit down, Lida.

LIDA: Petya says you asked me to drop by.

MARIA MIKHAYLOVNA: Yes, I wanted to ask you, Lida, to let Petya spend the night with us. Is that all right?

LIDA: There's no point in it.

MARIA MIKHAYLOVNA: But what's the sense in having him sit in the kitchen? He's lonesome all alone. And feels left out.

LIDA: It doesn't matter. He'd better get used to it. There are a lot of things in life that hurt, but you just have to put up with them.

MARIA MIKHAYLOVNA: Aren't you sorry for him at all? After all, you and I are mothers.

LIDA: Listen, Maria Mikhaylovna. Don't you go putting yourself on the same level as me. You've got a husband. But I'm a wife who's been ditched. When the guests go, he'll go to bed in the room.

MARIA MIKHAYLOVNA [*lowering her eyes*]: You distress me, Lida.

LIDA: Come on now, Maria Mikhaylovna. You'll never understand me. I'm grateful, of course, for the thought, for your kindness to Petya, for the books. But let's have done with this sort of talk once and for all.

[*The hall doorbell rings.*]

MARIA MIKHAYLOVNA [*raising her voice*]: Nina, go and open the door. [*To* LIDA] So, I can't understand you, can't I? All right, then. Perhaps you can understand me?

LIDA: If I had anything to understand with. [*Pointing to her heart*] Here there's nothing left. It's all gone. Excuse me. [*She goes out.*]

MARIA MIKHAYLOVNA: Mama, where are you?

[GRANDMA VERA *comes in.*]

GRANDMA VERA: I can't stand looking at her, or listening to her.

NINA [*sticks her head in the doorway and whispers*]: She's simply beautiful.

MARIA MIKHAYLOVNA: Who?

NINA: She's just arrived with Pavel Nikolaevich. [*She disappears.*]

[*The door is opened halfway. A man's voice says:* "May we come in?"]

GRANDMA VERA: Come in, Pavel Nikolaevich, come in.

[*Enter* VARVARA VASILEVNA (VARYA), *a beautiful woman of thirty; her husband,* PAVEL NIKOLAEVICH NEFEDOV, *thirty-four, with a good-natured face; and* NINA.]

GRANDMA VERA: Look, Masha, Pavel Nikolaevich has been hiding his wife, and she turns out to be just beautiful.

PAVEL NIKOLAEVICH: I haven't been hiding her. We're always on the go, that's all. Either I'm away on a trip or she is.

GRANDMA VERA: That's your modern family. Husband and wife only see each other at the station.

VARYA [*looking at* NINA, *to* MARIA MIKHAYLOVNA]: Is this your daughter?

MARIA MIKHAYLOVNA: Yes. Daughter and son all in one.

VARYA: She looks very much like her father.

NINA: Do you know Papa?

VARYA: Yes, at work. Very alike.

MARIA MIKHAYLOVNA: That's what people say.

GRANDMA VERA: And she copies all her father's mannerisms. Her father like to sit on the couch with his head back, and so does this one.

MARIA MIKHAYLOVNA: How about some tea?

PAVEL NIKOLAEVICH: We would have liked to very much, but—

VARYA: I have to leave today at ten thirty.

GRANDMA VERA: Well, then, there's still time. Come on with me, Nina. You lay the table.

[GRANDMA VERA *and* NINA *go out*.]

VARYA: Forgive me for talking business the first time I come here. But it just happened that way. I'm leaving and I have to hand over these few pages to Sergey Petrovich.

PAVEL NIKOLAEVICH: Varya dear, you shouldn't have . . .

VARYA: Oh, let me alone. This is my personal opinion on Sergey Petrovich's motor. A few observations.

PAVEL NIKOLAEVICH: A few observations! You've turned everything upside-down.

VARYA: Maybe so. But Sergey Petrovich will understand me. He'll read it and . . . [*She hands the papers to* MARIA MIKHAYLOVNA.]

MARIA MIKHAYLOVNA: And he'll be pleased.

VARYA: Oh, you don't know Sergey Petrovich!

PAVEL NIKOLAEVICH: Varya dear, what ever are you saying? Maria Mikhaylovna doesn't know Sergey Petrovich?

MARIA MIKHAYLOVNA: It doesn't matter. I understand what you meant.

VARYA: Oh! Forgive me. Sergey Petrovich will be upset,

of course. But he will understand me. He has to understand me. It is most important that he should understand.

MARIA MIKHAYLOVNA: Well, why are you going away? You
ought to stay a day or two and explain everything to him
yourself.

VARYA: I'm being sent on this trip. Or, to be more exact,
I'm being exiled. Just so that I shouldn't be able to
explain it and get in everyone's way.

PAVEL NIKOLAEVICH: That's your imagination, Varya.

VARYA [*irritated*]: Oh, don't be like that!

[*Enter* GRANDMA VERA.]

GRANDMA VERA: Tea's ready. Please come in.

VARYA: I'm sorry, but we must go.

GRANDMA VERA: It only takes a minute to drink tea. Pavel
Nikolaevich, I remember that you're a tea addict.

PAVEL NIKOLAEVICH: Yes, I am. One small cup, Varyusha.
[*He holds up one finger.*]

VARYA: Then in the meantime, if you'll allow me, I'll
scribble a note?

MARIA MIKHAYLOVNA: Of course. Here's Sergey Petrovich's
desk. Make yourself at home. And join us when you've
finished writing.

[*Everyone goes into the next room, except* VARYA.]

VARYA [*alone, passing her hand over the desk*]: So this is
how he lives. His wife . . . His daughter. Just like him.
[*She picks up a pen.*]

[*Enter* SERGEY PETROVICH PLATONOV, *suitcase in hand.
He is forty-five.*]

SERGEY PETROVICH: You? You here? What does it mean?

VARYA: I . . . My husband and I . . . Here are some
papers. . . . How are you, Sergey Petrovich?

SERGEY PETROVICH: How are you, Varvara Vasilev a?

[*Enter* MARIA MIKHAYLOVNA.]

MARIA MIKAYLOVNA [*standing in the doorway*]: The tea's getting cold. [*Seeing her husband*] Seryozha!

[*Leaving the door open, she runs up to him. They kiss.*]

Mama! Nina! Sergey's here!

[*Everyone gathers.*]

NINA: Papa dear! [*Clinging to him, she hangs on his neck.*]
GRANDMA VERA: Good Lord! She almost knocked him over!
MARIA MIKHAYLOVNA: Why didn't you send a telegram?
SERGEY PETROVICH: I came by air.
PAVEL NIKOLAEVICH [*shaking hands with* SERGEY PETRO-VICH]: Welcome back, Sergey Petrovich. I'm not sure if you've lost or gained weight. I've never been able to figure these things out. Varya and I dropped by before the train goes.
SERGEY PETROVICH: Who's leaving?
VARYA: I am. Today. I brought you my own individual opinion.
SERGEY PETROVICH: Your own individual opinion about what?
PAVEL NIKOLAEVICH: Better not ask. And in general this isn't a nice way to act. A man just arrives home from a trip and right away you start in about business. Varyusha, Sergey Petrovich is a human being too. He wants at least to have a cup of tea.
VARYA: About your motor. My observations . . .
SERGEY PETROVICH: Are they important?
VARYA: Yes.
SERGEY PETROVICH: Well, since you're in such a hurry, tell me briefly.
PAVEL NIKOLAEVICH: Varyusha, here's a man who hasn't seen his family for three months . . .
SERGEY PETROVICH [*to* VARYA]: Go on.
MARIA MIKHAYLOVNA: Come on, my friends, let's go and finish up the tea. Seryozha, when you're through, try and remember that you have a family in the next room.

[*All go out, except* VARYA *and* SERGEY PETROVICH.]

SERGEY PETROVICH: I'm listening.
VARYA: Read the conclusions. At the end.

SERGEY PETROVICH [*turning over the pages*]: Why are you leaving?

VARYA: I have to.

SERGEY PETROVICH: For a long time?

VARYA: Yes, for a long time.

[*Both of them stand over the open manuscript.*]

[*After a pause*] Have you read it?

SERGEY PETROVICH: No.

VARYA [*further pause—in the same tone*]: Have you read it?

SERGEY PETROVICH: No.

VARYA [*looking at him*]: You're not reading.

SERGEY PETROVICH: No.

VARYA: Well, all right. I'm off, then.

SERGEY PETROVICH: Yes, go.

VARYA: I knew I shouldn't have come here today.

SERGEY PETROVICH: No, you shouldn't.

VARYA: I felt that you weren't far away.

SERGEY PETROVICH: Why did you come?

VARYA [*after a pause*]: I've taken your pen. You won't be angry, will you? [*He says nothing.*] Well, thanks. Forgive me for coming here today. This is the first and last time. But I'm not taking anything away from anyone. I'm not hurting anyone. I just . . . It was hard . . . Well, now I've seen you. [*She is half crying, half laughing, trying to get hold of herself.*] I'll be all right . . . in just a minute . . . [*stubbornly*] I'll be all right . . . I'll be all right.

[SERGEY PETROVICH *looks silently into* VARYA'S *face as though he were seeing her for the first time. Pause.*]

VARYA [*in a low voice*]: Besides, do you know what? Do you know another reason why I came? I'd heard . . . My husband phoned here and they told him they were expecting a telegram from you. And I wanted to hear what you would say. What you would say to her. Forgive me, that's completely . . . Well, good-by. And farewell. And . . . And . . . Oh well, what's said is said. . . .

SERGEY PETROVICH: Will you write me?

VARYA: No.

SERGEY PETROVICH: Can I write you?

VARYA: No, you mustn't. [*She points to the next room.*] You mustn't. What's the use?

SERGEY PETROVICH: Well, I too . . . suddenly got the idea . . . and took the plane here.

VARYA [*pointing to the manuscript*]: Well, here's my own individual opinion.

SERGEY PETROVICH: We won't talk about that right now. After all, we are saying good-by.

VARYA: Yes. Good-by. Now you know everything.

SERGEY PETROVICH [*looking into her face*]: Farewell.

VARYA [*walks decisively up to the door*]: Pavel! It's time for us to go. [*She nods through the doorway.*] Good-by.

[PAVEL NIKOLAEVICH *comes in quickly. He is followed by* NINA.]

PAVEL NIKOLAEVICH: Well, Varyusha, have you given him all your science?

VARYA: Yes, let's go.

PAVEL NIKOLAEVICH: This is not my fault, Sergey Petrovich, I assure you. I consider . . .

[VARYA, PAVEL, *and* SERGEY PETROVICH *leave the room.*]

NINA [*seating herself astride the suitcase*]: Presents, presents, more presents!

[SERGEY PETROVICH *comes back. Enter* MARIA MIKHAYLOVNA.]

NINA: What surprises have you brought, Papa?

SERGEY PETROVICH: What? Oh, yes . . . Well, I thought— what can one bring to Moscow? I brought a blue dog made of clay. Very funny. [*He looks around the room.*] Very funny. [*His glance falls on the clock.*] Ah, the clock? No one touched it while I was away?

NINA: No, no one touched it.

SERGEY PETROVICH: Quite right, too. Winding the clock is a man's job.

MARIA MIKHAYLOVNA: That's something we won't forget for our whole life.

[SERGEY PETROVICH *goes up to the clock, winds it, and sets the pendulum in motion. He looks at his own wrist watch.*]

SERGEY PETROVICH: Nine exactly. [*He sets the clock.*] It's going to strike now. [*He puts one arm around* NINA, *the other around* MARIA MIKHAYLOVNA.] Well, once again . . . Greetings, my dear ones.

MARIA MIKHAYLOVNA [*looking searchingly into his face*]: Welcome home.

[*They stand together, listening to the clock strike.*]

SCENE II

A hotel room. December 31. A modest double room. A desk with a telephone. It is a winter evening. Sitting at the desk is MARGARITA, *a woman neither young nor old, but what is called "getting on." She is writing, occasionally glancing at a book. On the radio a symphony concert is just ending. The announcer says: "In one minute you will hear the New Year concert from Moscow."* MARGARITA *switches off the radio and goes on working.*

MARGARITA: Good for them! They made the same sort of glass in ancient Egypt! They didn't try to pull a fast one.

[*The door bursts open and in comes* VARYA *in a fur coat and fur cap, loaded with parcels.*]

VARYA: Bring it here, please. [*To* MARGARITA] Oh, Margarita! Help me quickly, please, or I'll spill everything.

[*Enter an aged* BELLBOY *with a small Christmas tree.*]

MARGARITA [*taking the parcels*]: A Christmas tree? Who's that for?

VARYA: It's for us, of course. [*To the* BELLBOY] Put it on the desk. Margarita dear, you'll have to clear off your papers.

MARGARITA: But I'm working here.

VARYA: On New Year's Eve? That's not right. [*To the* BELLBOY] Put it down, put it there, don't pay any attention to her.

MARGARITA [*hurriedly gathering up her papers*]: This is sheer despotism! What an idea! A Christmas tree in the middle of the desk! In the first place, a Christmas tree should go on the floor.

VARYA: And second?

MARGARITA: Second . . . well . . . why do we need a Christmas tree?

BELLBOY: It's a real young tree. Full of sap.

VARYA [*to* MARGARITA]: Did you hear that? Not like you and me.

MARGARITA: What stupid jokes!

VARYA: I only just managed to buy the tree. There's not a soul on the streets.

BELLBOY [*setting up the tree*]: Yes, this is not Moscow. People are all eating dinner by now. This is a quiet town. We don't have much in the way of historical sights. There's a furniture factory and a glass plant. And now we have our Machine Works. Is that, perhaps, what you came for?

VARYA: It is indeed.

BELLBOY: That's what I thought. Maybe our furniture isn't the very best. But they do a good job of cutting glass.

MARGARITA: Your glass is famous. For two centuries the whole world has been admiring it.

BELLBOY: Yes, that's right. Foreigners come here and they can't speak our language. But they tell us by signs what glass they want to buy. [*He points to the tree.*] *Is* it all right like that?

VARYA: Attach it a bit more firmly here, please.

BELLBOY: Quite right. I can see at once that you're an engineer. Otherwise, we have a quiet life here. We read in the papers about the congresses they have in Moscow. But, of course, we don't have anything of the sort here.

VARYA: What would you want congresses here for?

BELLBOY: Quite right. There'd be no sense in it. Just the same . . . [*He attaches the tree more firmly.*] Now it will stay in place till next New Year's Eve.

[VARYA *pays him.*]

Much obliged. I wish you the very best in the New Year.

VARYA: Thanks. The same to you. I'm curious to know what you think would be the very best for me?

BELLBOY: If, forgive me, you're not married?

VARYA: I am married.

BELLBOY: Do you have any children?

VARYA: No children.

BELLBOY: Then I'll wish you a child. It's not easy with children, but without them, you know, it's impossible.

MARGARITA [*challengingly*]: I'm not married.

BELLBOY [*after thought*]: Well, you don't have to be.

MARGARITA: Naturally not.

BELLBOY [*bowing*]: Good Health. [*He goes out.*]

MARGARITA: He didn't wish me a husband. He understood that it would be useless.

VARYA: Why useless?

MARGARITA: Because. There is a time, my dear, for everything. [*Changing the subject*] Now, what was the idea of dragging this Christmas tree up here?

VARYA: To celebrate the New Year. Don't be angry. It would be better if you'd help me decorate it. [*She unwraps the parcels.*]

MARGARITA [*irritably*]: Better. As though you knew what was better. Good Lord, what's this?

VARYA: Decorations for the tree. Here—take hold of this end and stand still.

MARGARITA [*pointing to another parcel*]: And what's here?

VARYA: All sorts of things. Wine, pastries, tangerines, salmon, and that sort of thing.

MARGARITA: This is madness. Who's it for?

VARYA [*decorating the tree*]: Here—loop it over the branch.

MARGARITA: You're out of your mind. Who are you going to celebrate New Year's with?

VARYA: With you, Margarita dear, with you.

MARGARITA: Just the two of us?

VARYA: Yes. Just the two of us. And please don't pester me today, do you hear?

MARGARITA: Two females celebrating New Year together? It's a sad picture.

VARYA: If you like, I'll be your boy-friend. Margarita, like a true gentleman, I tell you that in those down-at-the-heel slippers you look simply fascinating. But if you put something else on, you'd look even better.

MARGARITA: Go on with you . . . Who should I get dressed up for? By the way, there was a telegram for you.

VARYA [*quickly*]: Where?

MARGARITA: On the table under the books.

VARYA [*looking*]: It's not here.

MARGARITA: Look on the window sill.

VARYA [*still can't find it*]: Where on earth is it?

MARGARITA: Maybe I dropped it in the hall.

VARYA [*rushing into the hallway*]: Where?

MARGARITA: Oh, Varya, in my bag on the chair.

VARYA [*taking the telegram from the bag*]: Well, at last! [*Hastily she unseals and reads the telegram.*]

MARGARITA: It's written all over you that it's from a man.

VARYA [*her face expressionless*]: It's from my husband. New Year's greetings. And what made you think it was from a man?

MARGARITA: Because it's a long one. We women are stingier. Greetings, and that's it. Mmm, so, it's from your husband?

VARYA: Yes, that's right.

MARGARITA: You said that a bit sourly.

VARYA: No, it was because of the telegram. He writes: "Tests proceeding normally." That's rot! If everything were going all right, he wouldn't have written that.

MARGARITA: What are these tests?

VARYA: Tests on a motor.

MARGARITA: What motor?

VARYA: Do you understand anything about motors?

MARGARITA: How should I? I'm a historian. But I will try to understand, I really will.

VARYA: In general terms it's this way. There's an engineer there called Platonov. Sergey Petrovich Platonov. My husband works in his group. Do you understand?

MARGARITA: So far I understand.

VARYA: Well, this engineer and his group have constructed a motor for our plant. A government testing commission was appointed.

MARGARITA: To see if it was acceptable?

VARYA: More or less. It has various representatives. I'm the representative for our plant. It's important for us that the motor should have a small clearance gauge and very regular rotation.

MARGARITA: Halt. Explain to me without all these details. I belong to the humanities. Talk to me as you would to the janitor.

VARYA: How should I explain it? [*She takes one of the decorations off the tree.*] Here's a little donkey with a cart. Let's say that the donkey is the motor and the cart is the machine.

MARGARITA: That's better.

VARYA: The donkey must be small, but strong. But it's also important that the donkey should draw the cart smoothly, without bumps. Because we're transporting . . . well, let's say some wineglasses of fine crystal.

MARGARITA: We've heard of your crystal glasses!

VARYA: Well, they have constructed a motor of unusual design. It's really amazingly compact. But strong impulses in the transmission are unavoidable and the vibrations are passed on into the machine.

MARGARITA: Hold it, hold it. She's at it again. Talk to me like a human being. Tell me about the little donkey.

VARYA: The donkey is going to shake the cart. You understand what a mess that will make?

MARGARITA: And what can you do about it? Replace the donkey?

VARYA: That's what I think. But the commission has accepted the motor.

MARGARITA: So the commission is a pack of fools and you're the only clever one?

VARYA: They've carried out their assignment. But when their assignment was drawn up, this question was *overlooked*.

MARGARITA: And what does he think about it?

VARYA: Who?

MARGARITA: Not the donkey, of course. Pletnyov, or whatever his name is.

VARYA: Platonov. He admits that I'm right in principle. My husband wrote me that. Only he says that they can eliminate the defects. [*Sadly*] But he's wrong. It's the design itself that's at fault.

MARGARITA [*angrily*]: Where has he been all his life? He's a donkey himself.

VARYA: You can't calculate everything in advance. His superiors were against it, but he passed on my memorandum to the Minister. He wrote that my arguments were important and should be verified.

MARGARITA: The usual male trickery. If you hadn't been there, he'd have sneezed on your glassware.

VARYA: What glassware?

MARGARITA: The crystal glasses. Have you forgotten?

VARYA: No, he's not that sort of person. . . . He's very honest, upright. . . . He's a man of principle.

MARGARITA: So what happens next?

VARYA: Next? Next I climb onto the table. [*She places a chair on the table and climbs onto the chair*.] I hope I don't fall. . . . Will you hold it? I must put a star right at the top.

MARGARITA [*holding the chair*]: You're quite a nicely built wench, Varvara. Your husband must love you, doesn't he?

VARYA: Hold on to the chair.

MARGARITA: I am holding it. Well, does he love you?

VARYA: Yes, he loves me.

MARGARITA: And do you love him?

VARYA [*fixing the star*]: Does that look right?

MARGARITA: It looks fine. I was asking, do you love your husband?

VARYA: Hold on to the chair or I'll fall.

MARGARITA: I am holding it. Don't you try to throw me off the track.

VARYA [*getting down*]: I'm not trying to. You were asking about my husband? No, I don't love him. I'm in love with another man. Is that clear enough?

MARGARITA: Couldn't be clearer. And where's the other man? Is he in Moscow too?

VARYA: Yes.

MARGARITA: And where does he work?

VARYA: In the same place as my husband.

MARGARITA: Mmm, I see. Tell me more.

VARYA: There's nothing more to tell. He has a wife and a daughter. And I have a husband. I'll stay on here a little longer and . . . I'll get him out of my system.

MARGARITA: So . . .

VARYA: I'll pound this out of myself. I've got to pound this out of myself!

[*For several seconds they decorate the tree, only occasionally exchanging such remarks as "the basket," "the rabbit should go higher," etc.*]

MARGARITA: Yes. Everyone has his troubles. One person has too much, and the other hasn't got anybody.

VARYA: Margarita, you were married, weren't you?

MARGARITA: I don't look like an old maid, do I? I've been married. Three times. And every time I was the one who left. Every time it was the same thing that got me down. Why is everything so good to begin with and so bad afterward? Where does love go to? It's like water and sand. Is the beginning all an illusion? Do people pretend to be better than they are? Then I want no part of it. I'm an independent person. I have a higher degree and a profession. And I can afford to send you all straight to hell. Am I right?

VARYA: I don't know. I don't know anything any more.

MARGARITA: It turned out I was wrong. It turns out that you yourself have to make your man into a husband. Every day. It turns out that we deceive them too at the start. We seduce them. To begin with, we would never go to them without first looking in the mirror. And we'd be careful in every way. Thoughts, gestures, behavior, at first they were all kept in hand. Everything was important, necessary, and interesting. What a fool!

VARYA: Who?

MARGARITA: Me. I was a fool. And now I'm clever, only nobody gives a damn.

VARYA: Perhaps you're not clever in that way, Margarita.

MARGARITA: You're a child. Why, you child, didn't *he* send you the telegram?

VARYA: Because we agreed not to. No communication whatsoever. [*Laughing*] It's funny how it happens, Margarita: no one knew a thing about it, and I suddenly tell you the whole story.

MARGARITA: That's how it happens. We'll go our separate ways, and that'll be the end of it. But you told me because it's hard for a person to be alone. Particularly for a woman. But it is possible. After all, I am alive.

VARYA: Yes, it's hard.

MARGARITA: We need someone to powder our noses for, as

they say. It doesn't matter if you're an engineer or super-
engineer, the greatest scholar of them all, or a top-line
social worker.

VARYA: It's hard for him, too.

MARGARITA: Perhaps it is. But, you know, some men are
such beasts, they grit their teeth, bury themselves in
their work—and that's all there is to it. They don't so
much as bat an eyelid, the devils, even if you meet them
ten times a day. I admire that sort—they're made of
stone.

VARYA: Well, we finished decorating the tree while we were
talking. Now we must do something about ourselves.

MARGARITA: Perhaps you did invite someone after all?

VARYA: There's only you and me.

MARGARITA: Then I pass. I'll lay the table.

VARYA [*in front of the mirror*]: First the eyelashes.

MARGARITA: You look fine. Even without make-up.

VARYA: But better with make-up.

MARGARITA: Don't pout your lips. And don't put on too
much. It's not good.

VARYA: But it's good to be beautiful?

MARGARITA: Yes, it's good.

VARYA: But how can you be beautiful if God didn't provide
you with much in the way of health? You have to resort
to make-up.

MARGARITA: Of course, we women have no sense of measure.

VARYA: Well, that seems to be all. [*She goes up to the
table.*] Oh! How beautiful!

MARGARITA [*looking at* VARYA'S *face*]: That's not so bad
either. All right, I guess I'll change my shoes. [*She
changes her shoes.*]

VARYA [*to herself*]: Just to see him for one little minute.
[*Looking at her watch*] It's ten of twelve. Do you know
how to uncork bottles?

MARGARITA [*putting on lipstick*]: I'm busy.

VARYA: I'll have a try myself. Do you like salmon?

MARGARITA: Since the war I like everything. Turn on the
radio.

[VARYA *switches it on. The sound of automobiles in Red
Square is heard.*]

VARYA: Margarita dear, quickly. The Kremlin chimes will be striking any minute. [*Both sit down at the table.*]

MARGARITA [*pouring the wine*]: Who will propose the toast?

VARYA: I know one. We have a traditional toast in our family. Papa made it up. He is an austere man, irreproachably honest. He's a surgeon. We don't wish each other either good health or happiness or anything else of that sort. Papa usually says: "May each of us receive according to his desert."

MARGARITA: Most suitable.

VARYA: Well?

[*They clink glasses, raise them, and wait. The Kremlin chimes resound.*]

MARGARITA: May each of us receive according to her desert. Happy New Year, Varenka.

VARYA: The same to you.

[*They drink.*]

MARGARITA: Let's eat.

[*The telephone rings loudly.*]

It's long distance. For you, Varya.

VARYA [*about to rush to the phone; stops dead*]: But maybe . . .

MARGARITA: Take it.

VARYA [*picking up the receiver*]: Hello? . . . Yes, yes, Nefedova speaking. All right, I'll hold the line. . . . [*Pause*] Yes, it's me. . . . [*Gasping*] I can hear you, thank you. But why did you? . . . You shouldn't have . . . No, you mustn't . . . Don't say that. Oh, dear . . . Yes, I can hear . . . Well, you mustn't . . . I forbid you to say that, do you hear me? [*Affectionately*] You can't hear me? It's not true. That's not true, either . . . No, that's all not true . . . I can't bear to hear any more! I'm hanging up. [*She puts the receiver down hard, and looks at* MARGARITA.] You heard that? What does it mean?

MARGARITA: Right at midnight on New Year's Eve. He must have begged the operator on his knees.

VARYA: You heard, didn't you?

MARGARITA: What's going to happen to you two?

VARYA: Nothing is going to happen. Nothing. It's not in the cards. You'll see.

MARGARITA: *I* won't see.

VARYA: No. This is the end, the end, the end.

MARGARITA: They have a saying in the Orient: "You told me once—I believed you. You told me twice—I had my doubts. You told me a third time, and I knew you were lying."

C U R T A I N

ACT II

SCENE III

At work. March. Daytime. A building with white-painted glass walls. One door leads into the corridor, the other into the designer's office. A desk. A telephone. A very large drawing board. On the desk some blueprints. PLATONOV *in a white smock, is near the drawing board. He interrupts his work, goes to the door leading into the designer's office, half opens it, and calls: "Krasnushkin! Kolya!" He goes back to the board. Enter* KOLYA, *a young designer, in a white smock.*

SERGEY PETROVICH [*pointing to the drawing pinned on the board*]: Take the dimensions and work out the suspension.

KOLYA: What? Another suspension?

SERGEY PETROVICH: Yes. [*He goes on drawing.*]

KOLYA: I've no strength left, Sergey Petrovich.

SERGEY PETROVICH: You have no strength left?

KOLYA [*glumly*]: Perhaps I can summon up a little. [*He takes the dimensions and writes them down, grumbling.*] So I take them down . . . and I work it out . . . and what's the sense in it?

SERGEY PETROVICH: Do I have to explain to you too that

only by changing the suspension and the flywheel can
we get the motor right?

KOLYA: No, you don't have to explain it to me.

SERGEY PETROVICH: So don't waste time.

KOLYA: It's all right for you. You've got talent.

SERGEY PETROVICH: Decent people do not praise their superior to his face or curse him behind his back. Did
you know that?

KOLYA: I wasn't trying to flatter you. I was thinking of
something else. I was thinking that it's easy for a
talented person. He flits from one idea to the next.
From suspension to suspension. But for me it's torment.
[*He mutters figures to himself.*] Work it out. Drag it
out. Just like a donkey.

SERGEY PETROVICH: Rot!

KOLYA: Why rot?

SERGEY PETROVICH: It's the ungifted person who has things
easy. He's the one who flits from idea to idea. The
talented one has to suffer.

KOLYA: Is this a paradox?

SERGEY PETROVICH: It's the truth. An untalented man has
no reason to suffer. He doesn't see what he's looking
for. In general he's not looking for anything. Whatever
results he gets are all right with him. But the able man
will pull out all his veins with his own hands until he
gets where he wants to be.

KOLYA: Then everything is all right.

SERGEY PETROVICH: How do you mean?

KOLYA: Well, that means that I too have something like
. . . well, so to speak . . .

SERGEY PETROVICH [*smiling*]: We aren't modest. . . .

KOLYA: Maybe . . . [*He is about to leave.*]

SERGEY PETROVICH: Why don't you tell me about the tests
yesterday?

KOLYA: There's nothing to tell.

SERGEY PETROVICH: Just the same?

KOLYA: The people came from the plant.

SERGEY PETROVICH [*after a pause*]: Go on.

KOLYA: They brought Chivilikhin from the Ministry. You
remember, he used to work for you and you kicked him
out for laziness.

SERGEY PETROVICH: I remember.

KOLYA: Well, that's all.

SERGEY PETROVICH: Stop it, Kolya. I know you. What did happen? Were they up to something?

KOLYA: Nothing in particular. Only Chivilikhin asked about the results of the most recent tests.

SERGEY PETROVICH: Yes?

KOLYA: Well, as you know yourself, they were nothing to boast about.

SERGEY PETROVICH: Go on.

KOLYA: In general, everything turned out well.

SERGEY PETROVICH: I don't follow you.

KOLYA: Well, then you know who this Chivilikhin is. He's a schemer, a bureaucrat, and a tale-bearer. If he heard that we were having difficulties, he would raise the alarm through the whole Ministry. . . . So . . .

[SERGEY PETROVICH *maintains a menacing silence.*]

So . . . and he's a liar, too. . . . He's deceived us often enough. You write him a memorandum. He promises, but he doesn't do it. You know yourself.

SERGEY PETROVICH [*stopping work*]: What did you tell him about the results of our recent tests?

KOLYA [*despondently*]: I told him they were good.

SERGEY PETROVICH: You lied.

KOLYA: Yes. I had to. When in Rome, as they say . . .

SERGEY PETROVICH [*with restraint*]: You can leave. [KOLYA *clasps the drawings to his chest.*] Leave the drawings here. From now on I am not working with you any more.

KOLYA: Sergey Petrovich . . .

SERGEY PETROVICH: I could do without Chivilikhin, number one. And I don't need a number two, either.

KOLYA: But I saved the day.

SERGEY PETROVICH: With such methods? Turn over your things to Nefedov.

KOLYA [*almost in tears*]: Comrade . . . What is happening?

SERGEY PETROVICH: Go on, Krasnushkin. [*He begins to work.*]

KOLYA [*moves slowly toward the door, stops, then vehemently*]: I won't go! I won't leave you, do you understand? That's all there is to it! [*Silence.*] This won't happen again! And that's all! [*Silence.*] What am I? A

child? I won't do it again. On my honor as a Komsomol.
I swear. Well?

SERGEY PETROVICH [*Lifts the receiver and dials*]: Is that
the Technical Department of the Ministry? Get me
Chivilikhin, please. . . . This is Platonov. Yesterday you
were given incorrect information about the tests. The
results of the three last tests were bad. . . . What? What
has the name of our man to do with it? . . . You're going to write a memorandum? Then make your complaint
against me. It's my fault that I appointed someone who
did not know how to answer. Yes, yes, I take full
responsibility. [*He replaces the receiver. To* KOLYA]
What a brat!

KOLYA [*with adoration*]: Quite right!

SERGEY PETROVICH: You are the brat!

KOLYA: Yes, that's what I meant.

SERGEY PETROVICH: A puppy.

KOLYA: Quite right.

SERGEY PETROVICH: A whelp.

KOLYA: Absolutely right.

SERGEY PETROVICH: Go on, get out.

KOLYA [*cautiously*]: And the drawings?

SERGEY PETROVICH [*pause*]: You can take them with you.

KOLYA: The Lord be praised. [*As he collects his drawings
he sings quietly.*]

> "The birds they fly off in the autumn
> Fly off where the skies they are blue
> To far-off, warm lands they do wander
> [*As he passes* PLATONOV's *table*]
> But I shall remain here with you."

SERGEY PETROVICH: Flatterer.

KOLYA: Quite right. [*He is about to leave.*]

SERGEY PETROVICH: Wait!

KOLYA: Uh-oh.

SERGEY PETROVICH: Ask Nefedov to come in.

KOLYA: Without fail! [*He disappears.*]

[SERGEY PETROVICH *stands gloomily by the board. He
goes up to the calendar and leafs through it. Then he
returns to the board and goes on working. Enter* NE-
FEDOV.]

PAVEL NEFEDOV: What did you do to make Kolya so happy?

SERGEY PETROVICH: What do you mean?

PAVEL NIKOLAEVICH: He pinned a paper on the board and he's simply dancing with joy. What did you do, give him a commendation?

SERGEY PETROVICH: Sort of. How are things going with the flywheel, Pavel Nikolaevich?

PAVEL NIKOLAEVICH: One more day—and I'll bring you the drawings to be signed.

SERGEY PETROVICH: The flywheel is our main hope now. And we haven't much time. [*He whistles softly.*]

PAVEL NIKOLAEVICH: I'll do everything I can. I'm excited about it myself. And I'm not the only one. The other day I got a letter from Varya. Imagine, she's excited too. It's hard to understand what she wants more: that she should be right or that we should be right. Or, rather, that you should be right. Really.

SERGEY PETROVICH: Hmm.

PAVEL NIKOLAEVICH: Don't think I write her objectively. I even try to make the situation look better than it is. I pretend to be a big optimist. Everything is just fine, my dear spouse. The results are encouraging. And you're going to have to eat crow.

SERGEY PETROVICH: Hmm.

PAVEL NIKOLAEVICH: I didn't want to write about the tests at all. But she insists. I miss her, you know. . . . After all, it's been three months and . . . [*Counting to himself*] and four days. She left on the tenth. . . .

SERGEY PETROVICH [*interrupting*]: Well, that's all I wanted to talk to you about.

PAVEL NIKOLAEVICH: I'm going, I'm going. [*He heads for the door.*]

SERGEY PETROVICH: Pavel Nikolaevich! . . . No, it doesn't matter. . . . [*Decisively*] When is Varvara Vasilevna due to arrive?

PAVEL NIKOLAEVICH [*standing in the doorway*]: Well, you know, she's long since overdue. Really. They promised she'd be here by March first. Then they extended her stay again. I expected her last week. But she didn't arrive. Now I've simply given up guessing. They're giving her the run-around. That's the sort of person she is. She needs looking after like a child.

SERGEY PETROVICH: All right. Now, please, do your best on the flywheel.

PAVEL NIKOLAEVICH: Right away, Sergey Petrovich. Right away. [*He goes out.*]

SERGEY PETROVICH [*banging his fist on the table*]: Couldn't keep it in! Couldn't hold my tongue! You fool!

[*Enter* ANDREY VIKTOROVICH KRAVTSOV, PLATONOV'S *associate, a member of the Party committee. He is about fifty years old.*]

KRAVTSOV: Who are you paying such honor to?

SERGEY PETROVICH: Myself.

KRAVTSOV: I thought so. [*He sits down.*] Well, my friend, the Party committee is getting so many complaints from all directions about your iron character that I can only cry ouch! . . . They phone from the Ministry. They phone from the plant. Golovin is cursing you. He says that because of you we won't get a prize. When are you going to get that motor into the plant?

SERGEY PETROVICH: Andrey Viktorovich, you're an engineer yourself. You must understand. The Minister has given me time to make corrections. So don't let anyone push me around.

KRAVTSOV: Listen . . . I understand that. But I understand something else. A man has his pride. For example, they tell him: "It won't work." And he says: "Yes, it will work, and you can go to hell," etc. And then he himself grasps the fact that it isn't worth a damn, but he can't bear to have people see him eat his words. Especially if he is a distinguished engineer and she, for example, is only a young engineer. You understand what I'm getting at? But he should say straight out, like a real worker: "This is how it is, comrades. It seems that the woman is right." Understand me. It's not the prize I'm worrying about. It's the job. And the authority. The authority of this person.

SERGEY PETROVICH: What are you trying to talk me into? When Nefedova declared that the motor would not work, the motor had already been accepted. Who stood up for her? I did. But she thinks the defects cannot be corrected. And I think they can. We haven't entirely succeeded with the suspension, so we'll make the correction on the

flywheel. If I see that it's not working out, I'll be the
first to say so. I'm not trying to pull the wool over
anyone's eyes. Not for one second.

KRAVTSOV [*rising*]: That's all. Conversation finished. That's
what I'll tell the secretary. And you get on with the work
and spare your nerves. [*He is about to leave.*] I almost
forgot. The Party has an assignment for you. Ignatyuk's
wife has been in to see the committee. Crying. She says
he has got mixed up with some girl and is abandoning his
family. They've got two children. So please look into
this matter and report to the office. And this Ignatyuk
is even trying to justify his actions. "Love," he says,
"is free, and has the whole world in its spell." What a
cad!

SERGEY PETROVICH: Hold on a moment. You don't yet
know the whole story.

KRAVTSOV: Come on now, drop that kind of talk. My friend,
I know Ignatyuk and I've seen his wife. And, for better
or worse, I understand something about love. So don't
get sentimental, my friend, about this affair; stick to the
main facts.

[*Enter* KOLYA.]

KOLYA [*excited*]: Sergey Petrovich . . . It's about the suspension. Are you busy?

KRAVTSOV: He's free now. Psychologist . . .

[*All three go out. For a time the stage is empty. The
door leading into the corridor opens. Enter* VARYA. *She
looks around, and sees the jacket hanging on the chair.
Beyond the partition* PLATONOV'S *voice is heard. "Mistakes are necessary, you understand? Why are you all
afraid of making mistakes? That way we won't achieve
anything worth while." Then there is silence, but* VARYA
continues to listen. The phone rings.]

VARYA [*picking up the receiver*]: Hello? Sergey Petrovich
has gone out. Oh, it's from his home? His daughter? He
must be reminded that it's his birthday? I remember.
. . . That is, forgive me, I'll remind him. . . . He
shouldn't be late? His favorite cutlets? . . . And cran-

berry juice? . . . Very good, I'll tell him. [*She puts down the receiver.*]

[*Enter* PLATONOV. *He sees* VARYA *and quietly closes the door behind him. Then he goes slowly up to* VARYA. *They look at each other.* PLATONOV *takes her hands and covers his face with her palms.*]

SERGEY PETROVICH [*raising his head*]: At last . . .

VARYA: Yes . . .

SERGEY PETROVICH [*looking at her*]: Don't look at me just now.

VARYA: I can't.

SERGEY PETROVICH: What are we standing here for? Let's move. [*He leads her to the desk.*] It's unbelievable.

VARYA: Yes . . . What?

SERGEY PETROVICH: That you're here.

VARYA: May I touch you just a little? [*She feels his forehead and cheek with her finger.*]

SERGEY PETROVICH: You can do anything.

VARYA [*removing her hand*]: That's all . . .

SERGEY PETROVICH: It's not much. [*He puts his head close to hers.*]

VARYA: We'd better move apart. Move back.

SERGEY PETROVICH: I can't.

VARYA: Move back, darling. We can't stand like this. Someone may come in. They'd see us. . . . And they'd realize everything.

SERGEY PETROVICH: What would they realize?

VARYA: Everything.

SERGEY PETROVICH: Let them.

VARYA: Aren't you afraid of that?

SERGEY PETROVICH: I'm not afraid of anything any more.

VARYA: Then you must move back.

SERGEY PETROVICH: You belong to me. You understand? I have to be with you.

VARYA: Even today?

SERGEY PETROVICH: Always.

VARYA: But not today. There was a phone call from your home. You were to be reminded that today is your birthday. And you're not to be late. [*She moves over to the board.*]

SERGEY PETROVICH: You know, today really is my birthday.

[*Enter* IGOR ALEKSANDROVICH GOLOVIN, *the chief designer, a thick-set man of about fifty-five.*]

GOLOVIN: So this is where she's hiding. Your husband is looking for you. Greetings, Comrade Nefedova.

VARYA: Greetings, Comrade Golovin.

GOLOVIN: Sergey Petrovich, I've got a bone to pick with you.

SERGEY PETROVICH: What's the matter?

GOLOVIN: They're complaining about you in the Ministry. Your manner and so on.

SERGEY PETROVICH: I could also complain. About manners and so on.

GOLOVIN: That's not the point. You've got us in hot water with the plant. Now you're getting us in trouble with the Ministry. And for what? Your tests are a pure waste of time. Hold on. I know what you're going to say. The Minister gave us extra time and so on. But we can't stand on mere formalities. The motor has been accepted. We have the right to deliver it. But you . . .

SERGEY PETROVICH: So that's what you mean by standing on mere formalities.

GOLOVIN: The motor conforms to the technical requirements. And we ought to deliver it without wasting time.

SERGEY PETROVICH: Without wasting our prize, you mean?

GOLOVIN: Who's talking about a prize? What has a prize to do with it? Well, if you like, it has something to do with it. I don't see anything reprehensible about that. The whole collective worked on it.

SERGEY PETROVICH: The only reprehensible thing would be if another collective at the plant had to correct our motor.

GOLOVIN: We heard that one before. I'm going to insist that the Minister authorize the delivery of our motor. Do you want to ask me any questions?

SERGEY PETROVICH [*pause*]: Igor Aleksandrovich, I have considerable engineering experience. You have more than I have. But what good to us is this experience if we are not going to do everything we are capable of? Answer me that one. What good is our conscience—as engineers, as human beings, as citizens, as Party members, as anything at all? This I don't understand. I ask you to wait till our time is up. Don't go to the Minister.

GOLOVIN [*after thought*]: Dear Sergey Petrovich. You
know how much I like you. Conscience and all the rest
—this is, of course, all very fine. . . . But we have a
planned economy.

SERGEY PETROVICH: But don't they go together?

GOLOVIN: Yes, of course, they do magnificently. I express
myself rather clumsily. But, forgive me, you're looking
at everything from your ivory tower. But it is my duty—
I repeat, my duty—to take a broader view. The prestige
of the institute, the needs of the plant, the requirements
of industry . . . Please understand. I have to go to the
Minister. . . . And one thing more. This is only a small
plant. . . . I cannot allow you in the future—in your
own interests—to carry on discussions with the Ministry.

SERGEY PETROVICH: Unfortunately, I can see that I'll have
to carry on discussions.

GOLOVIN [*exploding*]: I forbid it! This is a disciplinary
matter! I think you're a member of the Party!

SERGEY PETROVICH: You think. I know.

GOLOVIN: You'll be sorry you talked to me like this.

[NEFEDOV *enters hurriedly.*]

PAVEL NIKOLAEVICH: Varyusha? My darling! Oh, excuse
me.

GOLOVIN: Please don't worry . . . I am finished. [*He goes
out.*]

PAVEL NIKOLAEVICH: Varyusha! I was looking for you all
over the institute. Let me kiss you. [*He kisses her;* VARYA
stands motionless.] Don't worry about Sergey Petrovich,
he's an old friend. . . . [*He laughs.*]

[PLATONOV *goes out.*]

You see what tact he has? It's time to quit. Let's go.

VARYA [*painfully*]: I can't go with you.

PAVEL NIKOLAEVICH: Why?

VARYA: I'm going to live at my father's.

PAVEL NIKOLAEVICH: What's all this about?

VARYA: I'm leaving you. . . . I've left you, Pavlik.

PAVEL NIKOLAEVICH: What? . . . How do you mean, leaving?

VARYA: Pavlik, dearest . . . forgive me. I'm sorry I have

to hurt you. . . . If you like, I'll kneel down in front of
you. . . . Hit me if you want to. . . . Maybe you'll
feel better. . . . But I have to tell you . . .
PAVEL NIKOLAEVICH [*slowly*]: What happened, Varya?
VARYA: I've fallen in love, Pavlik. . . . I've fallen in love
with someone else.

SCENE IV

*The Platonovs' apartment. March. Evening, the same day.
Same as Scene I. Laughter and the clatter of plates are
heard in the dining room.* MARIA MIKHAYLOVNA *is sitting
by the telephone.*

MARIA MIKHAYLOVNA [*replacing the receiver*]: No answer . . .

[*Enter* GRANDMA VERA.]

GRANDMA VERA: Perhaps he's gone to the Ministry.
MARIA MIKHAYLOVNA: Without phoning?
GRANDMA VERA: Something urgent.
MARIA MIKHAYLOVNA: Go in to the guests.
GRANDMA VERA: What did they say at the office?
MARIA MIKHAYLOVNA: He left a long time ago.
GRANDMA VERA: Did you phone Pavel Nikolaevich?
MARIA MIKHAYLOVNA: There's no answer.
GRANDMA VERA: You see, Nefedov's not home, either. The
same old story. They must have been called away some-
where. Let's go in to the guests, otherwise it'll be awk-
ward. First we made them wait. And now all the host-
esses have disappeared. That's not the way to behave!
MARIA MIKHAYLOVNA: Correct. See page so and so of the
rules of good etiquette. If you drop a fork at table, don't
pick it up. The footman will do it. Let's go now and
follow the rules of etiquette.

[MARIA MIKHAYLOVNA *follows* GRANDMA VERA *out.* NINA
*apears from the other door. Taking a cushion from the
couch to muffle her voice,* NINA *picks up the telephone.*]

NINA: Oh, Papa, Papa . . . He never pays attention when he's walking in the street. [*She dials.*] Is that Information? [*Crying*] Tell me, please, if someone was in an accident in the street, where should I phone to find out where he is? . . . Thank you. [*She writes down a number.*] Accident Information . . .

[*Enter* MARIA MIKHAYLOVNA. *She hears the last words.*]

MARIA MIKHAYLOVNA: What are you up to?

NINA: Mama, darling, I'm very worried about Papa. . . .

MARIA MIKHAYLOVNA: But why, may I ask?

NINA: I phoned Papa today. And asked them to tell him not to be late. And he must have been in a great hurry. Why did I bother him at work! [*She cries.*]

MARIA MIKHAYLOVNA: Don't be silly. I was worried too, but then I found that he had been called to the Ministry with Pavel Nikolaevich.

NINA: Is that true?

MARIA MIKHAYLOVNA: Well, Pavel Nikolaevich isn't home, either. And he was supposed to come to our party, too. Go wash your face and go back to the dinner table.

[*Knock on the door.*]

Come in.

[*Enter* LIDA *carying packages.*]

MARIA MIKHAYLOVNA: Oh, it's you, Lida. . . . Please come in. Nina, you heard what I told you?

[NINA *goes out.*]

LIDA: Maria Mikhaylovna, please don't think that I'm completely without feeling. . . . Petya and I . . . You're always doing so much for him . . . We decided that since you're having a party today— That's right, isn't it?

MARIA MIKHAYLOVNA: Right.

LIDA: Your husband's birthday . . . So I baked . . . I don't know if you'll like it. [*She uncovers the pastry.*] See his initials? *S* and *P*. And this is what Petya did.

A boat. He used matches and bark. And he carved the
wood. He worked on it a whole month. He thinks that
because he's interested in sailors, that's the best present
anyone could think of for anyone else.

MARIA MIKHAYLOVNA: What delicate work! . . . And the
pie's a great success.

LIDA: Yes, it came out all right.

MARIA MIKHAYLOVNA: Thank you, Lida, and thank Petya
for us. Why don't you go and fetch him and sit down
with us?

LIDA: No, no, that's impossible.

MARIA MIKHAYLOVNA: Why impossible?

LIDA: No, no, it's quite impossible. [*She goes toward the
door.*]

MARIA MIKHAYLOVNA: Just as you wish. Wait a moment!
I believe they have the same birthday. Isn't that right?

LIDA: Yes, that's right.

MARIA MIKHAYLOVNA: Then Petya must have a present too.
Just a minute. [*She looks around, then goes to the book
shelf and begins to search.*]

LIDA: No, please listen . . .

MARIA MIKHAYLOVNA: Don't argue with me.

LIDA: Please don't go to all this trouble, Maria Mikhaylovna. [*Smiling*] I bought him some paints. He's always
painting the sea. He had all sorts of different colors.
First he used up all the blue, and then he painted the
sea green and red and every other color under the sun.
So this time I asked them to put in an extra supply of
blue paint.

MARIA MIKHAYLOVNA [*handing over some books*]: Take
this one . . . and this one . . . and these three . . .
Stanyukovich's *Tales of the Sea,* Sobolev's *The Soul of
the Sea,* and Obruchev's travels. It's true he traveled on
land, but they're still magnificent stories.

LIDA [*taking the books*]: Thank you. He just lives on books.
He just sticks his ears in his hands and he's lost to the
world.

[*The hall bell rings.*]

LIDA: I'll open the door. Don't you trouble. [*She goes out.*]

[*A knock on the door.*]

MARIA MIKHAYLOVNA: Yes, come in.

[*Enter* NEFEDOV, *downcast. His hair and clothing are in disorder.*]

MARIA MIKHAYLOVNA: What's the matter, Pavel Nikolaevich? Has something happened to Seryozha?

PAVEL NIKOLAEVICH: He's just fine. But I'm not . . . we're not . . . you're not. [*He sinks wearily into a chair.*]

MARIA MIKHAYLOVNA: Tell me what's the matter. I'm waiting.

PAVEL NIKOLAEVICH: Right away. [*Slowly*] Right away . . . Although we ought to hurry . . . But there's still time . . . Only I beg you . . . Don't tell anyone.

MARIA MIKHAYLOVNA: Shall I get you some water?

PAVEL NIKOLAEVICH [*with a wave of his arm*]: No, it's all right.

[*Enter* GRANDMA VERA.]

GRANDMA VERA: Masha, how much longer? Oh, you're here, Pavel Nikolaevich? And where's Sergey Petrovich?

PAVEL NIKOLAEVICH [*with anger and malice*]: Your Sergey Petrovich is alive. He's alive and healthy.

MARIA MIKHAYLOVNA: Mama, Pavel Nikolaevich has something to discuss with me. I don't want anyone in here.

GRANDMA VERA: All right, all right. But where's Seryozha?

PAVEL NIKOLAEVICH: Seryozha's busy!

MARIA MIKHAYLOVNA: Sergey Petrovich has been delayed.

PAVEL NIKOLAEVICH: Yes, Sergey Petrovich has been delayed.

GRANDMA VERA: All right. I'll tell that to the guests. [*She goes out.*]

MARIA MIKHAYLOVNA: Well, I'm listening, Pavel Nikolaevich. Have you calmed down?

PAVEL NIKOLAEVICH: Yes, I've calmed down.

MARIA MIKHAYLOVNA: What's happened?

PAVEL NIKOLAEVICH: Nothing. You see what a fool I am? Something happened which I never expected. . . . It's just that your husband . . . and my wife . . . Do you understand?

MARIA MIKHAYLOVNA: I understand.

PAVEL NIKOLAEVICH: And they've gone . . . They've gone

off by themselves. They didn't give a damn about us. Well, what are we going to do? Why don't you say something? Why don't you say something?

MARIA MIKHAYLOVNA: Wait a minute. I'm thinking. Wait . . .

PAVEL NIKOLAEVICH: There's no time to wait! We've got to do something.

MARIA MIKHAYLOVNA: Don't shout! Do something yourself. . . . You're a grown man.

PAVEL NIKOLAEVICH: A grown man! You mean an idiot. How can I help shouting? It hurts, understand, it hurts! She's my wife. My love. You must stop him.

MARIA MIKHAYLOVNA: Why didn't you do that yourself?

PAVEL NIKOLAEVICH: I couldn't. As soon as she told me, I . . . I don't remember a thing. . . . Anyway, I couldn't have stopped them. But you can. They've gone to her place. We can take a taxi and be there in ten, in five minutes. I'll wait for you at the door. Downstairs . . . I beg you.

MARIA MIKHAYLOVNA: I can't do that.

PAVEL NIKOLAEVICH: I beg you. [*He grasps her hands.*] I beg you, Maria Mikhaylovna, dearest Maria Mikhaylovna.

MARIA MIKHAYLOVNA: I can't do that.

PAVEL NIKOLAEVICH: Are you made of stone? I implore you! After all, he's your husband! Don't you love him?

MARIA MIKHAYLOVNA: I can't do it.

PAVEL NIKOLAEVICH: Have pity on me. It's your duty. He . . . he's a Party member. You can go to the Party committee. They'll stop him. It's wrong to break up a family. Let's go. Let's go quickly! [*Stands up*] Remember that you have a daughter!

MARIA MIKHAYLOVNA: And for that very reason . . . I can't.

[PAVEL NIKOLAEVICH, *weeping, sinks onto the couch.*]

Be quiet. Control yourself. You're a man. Men aren't supposed to cry.

PAVEL NIKOLAEVICH: Who are supposed to cry? Women? Well, cry! Why aren't you crying?

[*The dining-room door is flung wide open.* NINA *stands*

in the doorway. Behind her, holding her back, is
GRANDMA VERA.]

NINA: Grandma, let me go! Mama, what's going on in
here? What's happened to Papa?!

[*There is complete silence in the dining room.* MARIA
MIKHAYLOVNA, *without hurrying, goes to the dining-
room door and addresses the guests.*]

MARIA MIKHAYLOVNA: My friends. Pavel Nikolaevich has
arrived, but he's not well. I must stay with him. And
Sergey Petrovich . . . Sergey Petrovich . . . has been
delayed on business. So please forgive me. And please
have a good time without me. [*With her eyes she asks*
GRANDMA VERA *and* NINA *to leave the room. She closes
the door behind them and remains alone with* NEFEDOV.]
PAVEL NIKOLAEVICH: Then I'll go.
MARIA MIKHAYLOVNA: Yes, please do.

[NEFEDOV *goes out.*]

MARIA MIKHAYLOVNA: What shall I do? What shall I do?
Perhaps it's a lie? No, it's true. I've felt it. When he
comes, what shall I say to him? Am I to talk about
myself? That wouldn't mean anything to him if he
doesn't love me anymore. His daughter? The family?
What am I to say? I can't believe it. Until he tells me
himself, I can't believe it! Perhaps it's just a passing
affair, a passion that won't last. And he'll come to his
senses. I'll tell him: "Be sensible, Seryozha!" After all,
he's not like the others. And he'll come to his senses.
That's how these things work out. So they say . . . Or
should I wait? Or should I go myself? No, not for anything in the world! . . . Let him be the first to speak
about it. He's not, after all, like the others. Let him
speak first.

[*The outside door bangs. Enter* PLATONOV.]

SERGEY PLATONOV: I'm very late, Masha. Please forgive
me. I—
MARIA MIKHAYLOVNA [*hurriedly interrupting him*]: It

doesn't matter. I do understand. Work. You . . . didn't meet anyone as you came in?

SERGEY PLATONOV: No, why?

MARIA MIKHAYLOVNA: Nothing. It doesn't matter. What am I thinking? Once again—many happy returns, Seryozha.

SERGEY PLATONOV: Thank you.

MARIA MIKHAYLOVNA: We were thinking . . .

SERGEY PLATONOV: What?

MARIA MIKHAYLOVNA: That you might have had an accident. Nina was very upset. . . . But I can't . . . I couldn't believe . . .

SERGEY PLATONOV: Masha . . .

MARIA MIKHAYLOVNA: Our guests are waiting. . . .

SERGEY PLATONOV: Oh, yes, the guests.

MARIA MIKHAYLOVNA: We must go in to the guests.

[*The door opens.* NINA, *seeing her father, runs up to him, clasps him round the neck and hangs on.*]

CURTAIN

ACT III

SCENE V

VARYA's *old home. April. A room in the apartment of* VARYA's *father. A door leading into the next room is open. The door into the hallway is closed. Two coats and a man's hat are hanging on the door. On the wall is a large photograph of a young couple. The woman might be* VARYA *if it were not for the short hair and the sacklike blouse with a round neck, like those worn in the twenties. The young man beside her is in a leather jacket and has dark hair and a mustache. A table. A couch. Sitting at the table in his shirt sleeves is a man of about sixty. He is reading the newspaper. His face is similar to the one in the photograph, but his mustache is gray and his hair is rimmed with gray. He wears glasses. This is* VARYA's *father,* VASILY FEDOROVICH. *Evening.*

VASILY FEDOROVICH: Do you hear, Varya?

VARYA [*from the next room*]: Yes?

VASILY FEDOROVICH: Dolukhanova is giving a concert on the eighteenth. We must buy tickets.

VARYA: All right.

VASILY FEDOROVICH: It isn't all right. You haven't been to the conservatory at all this season. To begin with, you were away on your trip. . . . Then this business . . .

VARYA: Yes, I didn't manage to go.

VASILY FEDOROVICH: And what have you managed to do?

[*The telephone rings in the next room.*]

VARYA [*from the next room*]: Yes? Hello, Grigory Stepanovich.

VASILY FEDOROVICH: I'm not home!

VARYA: Papa is not home. [*To her father*] What shall I tell him? A conference tomorrow?

VASILY FEDOROVICH: Another conference? I'm busy. I'm operating.

VARYA: I remember. Papa said he would be operating tomorrow. Is it very important?

VASILY FEDOROVICH: To hell with it! I'm operating, and that's all there is to it!

VARYA [*to her father*]: I'm to tell him that Kireev should operate?

VASILY FEDOROVICH: To hell with him! Does he expect me to trust Kireev with a stomach resection? Not on your life!

VARYA: I doubt very much if Papa will agree. . . . All right, I'll give him the message. Good-by.

[*Enter* VARYA *from the other room.*]

VARYA: He says it's a very important conference.

VASILY FEDOROVICH: Rot. If it were his stomach that needed a resection, he wouldn't think the conference was more important. That's the third conference in a week. They're out of their minds!

VARYA: I think he was offended. He knows you're at home. After all, he is your superior physician.

VASILY FEDOROVICH: Don't you tell me what to do. It reminds me, I didn't spank you enough when you were a child.

VARYA: You didn't spank me at all.

VASILY FEDOROVICH: That was my big mistake. All this is
    turning out very badly, Varya. This is very bad.

VARYA: And what is *this?*

VASILY FEDOROVICH: This? I don't know what they call it
    nowadays.

VARYA: The same as in your day.

VASILY FEDOROVICH: Don't be impertinent.

VARYA: But it's all right for you to be impertinent?

VASILY FEDOROVICH: That's my privilege. I am both father
    and mother to you. Your mother didn't live to see this.
    Some joy you would have brought her! And what got
    into your head? You were everything to Pavel. He's
    an honest man. Hardworking. Why are you looking for
    trouble? Have you gone out of your mind, Varya?

VARYA [*calmly*]: No, Papa, I'm not out of my mind. I've
    fallen in love.

VASILY FEDOROVICH: And your marriage with Pavel? Was
    that a marriage of convenience? You don't answer?
    Well, I'll tell you. You married him for love. And so
    now what's all this?

VARYA: All right. You are father and mother both? Then
    listen to me! I'll tell you what I would have only told
    to my mother. . . . I lived with Pavel. We had no
    children—and that was all right. It was even better
    that way. Work, science, and study don't go with diapers
    and children screaming. . . . That was the argument.
    You know the reasons people give. I figured there was
    no point in it. And he agreed. And in general he always
    agreed to everything.

VASILY FEDOROVICH: And is that bad too?

VARYA: Very bad. A woman needs sometimes to be told
    no. To have it explained and proved to her. To have
    someone say: "I want a child from you." Understand!
    A woman needs to have someone beg and demand that
    she have a child! But Pavel . . . He always agreed to
    everything. If it was no, it was no. But now I know
    what it means to want a child. And I want a child by
    Sergey Petrovich. I want to become a mother. I want
    it to be his child. And I want it to cry, I want diapers,
    I want everything. Only it must look like him. And he
    demands this of me.

VASILY FEDOROVICH: Are you going to have a child,
    Varenka?

VARYA: No. So long as he's living with his family, I'm not. Oh, Papa. How good it is to feel the comfort of a masculine will. . . . Yes, Pavel is a good man. And considerate. But nothing that came from him was really dear to me. Just as though I'd taken the wrong train. And the farther it went, the farther it took me out of my way. . . .

VASILY FEDOROVICH: And now? You've jumped off when you were halfway there and you're standing still. Alone.

VARYA: I'm alone? Don't you understand? I'm with him. And I don't need to find out anything about him, do you hear? If he's good and considerate or not. He's mine, just as he is. And the reverse. Everything about him interests me. Every little detail. Why he combs his hair this way and not that. Why he doesn't wear galoshes. Just as though these were facts of great importance.

VASILY FEDOROVICH: I understand.

VARYA: I breathe differently now. When I talk to people, I feel as though I had some special knowledge. When I walk along the street, everything around me seems to be shining. . . . Do you understand me, dear Papa? Do understand that for me Sergey Petrovich is everything. There is not and cannot be anyone better than he. I think about him all the time. So why shouldn't I be with him? He is my life. Do you understand? My life.

VASILY FEDOROVICH: Varya . . . If only he didn't have a family . . .

VARYA: What does his family matter if he loves me?

VASILY FEDOROVICH: Loves you . . . First he loves his wife, then you. Then some other woman.

VARYA: Don't you descend to such cheap talk. Think for yourself—what would he want with me, if it's not serious? He is a very serious person, Papa. He's not a kid. When you see him, you'll understand yourself. He's coming today. I'll introduce you.

VASILY FEDOROVICH: No, thanks, spare me that. I don't want to meet him. When's he coming?

VARYA [*looking at her watch*]: He should be here already.

VASILY FEDOROVICH: Then I'll leave.

VARYA: Papa!

[*The bell rings.*]

That must be him.

VASILY FEDOROVICH: Don't you dare introduce us, do you hear?

[VARYA *goes out. She is heard saying: "Just a minute." Then she enters rapidly, closing the door behind her.*]

VARYA [*in a low voice*]: Papa, it's Pavlusha. . . . How unfortunate. I'll go out with him for a few minutes, and when Sergey Petrovich arrives, you keep him here.

VASILY FEDOROVICH: I want no part in this.

VARYA: Please, I beg you . . .

VASILY FEDOROVICH: Don't waste your time.

[*Enter* NEFEDOV, *wearing a hat and coat and carrying a suitcase and a parcel.*]

PAVEL NIKOLAEVICH: Hello, Vasily Fedorovich.

VASILY FEDOROVICH: Hello, Pavlusha. It's a long time since you've been here.

PAVEL NIKOLAEVICH: Yes, well . . .

VASILY FEDOROVICH: Well, come here. [*They kiss.*] What's the suitcase for? Are you going away?

PAVEL NIKOLAEVICH: No, these are Varya's things. You must need them, Varya.

VARYA: Thank you, Pavlik.

VASILY FEDOROVICH: Will you have some tea?

PAVEL NIKOLAEVICH: With pleasure.

VARYA: You're forgetting, Papa. I have to leave at once. Won't you come along with me, Pavel? [*She puts on her coat.*]

PAVEL NIKOLAEVICH: Of course.

VASILY FEDOROVICH: There's no use in his going with you. Let him sit and talk to me. Won't you stay, Pavlusha?

PAVEL NIKOLAEVICH: I would like to, Vasily Fedorovich, but Varyusha has asked me . . . Another time, if you'll allow me.

VASILY FEDOROVICH: Varyusha has asked you. . . . Oh, Pavel, you're a fool.

PAVEL NIKOLAEVICH: Yes, I'm afraid you're right. . . . Varya, I got your summer coat from the cleaners. And in the parcel you'll find your papers and books. Perhaps

you'd like to look and see if I haven't forgotten something?

VARYA: Thanks very much, Pavlik. I'll look later. I'm in a
hurry.

PAVEL NIKOLAEVICH: Let's go, then.

VASILY FEDOROVICH: Go on, go on. You can see she's in
a hurry.

PAVEL NIKOLAEVICH: Good-by, Vasily Fedorovich. Another
time.

VASILY FEDOROVICH: Ah, Pavlik . . . Sometimes there
aren't any other times.

[VARYA *and* NEFEDOV *go out.*]

VASILY FEDOROVICH [*alone*]: The wrong train . . . Maybe.
But this train? I wonder if it isn't going off the rails.

[*The outside door slams.*]

That would be fine if they met. Hmm . . . A bad business. [*He goes up to the portrait and stands in front of it,
swaying slightly backward and forward.*] There you are,
Lenochka. . . . You see what happens without you? I'm
no mother. This is where your womanly understanding
is needed. . . . She loves him. But is this the same sort
of love as ours? Here am I ready to believe in a life
hereafter, just so I can see you again. . . . Her face is
just like yours, but her life is not like yours. Somewhere
along the way I failed to teach her something. . . . *Mea
culpa.* It's my fault. They're pretty free and easy with
themselves. . . . And your daughter is a serious woman.
What are the others like, those who aren't serious? Abor-
tions, husbands—their own or someone else's—it doesn't
seem to matter. What does matter for them? Don't
generalize, Vasily Fedorovich, don't generalize. Medicine
teaches us that in life and in man everything is individual. . . . [*The bell rings.*] So the trains didn't meet.
[*He starts for the door.*] Let my neighbor open it.[3] [*He
takes the suitcase and the parcel into the next room. A
knock on the door.*] Come in.

[*Enter* SERGEY PETROVICH. *He stops in the doorway.*]

SERGEY PETROVICH: Good evening. May I speak to Varvara Vasilevna?

VASILY FEDOROVICH: She's not at home.

SERGEY PETROVICH: My name is Platonov. Didn't she leave a message for me?

VASILY FEDOROVICH: She wanted you to wait for her.

SERGEY PETROVICH: Are you her father?

VASILY FEDOROVICH: Yes—I'm not her husband, in any case.

SERGEY PETROVICH: Where may I wait for her?

VASILY FEDOROVICH: Wherever you like.

SERGEY PETROVICH: Then I'll wait outside on the street.

VASILY FEDOROVICH: Why do that? Take off your coat and [pointing to the couch] please sit down.

[SERGEY PETROVICH takes off his hat and coat and sits down. Pause.]

SERGEY PETROVICH [looking at the photograph]: That must be Varvara Vasilevna's mother.

VASILY FEDOROVICH: Yes, her mother and my wife. A rare combination today, isn't it?

SERGEY PETROVICH: Tell me, why do you take this tone with me?

VASILY FEDOROVICH: What tone?

SERGEY PETROVICH: Unfriendly, to put it mildly.

VASILY FEDOROVICH: And why, if I may be permitted to ask, young man, should I talk to you any differently?

SERGEY PETROVICH: I'm not a young man.

VASILY FEDOROVICH: That's of no importance.

SERGEY PETROVICH: Yes, it is. I'm in my forties. My hair is gray. And the fact that I've fallen in love with your daughter doesn't make me a criminal.

VASILY FEDOROVICH: Do you have a daughter?

SERGEY PETROVICH: Yes.

VASILY FEDOROVICH: And you love her?

SERGEY PETROVICH: Of course.

VASILY FEDOROVICH: Would you want her to be in a similar . . . situation? What tone would you adopt in talking to the man who . . . [He waves his hand. Pause.]

SERGEY PETROVICH: Am I to blame because it all came so late?

VASILY FEDOROVICH: Surely you know that you don't have to let in everything that comes.

SERGEY PETROVICH: Even if it's a chance for rare happiness? I always thought people wrote too much about love. But now I understand: they don't write enough. When every little hair of some other person, every little piece of paper on which that person has scrawled even one word—everything becomes a sacred relic . . . And now that I've waited and found my happiness, you want me to smother it?

VASILY FEDOROVICH: You think you've found happiness? I think that your wife and Nefedov must have different views. You know, I'm a surgeon. All my life I've been cutting up live human beings. It hurts them, but I've got used to it. But if I cut them up in order to make it hurt instead of to make it stop hurting, then I'd be a torturer, not a surgeon.

SERGEY PETROVICH: I'm cutting into my own flesh.

VASILY FEDOROVICH: That's not true. Your pain is not so great as theirs. It would be different if your family life had been a nightmare. No one asks you to go on living a nightmare. But it wasn't a nightmare, was it?

SERGEY PETROVICH: No, it wasn't.

VASILY FEDOROVICH: It wasn't. And that means that if love has gone, duty still remains.

SERGEY PETROVICH: Doesn't it seem to you that this duty of yours and the nightmare are one and the same thing? It would be interesting to see what decision you would make if you were in my shoes.

VASILY FEDOROVICH: Listen . . .

SERGEY PETROVICH [*abruptly*]: I know. You're going to tell me that you never would be in my position. Or something else equally hypocritical and edifying. With vitamins, but without taste. It's a lie. Perhaps you were one of the lucky ones who met right at the start the person you could love all your life. But few people are that lucky. Much more often a person lives his whole life without any great love. He just doesn't meet the right person. Or he meets her too late and he's afraid to do anything about it. What shall he do about his wife? What will the people around say? What about his friends?

VASILY FEDOROVICH: And how do *you* intend to act in this situation?

SERGEY PETROVICH: I don't know.

VASILY FEDOROVICH: That's great! [*The bell rings.*] That's Varya now.

SERGEY PETROVICH: I'll open the door. [*He goes out.*]

[VASILY FEDOROVICH *picks up his cigarette case from the table, takes out a cigarette, puts it back, puts on his jacket, hat, and coat, hides the cigarette case, and starts for the door. Enter* VARYA *and* SERGEY PETROVICH.]

VARYA: Where are you going, Papa?

VASILY FEDOROVICH: I must get some cigarettes.

VARYA: Have you two met?

SERGEY PETROVICH: Yes.

[VASILY FEDOROVICH *leaves the room.*]

VARYA: What happened here? [*She starts to follow her father.*]

SERGEY PETROVICH [*holding her back*]: Let him go. Sit down. [*He sits her down.*] Let's sit together for a minute. . . . [*He takes her hands in his.*] Where have you been?

VARYA: Pavel was here.

SERGEY PETROVICH: Oh.

VARYA: He brought my things.

SERGEY PETROVICH: Where have you been?

VARYA: I went out with him. I didn't want you two to meet here.

SERGEY PETROVICH: What did you talk about?

VARYA: Always the same thing. He begged me to go back to him. He told me how much he was suffering. . . . He said that I'd left him, but that you don't love me enough to leave your wife and daughter. He talked a lot. He was crying. Great big tears.

SERGEY PETROVICH: And what did you say?

VARYA: I tried to console him and quiet him down. I told him I wouldn't go back to him because I loved you. And I begged him not to cry. . . . It's terrible to see a man crying. I cried myself. I told him you loved me. You do, don't you?

SERGEY PETROVICH: I do.

VARYA: But, really, what are we going to do now?

SERGEY PETROVICH: I don't know.

VARYA: Do you want things to stay the way they are now?

SERGEY PETROVICH: No, I don't.

VARYA: I don't either. Why can't we love each other openly? And besides, I need all of you. Always. And I want everyone to know that you're mine. And I want us to have a family. [*Leaning against his back*] I want to be your wife. . . . A woman doesn't need anything in particular. . . . She wants a family, enough to live on . . . a job she likes. But the most important thing is that she should have a good husband.

SERGEY PETROVICH: What do you mean—good?

VARYA: I mean like you. Sometimes kind. Sometimes mean. Sometimes tender. And sometimes harsh. I need your hands and this broad back. To protect me . . . to be beside me . . . so that I shouldn't have one single thought, one joy or one sorrow without you. . . . Are you listening?

SERGEY PETROVICH: Yes.

VARYA [*imitating him*]: Yes . . . And that rough voice . . . And I want you to be shaven. [*She passes her hand over his cheek.*] And once in a while, only very seldom, I want you unshaven. . . . [*She laughs.*] Now do you understand what sort of husband I want?

SERGEY PETROVICH: I understand. [*He looks her straight in the eye.*] Listen. I want to tell you something. . . . [*In a firm voice*] I can't leave my wife and daughter.

VARYA: So . . . Pavel was right.

SERGEY PETROVICH: No, he wasn't. I love you as much as it's possible for anyone to love.

VARYA: Maybe . . . And what's the way out for us?

SERGEY PETROVICH: If I only knew.

VARYA: Well, I know. [*Getting up*] I'm asking you to leave.

SERGEY PETROVICH: Right now?

VARYA: Leave and don't come back.

SERGEY PETROVICH: Varya . . . Not this way . . .

VARYA: This is the only way. . . . There's the door! And the way home you can find yourself, I hope. [*She goes into the next room and closes the door behind her.*]

[*For a moment* PLATONOV *stands motionless, then picks up his hat and coat and, without putting them on, goes out immediately.* VARYA *runs out from the next room, dashes toward the door, then stops. She then rushes to the window, is about to put her head out, but stops.*]

[*Breathing hard*] No, no . . . The main thing now is not to lose my self-respect . . . To preserve my dignity . . . As they say, to be a man . . .

[*The outer door bangs.*]

Good Lord, Seryozha?

[*Enter* VASILY FEDOROVICH.]

VASILY FEDOROVICH: The outside door was open.
VARYA [*at a loss*]: Yes, yes . . .
VASILY FEDOROVICH: I'll put the tea on. [*He picks up the teapot and goes out.*]
VARYA: Poor Papa. He must have been standing in the street waiting. . . . He's old . . . and gray. . . . He brought up a daughter. And she's messed up everything.

[*Enter* VASILY FEDOROVICH.]

Did you put the tea on?
VASILY FEDOROVICH: Yes, a full pot.

[*Pause.* VARYA *sits down on the couch.* VASILY FEDOROVICH *goes up to her and, drawing her head close, caresses her hair.*]

What's the trouble, daughter?
VARYA [*despairingly*]: It's not fair! I tried. I ran away from it. I didn't want it to happen. . . . And now that this great . . . marvelous . . . thing has happened . . . now I have to kill it? Myself? . . . Oh, Papa, it hurts. . . . Do you hear? I can't stand it . . . I can't stand it . . . [*She weeps bitterly.*]
VASILY FEDOROVICH: Yes, it hurts. . . . It's the same thing in surgery. You amputate someone's arm and the arm hurts. The arm is gone, but the person can still feel it. He wants to stroke it, to touch it. He can feel

each one of his fingers. But then it passes. It passes,
do you hear, daughter?

VARYA: Papa, dear Papa . . . I'm not to blame. Honestly,
I'm not to blame. . . .

VASILY FEDOROVICH [*caressing her*]: Ssshhh . . . gently
now . . . We'll drink our tea, and everything'll be all
right. Everything'll be fine.

SCENE VI

*At the Platonovs' home. May. Daytime. Same as Scene I.
Above the couch there is now a map of the Soviet Union,
studded with small flags. More flags are pinned on the sides
of the map.* NINA *is kneeling on the couch, running her
finger over the map.* MARIA MIKHAYLOVNA *is seated at the
table reading a letter.*

NINA: Perezhival'sk . . . Perezhival'sk . . . There is no
Perezhival'sk! Here it is! You clever place! That's where
you go to. For that you get a flag. [*She sticks a flag in.*]
Mama! I've found Perezhival'sk.

MARIA MIKHAYLOVNA: Not "Perezhival'sk." Przheval'sk.

NINA: All right, "Przheval'sk."

MARIA MIKHAYLOVNA: Do you remember Kolya Ostrovtsov?

NINA: The one with the white eyelashes? And the wart?

MARIA MIKHAYLOVNA: Yes. The wart is now a big official in
the Ministry of Finance.

NINA: Where?

MARIA MIKHAYLOVNA: In Vladivostok.

NINA: Good for him. Otherwise we wouldn't have a single
flag there. [*She looks at the map.*] Vladivostok . . .
Vladivostok . . . Here's a flag for you. [*She sticks a
flag in.*]

MARIA MIKHAYLOVNA: Haven't you given up that game yet?

NINA: It's not a game. I want *everyone* to see how many
people write you, from all parts of the Soviet Union.

MARIA MIKHAYLOVNA: Who is everyone?

NINA [*looking down, stubbornly*]: Everyone. There isn't a
republic that hasn't got some of your former students.

MARIA MIKHAYLOVNA: In the last fifteen years there are a
lot of kids whose lives I've made miserable!

NINA: Not so miserable. Since they write you.

MARIA MIKHAYLOVNA: That's just because I did make their lives miserable.

[*Enter* GRANDMA VERA.]

NINA: Grandma Vera, today Vladivostok got a flag, and so did Przheval'sk. Did you ever hear of the town of Przheval'sk? Here it is. . . . It's got lost again. . . . Here it is. Great?

GRANDMA VERA: What does that expression mean— "great"? Why don't you do what you're supposed to do?

NINA [*throwing up her arms*]: Oh, I'm supposed to iron Papa's handkerchiefs!

GRANDMA VERA: "Oh, I'm supposed to iron Papa's hand-kerchiefs!"

NINA: Granny Grandma Verusenka, did you put the iron on?

GRANDMA VERA: I didn't even think of it.

NINA: That means you did put it on. [*She kisses* GRANDMA VERA, *runs to the door, comes back, kisses her mother, and runs off.*]

GRANDMA VERA [*looking at the map with some pride*]: Tell me, what is this idiocy she's thought up?

MARIA MIKHAYLOVNA: We ought to take it down.

GRANDMA VERA: Let it hang there. It's not in anyone's way. What a lot of flags. It looks as though you really are needed by everyone.

MARIA MIKHAYLOVNA: Not quite everyone, Mama, I know that.

GRANDMA VERA: A lot you know. You don't know a thing. It's your duty to hold on to your husband if you love him.

MARIA MIKHAYLOVNA: If he loves me. I don't want a husband I have to hold on to. And that's enough about that.

GRANDMA VERA: All right. Enough. [*Pause.*] But then you should tell him yourself, "Get out," and that's all.

MARIA MIKHAYLOVNA: That's what I will do.

GRANDMA VERA: You're taking a long time to get ready.

MARIA MIKHAYLOVNA: I'll tell him today, when he comes in.

GRANDMA VERA: You're out of your mind. Don't dare to so

much as think of it. I thought I was talking to a human being, but you . . .

MARIA MIKHAYLOVNA: But I am a human being. You're right. Enough. A person has to have some dignity, after all. I've been clinging to him long enough.

GRANDMA VERA: You're mad. I'm certainly sorry I started this conversation.

[*The sound of a lock being turned.*]

MARIA MIKHAYLOVNA: Sergey has arrived. . . . Leave us, Mama.

GRANDMA VERA: Be careful, Masha. You'd do better to hold your tongue.

[*Enter* PLATONOV. *He has lost weight, his eyes have lost their former alertness, and he is somewhat stooped. He is carrying some magazines.*]

SERGEY PETROVICH: Good evening. I brought you a magazine, Vera Aleksandrovna. There's an article here about an atomic-power plant. With illustrations, just as you asked.

GRANDMA VERA: That's better. They write on and on about these things, and they probably don't understand themselves what it's all about. [*She takes the magazine.*] I'll go and warm up dinner. [*She goes out.*]

SERGEY PETROVICH: I'm not late?

MARIA MIKHAYLOVNA: No. By the way, the clock is slow. You forgot to wind it last Sunday.

SERGEY PETROVICH: Oh, yes, the clock. [*He winds the clock.*] No one called?

MARIA MIKHAYLOVNA: No one. I'll clear off the desk for you.

[MARIA MIKHAYLOVNA *moves her things over onto the couch.* PLATONOV *sits down at the desk, in a hunched-up position. He wearily pulls out one drawer, then another. He is lost in thought.* MARIA MIKHAYLOVNA *watches him.*]

SERGEY PETROVICH [*involuntarily speaking aloud*]: I can't . . .

MARIA MIKHAYLOVNA: What can't you?

SERGEY PETROVICH: Oh, I beg your pardon. . . . There's something here I can't find.

MARIA MIKHAYLOVNA: What's new at work?

SERGEY PETROVICH: Nothing. Golovin is stirring up trouble. And we've finished the new flywheel.

MARIA MIKHAYLOVNA [*gently*]: Perhaps, after all, you shouldn't have tried to reconstruct it?

SERGEY PETROVICH [*irritably*]: Don't talk about things you don't understand! Shouldn't have, shouldn't have! I like the way you teachers always see everything so clearly!

MARIA MIKHAYLOVNA [*pause*]: What's the matter with you, Sergey? You're always so abrupt and irritable these days.

SERGEY PETROVICH: I'm just tired. Worn out . . .

MARIA MIKHAYLOVNA: Why? Perhaps if you told me, you'd feel better. Perhaps you . . . will tell me, Seryozha?

SERGEY PETROVICH: It's nothing. . . . It's just that human beings have a lot of different things on their minds. . . . And I'm human.

MARIA MIKHAYLOVNA: All right. But just don't forget that I'm a human being too.

[*Enter* NINA.]

NINA: Mama . . . Oh, Papa's arrived! How angry you look.

MARIA MIKHAYLOVNA: Wait, Nina. You started to say something?

NINA: Some of your kids have arrived. With dirty feet. And no galoshes. They say you sent for them.

MARIA MIKHAYLOVNA: I'd completely forgotten. [*She goes out.*]

NINA [*pointing to the map*]: Did you see it?

SERGEY PETROVICH [*sitting down on the couch with his back to the map*]: Yes, I saw it.

NINA: I've stuck in some new flags!

SERGEY PETROVICH [*mechanically: without thinking*]: Yes, yes.

NINA: Why are you so lifeless?

SERGEY PETROVICH: I don't feel well. Sort of shivery.

NINA: We must take your temperature.

SERGEY PETROVICH: There'll be time enough for that.

NINA: No there won't. [*She runs out of the room.*]

SERGEY PETROVICH: Maybe I really am ill. I'd just like to lie down and die. . . .

[*Enter* NINA *with handkerchiefs and a thermometer.*]

NINA: Here are your handkerchiefs. And here's your thermometer. Here, let's get it under your armpit.

SERGEY PETROVICH: It tickles. . . . Thank you, Nina, for the handkerchiefs.

NINA: Quite right. Thank you. Good health. I am fulfilling my duties.

SERGEY PETROVICH: And what comes next?

NINA [*sighing*]: Nothing. [*She sits down on the couch.*] What about my shoes? You promised to buy me high-heeled shoes.

SERGEY PETROVICH [*joking*]: Good heavens! Can't you see anything with low heels on?

NINA: Now Papa! Just some teeny little high heels. All the girls have a pair of high heels for going out.

SERGEY PETROVICH: And how are you doing in mathematics?

NINA: Fine.

SERGEY PETROVICH: Fine? Does "fine" mean three, or does "fine" mean a five?

NINA: A four. It will be a five. Word of honor. I'm persistent. Like you, Papa.

SERGEY PETROVICH: Don't flatter your father. [*He pulls her ear.*] Ugh! Where did you get that hair-do with the ribbon?

NINA: I've had it a long time. Oh, Papa, you don't notice . . .

SERGEY PETROVICH [*gloomily*]: It's true. [*Tenderly*] You're quite grown up. All right. You'll get your shoes. . . . No sound from Maria's boys. They must be a hard-working bunch.

NINA: They're such an awkward lot. Why is it that there used to be people like you, but not any more?

SERGEY PETROVICH: What do you mean "not any more"? Am I dead or something?

NINA: No, I meant when you were a youngster. I meant there used to be other boys like you.

SERGEY PETROVICH: And nowadays?

NINA: Nowadays they all have such big ears. . . .

SERGEY PETROVICH: I did too.

NINA: When they talk to you, they can't look you in the eye. . . .

SERGEY PETROVICH: I couldn't either.

NINA: They wave their arms . . . and they dig at the ground with their feet.

SERGEY PETROVICH: I was just the same. I used to wave and dig.

NINA: That's not true. I've seen a photo of you when you were a youngster.

SERGEY PETROVICH: And how did I look?

NINA: Now you're fishing for compliments. . . . Let's have the thermometer.

[*The bell rings.*]

SERGEY PETROVICH: First of all, go and open the door. It must be Kravtsov.

[NINA *goes out.*]

[*He takes the thermometer from under his arm.*] Hmm. [*He shakes it down.*]

[*Enter* NINA *and* KRAVTSOV.]

NINA: How much was it? Let's see the thermometer.

SERGEY PETROVICH: I didn't hold it right. I'll put it back. [*He does so.*]

KRAVTSOV: Are you ill? You don't look so good.

[*Enter* MARIA MIKHAYLOVNA.]

MARIA MIKHAYLOVNA: Dinner's ready. Andrey Viktorovich, will you have dinner with us?

KRAVTSOV [*greeting her*]: Many thanks, Maria Mikhaylovna, but my wife is waiting to give me dinner at home.

SERGEY PETROVICH: And I'll eat a bit later, Masha.

KRAVTSOV: But why? I can wait.

SERGEY PETROVICH: I haven't any appetite anyway.

NINA: Papa is ill.

MARIA MIKHAYLOVNA: Are you really?

SERGEY PETROVICH: It's nothing. Masha, Andrey Viktorovich and I are going to have a little talk.

MARIA MIKHAYLOVNA [*to Nina*]: Off we go. [MARIA MI-
KHAYLOVNA *goes out.*]

NINA [*pointing to her armpit and wagging a threatening
finger at her father*]: Hold it properly. [*Nina goes out.*]

SERGEY PETROVICH: Let's have it. What's happened?

KRAVTSOV: It's a nasty story. Golovin is hinting that you
are carrying out the tests for reasons other than technical ones, and . . . well, you understand. He says that
you don't give a damn for the collective. And then
just to make matters worse, these rumors start circulating . . . and Nefedov is acting very strangely . . .

SERGEY PETROVICH: Rumors?

KRAVTSOV: Yes. Ignatyuk is telling everyone in sight. "He
gave me the works," Ignatyuk says, "rubbed my nose in
the dirt, and what's he up to himself?"

SERGEY PETROVICH: Ignatyuk is a woman-chaser and no
good. He can't open his mouth without talking filth.

KRAVTSOV: Maybe Ignatyuk is a woman-chaser. But you
don't look any better.

SERGEY PETROVICH: In whose eyes? In yours?

KRAVTSOV: Stop it. I know you. I know that you are an
honorable man. But, Sergey Petrovich, I also disapprove
of what you're doing.

SERGEY PETROVICH: Why?

KRAVTSOV: You've really made a hell of a mess. There's a
right age for everything, my friend. But you have a
family. You must get hold of yourself. And if you
can't, to hell with you. . . . Surely you could make a
better arrangement than this? Maria Mikhaylovna is
suffering, Nefedov is suffering, and your daughter is
suffering. . . . [*In a whisper*] Can't you keep it a bit
quieter!

SERGEY PETROVICH: What advice are you giving me?

KRAVTSOV: I'm not giving you any advice. But you can't
treat people that way. Everyone will hold it against you.
They'll say, "He abandoned his wife and daughter."
This Ignatyuk will pour all the dirt he can on you.

SERGEY PETROVICH: To hell with Ignatyuk!

KRAVTSOV: All right. What about Golovin? He's no
Ignatyuk. He'll tie everything into such a package that—

SERGEY PETROVICH: To hell with Golovin too!

KRAVTSOV: Well, but you're not going to say to hell with Maria Mikhaylovna, are you? Surely you have some pity for her.

SERGEY PETROVICH: What does that mean—"pity"? Am I to lie? Or tell the truth?

KRAVTSOV: Don't be in such a hurry to tell the truth. Sometimes it's better to keep quiet than to blurt out to your wife, "I don't love you any more, I'm going off with someone else, good-by."

SERGEY PETROVICH: Why? Why is it better?

KRAVTSOV: Because you know how women sometimes talk. They'll say that their husband is running around but he'll come back. And if you say nothing, it's as though nothing ever happened. . . . Why are you looking at me like that?

SERGEY PETROVICH: I'm learning the fine points of your higher wisdom. So you think that Masha wants that sort of pity?

KRAVTSOV: I don't think anything. But if you have no pity for anyone, at least respect public opinion. Keep quiet. Everyone understands that things sometimes happen. We're not all angels. But you're trying to kick against the pricks. And for that, people are going to hit you over the head. And quite right, too. Don't get carried away.

SERGEY PETROVICH: Well, Andrey Viktorovich, you've had your say.

KRAVTSOV [dumfounded]: What?

SERGEY PETROVICH: The devil knows to what depths you manage to sink.

KRAVTSOV [wearily]: It's you that's sunk. [Angrily] Just understand that I don't want to see you pushed around. You're no worse than the rest. You're a hundred times better than I am. Ignatyuk was expelled from the Party. And this will be an even worse mess. They'll take away your card, too.

SERGEY PETROVICH: I earned my card at the front. And I'll manage to defend it. The Party doesn't want me to lie. The Party wants me to be an honest man. It wants me to work honestly. It wants my family to be founded on love. That's what the Party wants. It wants me to be honest in all things at all times. That's right.

We have only one life to live. And whoever lies is deceiving both himself and the Party.

KRAVTSOV [*jumping up*]: To hell with you! The devil take you! Go ahead and destroy yourself! Everything you say is right, Sergey Petrovich. That's not what I was advising you to do. That's not it. I understand. It hurts me to talk that way. But, after all, I am your friend. I know you. I believe you. But the others? After all, you're not going to tell everyone everything!

SERGEY PETROVICH: Why shouldn't I! I will. My conscience is clear. Don't I have a right to happiness?

KRAVTSOV [*after a pause*]: You know what, Sergey Petrovich? If we're really going to talk about conscience, then I don't think you do have the right. . . . Your happiness has come too late. What is it to do, this happiness of yours—ride rough-shod over your daughter, your wife, and Nefedov? They've done you no harm. . . . And what I wonder is—will you invite people to your wedding and have them shout "bitter" to you, when it really is bitter? [4] Or won't you invite them? Will you do it on the quiet?

SERGEY PETROVICH: Yes . . . the wedding . . . All right, that's enough about that. We've broken off.

KRAVTSOV: How do you mean, broken off?

SERGEY PETROVICH: About a month ago. Everything's over between us.

KRAVTSOV: Whew! What a relief! What a load off my shoulders. . . . So why have you been fooling me all this time? Well, that's fine. All the better. Now Golovin hasn't a leg to stand on. Well, my friend, you've certainly given me a bad time. I feel worn out. . . .

SERGEY PETROVICH [*removing the thermometer*]: Temperature's the same.

KRAVTSOV: What is it?

SERGEY PETROVICH: Normal.

KRAVTSOV: Then enjoy your dinner, my friend. [*He takes his leave and goes out.*]

SERGEY PETROVICH [*alone*]: My happiness came too late? [*He lifts the receiver and dials a number. Waits. Then quietly replaces the receiver.*] Like a kid . . . or like a drunkard looking for vodka . . .

[*Enter* MARIA MIKHAYLOVNA.]

MARIA MIKHAYLOVNA: We've already eaten. We'll have to
warm it up again for you.
SERGEY PETROVICH: No, don't bother. I don't want to eat.

[*The telephone rings.* PLATONOV *reaches for the receiver,
but* MARIA MIKHAYLOVNA *is there before him.*]

MARIA MIKHAYLOVNA: Hello? . . . Hello? . . . They've
hung up. [*She replaces the receiver.*] Sergey, I can't go
on like this.
SERGEY PETROVICH: Why, what's happened?
MARIA MIKHAYLOVNA: I can't go on like this. I try to teach
the children to tell the truth. But here everything is a
lie. There's no sense in anything when it's false. . . .
What's the use in our being together?
SERGEY PETROVICH: What are you talking about, Masha?
You and I have spent seventeen years together.
MARIA MIKHAYLOVNA: That's right. We've spent them.
That's behind us. How are we to go on in the future?
SERGEY PETROVICH: Stop it.
MARIA MIKHAYLOVNA [*touches his forehead*]: You've got a
fever! [*She looks at the thermometer.*] A hundred and
three point six. Nina!

[*Enter* NINA *and* GRANDMA VERA.]

Mama, Sergey has a fever.
GRANDMA VERA: I knew it. He had no appetite.
MARIA MIKHAYLOVNA: Nina, go and get Grigory Pavlo-
vich. Ask him to come over.

[NINA *rushes to the door.*]

Put on your coat.
NINA: It doesn't matter. [*She runs out.*]
MARIA MIKHAYLOVNA: I'll take the phone in the next room
and call up the clinic. Mama, give Sergey his dressing
gown and slippers. [*She takes the phone and goes out.*]
SERGEY PETROVICH [*to Grandma Vera*]: I can do it myself.
GRANDMA VERA: You sit where you are. [*She goes out.*]
SERGEY PETROVICH: Happiness has come too late? Why too
late when we're both alive?

C U R T A I N

ACT IV

SCENE VII

A cottage in the country. June. A sunny day. In the background, part of the cottage may be seen. On the other side, a fence and garden gate. A table and chairs stand in the garden. GRANDMA VERA *is watering the flowers. Enter through the gate* MARIA MIKHAYLOVNA, *wearing a light coat and carrying a bag.*

GRANDMA VERA: Why so late?

MARIA MIKHAYLOVNA: It's a holiday. The streetcars were jammed. And the neighbors kept me. Lida was seeing her boy off to pioneer camp. They came to say good-by.

GRANDMA VERA: And Lida, of course, had been drinking.

MARIA MIKHAYLOVNA: A bit. From happiness. Petya got fives in every subject.

GRANDMA VERA: She has the same recipe for joy and sorrow.

MARIA MIKHAYLOVNA: Where's Nina?

GRANDMA VERA: She went to the river.

MARIA MIKHAYLOVNA: How's Sergey?

GRANDMA VERA: He's lying down, face to the wall. And he doesn't say a word. He got up this morning. Right now he must be sleeping. [*Pointing to the window*] You see? He's closed the shutters. You ought to have a nap in the fresh air yourself.

MARIA MIKHAYLOVNA: Why not? [*Pointing to the bag*] Take it in, Mama, there are some vegetables.

[GRANDMA VERA *takes the bag and goes off.*]

It's horrible in town, and no better here. [*She sits down in a chair, covering her eyes with her hands.*]

[NINA, *carrying a towel, appears on the other side of the gate.*]

NINA: Ah, Mama is here. I have to complain to you about Papa. He got up this morning and went all over the place.

MARIA MIKHAYLOVNA: Grandma Vera has already told on him to me. I'll give Papa a reprimand.

NINA: He could hardly stand on his legs.

MARIA MIKHAYLOVNA: No wonder. Two weeks flat on his back.

NINA: What's happening in Moscow? How is Papa's business?

MARIA MIKHAYLOVNA: Kolya is coming down. He'll tell us.

NINA: Did you see Kolya?

MARIA MIKHAYLOVNA: He called me up. Well, I'm going to lie down for a bit. [She goes off.]

NINA [hangs her towel over the chair and speaks, addressing the chair]: Hello, Kolya . . . Hello, Ninochka . . . No, not like that. [Offhandedly] Hello, Kolya . . . Hello, Ninochka . . . Or this way. [Her voice charged with meaning.] Hello, Kolya . . . Hello, Ninochka . . . That's no good either. [She thinks.]

[PLATONOV has half opened his shutters and is watching her.]

This way, then. [Her face stony.] Hello, Kolya . . .

SERGEY PETROVICH [smiling]: Hello, Ninochka.

NINA: Oh, Papa! What a beast you are. [She turns her back on him.] Aren't you ashamed to spy on me?

SERGEY PETROVICH: Trying to shift the blame, are you? Come here. [He touches her head.] You've wet your hair again. Swimming?

NINA: Yes. [She rubs her cheek against his hand.]

SERGEY PETROVICH: Shall I scratch you behind the ears?

NINA: Yes, scratch. [She kisses his hand.] You're a very sweet and gentle Papa.

SERGEY PETROVICH: And you're my very sweet and gentle daughter.

NINA: Yours?

SERGEY PETROVICH: And Mama's.

NINA: Tell me, Papa . . . Don't you love Mama at all any more?

SERGEY PETROVICH: What a question! Where did you get that idea from?

NINA: Answer me. Give me a straight, honest answer.

SERGEY PETROVICH: You see, Nina . . . when you're grown up, you'll understand that—

NINA: I'll understand right now.

SERGEY PETROVICH: No. Right now you only know the words. You don't really know what they mean. You say "love." What is love?

NINA: I love you. And Mama.

SERGEY PETROVICH: And Grandma Vera. And Kolya.

NINA [*quickly*]: I'm indifferent to Kolya.

SERGEY PETROVICH [*smiling*]: All right. You're indifferent to Kolya.

NINA: There's nothing funny about that. But I do love you and Mama more than anything on earth.

SERGEY PETROVICH: You love us. . . . But mightn't you stop loving us?

NINA: Never.

SERGEY PETROVICH: But when you meet a young man like Kolya—[*Noticing her gesture of protestation*] Not Kolya, of course, but someone like him . . . And when you get so that you need him more than life itself, then you'll be ready even to stop loving us if we try to prevent you from loving him. Then you'll understand what love is. . . . But right now the best thing for you would be to go and meet Kolya. Here he comes now.

NINA [*embarrassed*]: What? Is he here already?

SERGEY PETROVICH: Yes, here already. How unpleasant, isn't it?

[*Enter* KOLYA.]

KOLYA: Sergey Petrovich, Ninochka . . . [*He bows.*] I missed five—no, three—streetcars. [*Bows.*] I almost got smashed flat as a pancake. [*Bows.*]

SERGEY PETROVICH: That's enough bowing. When is the board meeting?

KOLYA: Tomorrow.

SERGEY PETROVICH: A pity I can't be there.

KOLYA: Never mind. The results of the tests are brilliant. Golovin is eating crow. Hurrah for us, eh, Sergey Petrovich? I brought you the form to sign for the delivery of the motor.

SERGEY PETROVICH: Who signed for the plant?

KOLYA: Nefedova.

SERGEY PETROVICH: All right. Come inside. [*He withdraws his head.*]

NINA: So Papa was right, was he?

KOLYA: Absolutely right.

NINA: Oh, Kolya, how clever you are!

KOLYA: You said it!

SERGEY PETROVICH [*from off stage*]: Kolya!

KOLYA: I'm coming. . . .

NINA: But please remember that Papa is ill. He mustn't work a lot now.

KOLYA: But can we go boating a lot?

NINA: Yes, we can.

SERGEY PETROVICH [*from off stage*]: Kolya!

KOLYA: I'm coming right away! I'll do everything I can, Ninochka.

NINA: I'll go and make arrangements about the boat.

SERGEY PETROVICH [*from off stage*]: Kolya!

[KOLYA, *putting a finger to his lips, goes into the cottage on tiptoe.* SERGEY PETROVICH'S *head appears in the window.*]

SERGEY PETROVICH: Where's Kolya?

NINA: He went in to see you a long time ago.

[SERGEY PETROVICH *disappears.* NINA, *dancing merrily, goes toward the gate. Coming toward her is a middle-aged man with a bloated face. This is* IGNATYUK.]

IGNATYUK: Excuse me. Hello. Does Comrade Platonov live here?

NINA: Yes, he does.

IGNATYUK: I would like to speak to his wife.

NINA: I'll call her right away. [*She goes off.*]

IGNATYUK [*looking around*]: The cottage is nothing wonderful. . . .

[*Enter* MARIA MIKHAYLOVNA *and* NINA.]

MARIA MIKHAYLOVNA: You wanted to see me?

IGNATYUK: If you are, excuse me, really Sergey Petrovich's wife.

MARIA MIKHAYLOVNA: Yes, I am.

IGNATYUK: Then I'd like to have . . . a little talk with you. Just the two of us.

MARIA MIKHAYLOVNA: All right. Come in.

NINA [*to her mother, in a low voice*]: He looks kind of suspicious.

MARIA MIKHAYLOVNA: Don't worry. You go now.

[NINA *goes into the house.*]

IGNATYUK [*coming through the gate*]: You don't, forgive me, have any dogs, do you?

MARIA MIKHAYLOVNA: No, there are no dogs. [*She looks questioningly at her visitor.*]

IGNATYUK [*removing his coat, hat, and scarf, and putting them all on the chair*]: You don't mind? [*He sits down in a wicker chair, feels it.*] Light, practical, and convenient! Please don't think me presumptuous, but I wonder if I might have a small glass of water.

MARIA MIKHAYLOVNA: Perhaps you'd like some tea?

IGNATYUK: No, it's too hot.

MARIA MIKHAYLOVNA: Then some kvass?

IGNATYUK: Is it cold?

MARIA MIKHAYLOVNA: Yes.

IGNATYUK: Then I won't refuse.

MARIA MIKHAYLOVNA [*turning toward the house*]: Nina, bring out some kvass.

IGNATYUK: Do you mind if I smoke? [*He has already lit up.*]

MARIA MIKHAYLOVNA: Please do.

[*Enter* NINA, *carrying the kvass and glasses.*]

NINA: Mama, I'm running down to make arrangements about the boat. I won't be long. [*She runs off.*]

IGNATYUK [*pointing after her with his little finger*]: Your daughter?

MARIA MIKHAYLOVNA: Yes.

IGNATYUK: Of course. [*Pause.*] My name will hardly mean anything to you. Ignatyuk. Your husband didn't mention me?

[MARIA MIKHAYLOVNA *shakes her head.*]

I don't wonder.

MARIA MIKHAYLOVNA: What can I do for you?

IGNATYUK: In general terms, this is the essence of the matter. Your husband, one may say, did everything he could. . . . Thanks to your husband, I've been kicked out of the Party. Of course, I shall appeal, but . . . My, so to speak, fair name has temporarily been sullied. [*Short pause.*] And why? The Party committee received a complaint about me. From my wife. So far so good. My wife and I didn't get along, I don't deny it. I don't deny that I took up with another woman. What's going to happen in the future I don't know. Maybe I'll go back to my family, think things over, and settle down, and maybe the new passion will win the day. Only the future will tell. But Sergey Petrovich took it upon himself to prove that I was at fault. I understand that this was an assignment the Party had given him. But assignments can be carried out in various ways. And what did he do? He went at it tooth and nail, as they say. What I want to know is, who are fit to be my judges? [*Pause.*] And what about Sergey Petrovich himself!

MARIA MIKHAYLOVNA: Why did you come here?

IGNATYUK: Quite right. That's a good question. And I'll answer it. I came here so that we could open each other's eyes. Why don't you complain to the Party committee? Let them investigate Sergey Petrovich, too. People think that with him everything is perfect harmony at home. But is it really? I beg your pardon, it's even improper to call a spade a spade.

MARIA MIKHAYLOVNA: I don't wish to listen to dirty gossip about my husband. [*She rises.*]

IGNATYUK [*remaining seated*]: Dirty? Perhaps you're right. But gossip? That I deny. His affair with Nefedova is a fact, and not gossip. . . .

MARIA MIKHAYLOVNA: You will have to leave.

IGNATYUK [*rising*]: I understand. [*He puts his wraps back on as he speaks.*] But I shall make it my business to take this story everywhere. To all levels. I've been expelled, but that's nothing compared to what's coming to him. [*He goes toward the gate.*]

MARIA MIKHAYLOVNA: Wait a minute . . . I would like just the same to explain to you. All this is completely untrue. . . .

IGNATYUK: What do you mean?

MARIA MIKHAYLOVNA: You've been misinformed. . . . The Nefedovs are acquaintances of ours. They come to our home. . . .

IGNATYUK: What is this? Are you trying to protect him? She wouldn't dare to come within gunshot of this place, to meet you face to face.

[VARYA *appears at the gate*.]

VARYA: Forgive me . . .

MARIA MIKHAYLOVNA [*to Ignatyuk, distractedly*]: There . . . you see?

IGNATYUK: Well, that's the last straw! Such goings on! This is it, the decadent intelligentsia! [*He goes off, slamming the gate*.]

MARIA MIKHAYLOVNA [*to herself*]: And I've got to put up with this too. . . .

VARYA: Did he insult you?

MARIA MIKHAYLOVNA: He? No, he didn't.

VARYA: I came to find out: how is Sergey Petrovich's health?

MARIA MIKHAYLOVNA: It's getting better. He's improving.

VARYA: Thank you. The board is meeting tomorrow. . . . I wanted to tell him that he has nothing to worry about. I'm going to make a statement. Everything is all right with the motor.

MARIA MIKHAYLOVNA: I'll give him your message.

VARYA [*turns away to leave, then stops*]: Perhaps . . . I might see him?

MARIA MIKHAYLOVNA: See him? [*Pause. She goes off*.]

VARYA: I don't care. She can think what she likes about me . . . I don't care. But maybe he won't come out. . . . [*She listens*.] Well, let him stay there, I don't care. [*She covers her face with her hands*.]

[*Enter* PLATONOV. *He looks at* VARYA *without speaking. She uncovers her face*.]

SERGEY PETROVICH [*comes slowly down the steps, hanging on to the rail; he nearly falls*]:

[VARYA *makes a movement in his direction*.]

It's all right. [*He goes up to her.*] Let's go. I'll see you
down to the corner. . . .

[*They walk side by side to the gate without looking at
each other.*]

VARYA: I've brought you only unhappiness. . . . Forgive
me.

SERGEY PETROVICH [*in a choking voice*]: Can you get along
without me?

VARYA: No.

SERGEY PETROVICH: And I can't get along without you.

VARYA: I'm willing to be anything you like to you. . . .

SERGEY PETROVICH: Could you be everything?

VARYA: Everything?

SERGEY PETROVICH: Yes, everything.

[SERGEY PETROVICH *and* VARYA *go off. Enter* NINA. *She
looks at them from a distance, then runs into the
garden.*]

NINA: Mama! Mamochka! Mama!

[*Enter* MARIA MIKHAYLOVNA.]

NINA [*looking down*]: Why did she come here?

MARIA MIKHAYLOVNA: To find out about your father's
health.

NINA: How dare she come here!

MARIA MIKHAYLOVNA: That's not your business.

NINA [*raising her head*]: Yes, it is my business! And you!
Why didn't you throw her out? Why didn't you hit her?

MARIA MIKHAYLOVNA: Hold your tongue!

NINA: If you don't care, if you don't love Papa, *then you
deserve it!* You deserve it!

MARIA MIKHAYLOVNA: Go away! [*In a strained voice*] Or
I'll hit you. [*She raises her arm.*]

[NINA *staggers back. Enter* GRANDMA VERA, *followed by*
KOLYA.]

GRANDMA VERA: What's going on here? Nina, what's the
matter with you?

NINA: Nothing.

GRANDMA VERA: Kolya, please take Nina for a walk.

KOLYA: All right, Vera Aleksandrovna. Let's go, Ninochka.

NINA: I don't—

GRANDMA VERA: Go on with you! Go for a walk!

NINA: Mama . . . Mamochka . . .

MARIA MIKHAYLOVNA: Yes . . . Go and take a walk with Kolya. . . .

KOLYA: Let's go, Ninochka.

[NINA *and* KOLYA *go off.*]

GRANDMA VERA: What has happened to you here? I heard you shouting at her. The first time I ever heard you shout at her.

MARIA MIKHAYLOVNA: Yes . . . there's always a first time.

GRANDMA VERA: So it happened at last. She came down here. You ought really—

MARIA MIKHAYLOVNA: I beg you. Keep quiet! What do you all expect of me? You want me to kill her? Or him? Or myself? What do you want of me? Leave me in peace, in peace, do you hear? I keep quiet, so don't torment me with questions and advice. I keep quiet, so let me keep quiet! Leave me alone! I insist!!

GRANDMA VERA: All right, all right, Mashenka . . . I'll leave you alone. But for God's sake, calm down. I won't say a word now . . . Only calm down. [*As she leaves*] Good Lord, what did we do to deserve this? [*Goes off.*]

MARIA MIKHAYLOVNA [*alone*]: It's true: what did we do to deserve this? I won't be able to stand it. . . . How dare she come here! And I'm a fool, a complete fool. I let them meet. . . . But he used to love me. Could he have stopped loving? I can't believe it . . . as I can't believe in death.

[*Enter* PLATONOV. *He goes up to* MARIA MIKHAYLOVNA.]

We must have a talk, Seryozha. But without lying.

SERGEY PETROVICH: Yes, lying is the easiest way—and the worst. [*Pause.*] I'm leaving you, Masha.

MARIA MIKHAYLOVNA: So that's it. Well, go ahead. You will pay dearly in life, Seryozha, for what you've done to us. I don't believe that you two will be happy. . . .

No, don't think I want to hold you back. What good are you to me without love? [*Pause. With torment in her voice*] Have you . . . thought everything over, Seryozha?

SERGEY PETROVICH: Yes, I have.

MARIA MIKHAYLOVNA: All right. Then there's nothing more to be said.

SERGEY PETROVICH: Try to understand . . . I can't . . . I don't dare to act otherwise . . . but all my life I will—

MARIA MIKHAYLOVNA: All your life . . . I heard those words somewhere before . . . seventeen years ago. . . . [*She goes off toward the cottage.*]

SERGEY PETROVICH: Masha, wait a minute . . . I'll explain . . .

MARIA MIKHAYLOVNA: You don't have to explain. . . . There's nothing to explain. . . . That's all there is to it . . . that's all [*She stands in the doorway, looks at* PLATONOV, *and says, as though she were listening to herself for the last time*) Seryozha. . . .

SCENE VIII

At the Platonovs'. October. Evening. Same as Scene I. The drawing board and the rolls of paper have gone. It is raining outside. There is no one in the room. The outside door bangs. Pause. NINA *runs in, falls on the couch, and begins to sob. Enter* GRANDMA VERA.

GRANDMA VERA: What's the mater with you? What's happened?

NINA [*crying*]: Oh, Grandma Vera, Grandma Vera . . .

GRANDMA VERA: Well, what has happened? Tell me.

[NINA *continues to cry.*]

Do you want to drive me out of my mind? Stop crying, do you hear? Your mother will be coming, and you're not going to cry in front of her, are you? She's had enough grief as it is.

NINA [*through her tears*]: I . . . I'll stop right away. I was just coming home from a friend's house and . . .

[*Whimpering*] I met Nefedova . . . **I'll stop** . . . I met Nefedova . . . with that person . . .

GRANDMA VERA: It's wrong to talk that way about your father. [*Pause.*] Well, what happened?

NINA: He came up and asked how I was.

GRANDMA VERA: And what did you say?

NINA: I didn't say anything. I ran away. [*She is still crying.*]

GRANDMA VERA: Just a minute. [*Changing the subject*] Just tell me this. What friend do you always go to when you leave school?

NINA: I've got only one friend now. . . . Her father died too.

GRANDMA VERA: Don't dare to talk that way! What idiocy! [*Pause.*] Are you going to eat now or are you going to wait for your mother?

NINA: I don't want to eat. I ate at my friend's house.

GRANDMA VERA: More foolishness! As if you didn't have a house of your own.

NINA: Granny Verochka, don't be cross with me today, please. [*She snuggles up to her.*]

GRANDMA VERA [*caressing her*]: You're a bad girl. [*She kisses her.*] You make your granny unhappy. You don't care about your granny. . . .

NINA: You know how much I care about you, Grandma Vera.

GRANDMA VERA: How much?

[NINA *embraces her without speaking.*]

NINA: There, there, I'll go and lie down, all right?

GRANDMA VERA: It's rather early.

NINA: Just the same, I feel sleepy.

GRANDMA VERA: Wouldn't you like to lie down on the couch? Then you can sleep near your grandma.

NINA: No, I'll never sleep here again. [*She kisses* GRANDMA VERA.] Good night, Grandma.

GRANDMA VERA: Sleep well. And get all that nonsense out of your head.

NINA [*nodding her head*]: I have. [*She goes out.*]

GRANDMA VERA [*alone*]: Oh, what a girl . . . still just a little girl . . . "That person" . . . she thinks she doesn't have a father. As though he were dead . . . But he's not dead. If he were dead, then death would be to blame for everything. I see him now as he was when he said good-by and left . . . White as a sheet. He stood in front of me, his hands trembling, and he said: "Vera Aleksandrovna, understand, I have not chosen an easy path." Just the same, he should not have left. . . . If they had got on badly together . . . If Masha had been at fault . . . But Masha never so much as looked at anyone else. And a lot of men looked at her. . . . She never even thought about it . . . only about him and the family and work. To deal her such a blow . . . No, human happiness is not built that way. . . .

[*There is the sound of a key in the outside-door lock. Pause. Enter* MARIA MIKHAYLOVNA. *From her brief case she takes out a thick pile of exercise books.*]

GRANDMA VERA: So you've arrived at last.

MARIA MIKHAYLOVNA [*kissing her mother*]: Hello.

GRANDMA VERA: Did you get your feet wet?

MARIA MIKHAYLOVNA: No, they're dry.

GRANDMA VERA: What do you mean, dry! I wasn't watching this morning and you wore the wrong shoes.

MARIA MIKHAYLOVNA: Where's Nina?

GRANDMA VERA: She went to bed. She said she was tired. That geography teacher phoned you, asked you to come over for her birthday.

MARIA MIKHAYLOVNA: I'm busy today. I've got a pile of exercise books.

GRANDMA VERA: She didn't invite you for today. It was for tomorrow.

MARIA MIKHAYLOVNA: Tomorrow I have to work too.

GRANDMA VERA: Work, work. You ought to go. See people a bit.

MARIA MIKHAYLOVNA: So that's what it is. [*She smiles.*]

GRANDMA VERA: There's nothing to laugh at. You'll be alone now . . . Nina will soon get married. And I'll leave you.

MARIA MIKHAYLOVNA: And who's going to give you your discharge?

GRANDMA VERA: Everyone gets a discharge to where I'm going.

MARIA MIKHAYLOVNA: What gloomy thoughts you have today. Do you want me to cheer you up?

GRANDMA VERA: No, I don't.

MARIA MIKHAYLOVNA: Today I went into my classroom and
I heard some peculiar sort of noise. Well, I thought,
there's more here than meets the eye. I looked at the
class book, looked over the children, and I saw that
Misharev was not in his seat. And alongside me there's
a box for textbooks. It's just a bit higher than a stool.
And that's where those wheezing noises were coming
from.

GRANDMA VERA: How on earth did he get in there?

MARIA MIKHAYLOVNA: What do you think? He wanted to
be a hero. It was to be a big joke: I would call the roll,
and he would answer me from the box. That would
have given the whole school something to talk about
for a year.

GRANDMA VERA: Good Lord!

MARIA MIKHAYLOVNA: I figured it all out in a second. And
so I didn't call the roll. And I went through the whole
lesson as though there were nothing wrong. And when
the bell rang I said: "Now, Misharev, you can come
out of the box." Then it really started. Everyone roared.
He pushed back the lid, but he couldn't climb out by
himself. We only just managed to drag him out. His
legs wouldn't unbend. [*Laughs*] And he squats there on
his haunches and says: "Forgive me, Maria Mikhaylovna
. . . I didn't do it on purpose, Maria Mikhaylovna . . ."

GRANDMA VERA [*laughs*]: And what did you say?

MARIA MIKHAYLOVNA: I said, "Of course, Misharev, I
realized you must have got in there by accident. Who
would want to sit out a whole lesson in a box on purpose?"

[*The two women laugh. There is a knock on the door.*]

Come in!

[*Enter* LIDA *in a dressing gown.*]

LIDA: Forgive my coming so late . . . and dressed like
this. I wonder if you happen to have a little vodka.

MARIA MIKHAYLOVNA: Mama, do we have any vodka?

GRANDMA VERA: There's a little in the carafe. [*She goes out
and returns with a small carafe of vodka.*]

LIDA [*laughs*]: That's not much for me. . . . Thank you very much just the same. I'll have to go out for some.

[GRANDMA VERA *goes out.*]

Your mother doesn't approve of me. . . . But do you know why I decided to drink today? I thought about you.

MARIA MIKHAYLOVNA: Come now, Lida, you drink when you're sad, you drink when you're happy, and now you're drinking on other people's behalf.

LIDA: Not other people's, ours. I must go and buy some vodka.

MARIA MIKHAYLOVNA: Perhaps it would be better not to. It won't do you any good.

LIDA: Ah, Maria Mikhaylovna, what harm can it do me? All the harm has already been done. . . . Now I look at this business differently. . . .

MARIA MIKHAYLOVNA: What business?

LIDA: Men. Do you think I can't see that everyone disapproves of me? Vera Aleksandrovna, for instance . . . She must think of me as . . . I know how people talk: "Today it's one man, tomorrow another, and so on . . ." But I think it's better to be with them than to be alone. And, besides, I wanted to make a test, find out where I stand. Am I really of no use to anyone? Well, it's turned out that I'm still attractive. As many as I want . . . In the daytime I work as a timekeeper and in the evening I have a good time. And now I've got to like it that way.

MARIA MIKHAYLOVNA: But why do you drink if you like it?

LIDA: You think I drink because I'm sad? No . . . It's simply . . . You have to know how to get everything you can out of life. Now I . . . I loved Fedya and I thought I would spend my whole life with him. But he didn't give a damn about it. I thought one way, he thought differently. And now I don't give a damn either. If it isn't him, it doesn't matter who it is. . . .

MARIA MIKHAYLOVNA: You should spare yourself, have pity on yourself.

LIDA: For whom? For people? Anyway, no one is going to set up a golden monument to me. For myself? For myself I'm all right as I am. For my son? Petya is my consolation. He won't condemn me. He'll forgive me. And you too—I don't give a damn for the others—you don't condemn me.

MARIA MIKHAYLOVNA: I will condemn you.

LIDA: You mustn't. Let the others do the condemning. Those who all their lives have been sheltered behind their husband's back. There are women who don't care whether their husbands love them or not. As long as they have a husband's pocket to dig into. As long as they can call themselves married women. You're not like that, I know. I can never be as good as you are. But I'm better than they are. I'm not hanging on to anyone. I stand on my own feet. And I can do for myself what I want with myself. If I want to drink vodka, I will! I have the right!

MARIA MIKHAYLOVNA: Stop it, Lida. What right can one have to drink?

LIDA: Do you want me to hang myself from misery?

MARIA MIKHAYLOVNA: Is that the only thing you can think of? Either get drunk or hang yourself? That's some solution! . . . [*Pause.*] Hanging yourself is the first thing that comes to mind. . . . When you're lying awake nights and biting your fingers so as not to start bawling out loud. When you think it all over . . . Getting drunk, hanging yourself . . . and how to go on living . . . [*She fights with tears.*]

LIDA: Maria Mikhaylovna! What a fool I am. Please don't cry. . . .

MARIA MIKHAYLOVNA: Not on your life! I'll tell you something: this is how it is. You turn over to the wall and lie still and just wish that no one would ever touch you. But life touches you. . . . This thing has to be done and that . . . I began to get bitter and angry against life. But then I began to understand that it was right that life should touch me. And now I know for sure that I am deeply thankful to life for touching me! More than that. You have to go out and meet life as it comes. The air? Breathe it in deeply. The sun? Let it warm you. The rain? Let even the nasty rain wet you. And worries? Give me my worries! And clothes? I'm a woman, and I need new clothes. I need everything—the small and the great. Otherwise you can withdraw into your own hurt feelings to such an extent that you really feel like drowning yourself. You live on your pain. You think of nothing but your pain! But this is humiliating! In life there are so many sorrows as it is, illnesses, deaths, wars . . . that I should allow someone else to spoil my life? I won't allow it! I won't let him! Not a single day shall be spoiled! They all belong to me. And that's that!

LIDA [*sighing deeply as if surprised*]: Well, what do you know? [*She goes toward the door; smiles.*] You've persuaded me for today.

MARIA MIKHAYLOVNA: That's something, anyway.

[LIDA *goes out.*]

Oh, exercise books, exercise books . . . It's a good thing that there are so many of you. . . .

[*Enter* GRANDMA VERA.]

GRANDMA VERA: What can you see in her? She's a lost soul. [*She walks toward the clock; starts to tinker with it.*]

MARIA MIKHAYLOVNA: First of all, she's not lost. And, second, she is a human being. What are you up to, Mama?

GRANDMA VERA: The clock must be wound.

MARIA MIKHAYLOVNA: Wait . . . From now on I'll do it. [*She winds the clock, then speaks, as though she were remembering something.*] Greetings, my dear ones . . . Greetings, my dear ones . . . Greetings, my dear ones.

[*The clock strikes nine.*]

CURTAIN

NOTES

1. A bad mark. The Russian marking system ranges from 0 to a maximum 5.
2. By Howard Fast.
3. This is the outside door leading into the hall which serves more than one apartment.
4. The custom at Russian wedding parties is for the guests to shout "bitter," whereupon the bride and groom must kiss.

VERSE

[Vladimir Mass and Mikhail Chervinsky are a lively team of young Soviet satirical poets. The two pieces translated here, which are self-explanatory, appeared in *Den' poèzii, 1956*—a publication almost as much criticized as the second volume of *Literaturnaya Moskva*.]

AROUND AND ABOUT

(A GUIDE FOR TOURISTS WISHING TO WRITE TRAVELERS' DIARIES)

Vladimir Mass and Mikhail Chervinsky

FROM THE AUTHORS

On the steamboat *Pobeda* we haven't as yet
Toured through Europe's fair lands—which we greatly
    regret.
At first we intended to sail on this boat
And even our traveler's diary we wrote,
Our notes—with omissions perhaps—did compile
In the usual, standard and long-approved style.
If some of our tourists should use in it find
(And we have the journalists mostly in mind)
For their articles, sketches, whatever you ask,
Then we'll have succeeded, we feel, in our task.

NOTE

What we offer's no more than a general scheme,
But we've given examples and got the main theme.
If superfluous passages here you should find,
Please just cross them out—we really don't mind.

DEPARTURE

At what point should we launch on our travelers' tale?
Our dear ones are thronging the dock; from the rail
We wave them good-by and we leave them astern,
And, homesick at once, we just long to return.

WHAT WE SAW AND LEARNED

Our journey enriched us, enriched us inside,
And all that we saw left us standing wide-eyed.

At sea and on land, in the air, on the ground,
There was nothing we gazed on that did not astound.
In Holland the tulips most truly amaze.
The Acropolis Athens revealed to our gaze.
Paris showed us its chestnuts: Montmartre by night,
The Champs Elysées all a-sparkle with light.
The silks of Lyon and well-built Amsterdam's
Old cathedrals inspired us to sing dithyrambs.
Of Italy's vistas the great Colosseum
Was only the first of ten marvels *per diem.*
In Norway the fiords captivated the eye.
Switzerland's mountains are snow-capped and high.
The grandeur of Rome did our wonder excite.
In London the fog was a wonderful sight.

MEETINGS

We met, I recall . . . (on the walks of Hyde Park,
On the quai at Le Havre, on the square of Saint Mark)
A man wearing . . . (glasses, a hat, a beret).
At first he was naturally somber and dour;
When he learned who we were, he decided to stay
And cried . . . (*"Guten Tag!" "Buona sera!" "Bonjour!"*),
And tears of emotion welled forth from his eye.
We badges exchanged as we bade him good-by.
And then after that wherever we'd walk,
All the people came up to us simply to talk.

CONVERSATIONS

Our shaky command of each alien tongue
Caused us some slight embarrassment, strangers among.
But soon we abandoned all weak hesitation
And found other methods of communication.
We accosted a gendarme and asked him the way,
We asked him in Russian: *Gde rue de la Paix?*
He was able by using his hands to reply . . .
We badges exchanged as we bade him good-by.

CHILDREN

Along Piccadilly all colored with lights
We walked and inspected the various sights.
By the cars that we saw we were greatly impressed,
But it was the children that pleased us the best.

LITERATURE

(First Alternative)

While standing and gazing with reverent eye
On the palaces, fountains, and parks of Versailles,
We thought of the lines of immortal . . . (Flaubert,
Of Heine, Stendhal or Corneille or Voltaire).

(Second Alternative)

As we gazed on the Tower so grim and austere
(The prisoner enters but never returns),
We thought of the lines of immortal . . . (Shakespeare,
Of Milton, Ben Jonson or Shelley or Burns).

MUSIC

(First Alternative)

As soon as we wandered ashore in Marseille,
Some people there started "Katyusha" to play.

(Second Alternative)

On Capri's fair isle
They sang us "Katyusha" with heartwarming smile.

PAINTING

We went to the Louvre and we spent there one hour,
But for literally hours—you can say what you like—
We, breathless, admired . . . (the extraordinary power,
The vision, the technical skill) of . . . (Van Dyck,
Leonardo da Vinci, Matisse or Rodin,
Van Gogh or Rembrandt or Cézanne or Gauguin).

CONTRASTS

In . . . (Naples, in Stockholm, in Paris, in Rome,)
In whatever city you happen to roam,
There's something that's hard for our eyes to endure:
The contrasts that set off the rich from the poor.
On the gay boulevards there wander along
Ladies and gentlemen—elegant throng!
While there a poor artist with nothing to eat
Works with chalks on the sidewalk right under their feet.
Outside a shop window there mournfully plays
A poor homeless fiddler whose sufferings we feel.
Inside living models! Exposed to our gaze!

Their transparent negligées scarcely conceal. . . .
But we from the models averted our eyes,
The pity we felt all description defies.

GENERAL IMPRESSIONS

Into the bay of Sorrento we sail,
But to describe it—
                          the words simply fail.
Venice in palaces old does abound,
But to describe them—
                          no words can be found.
The beauties of Rome all entranced we imbibe,
But to describe them—
                          no words can describe!

CONCLUDING REMARKS

Now in case there are those who would plagiarists call
Us, we wish to announce and in print to proclaim
That this diary's not our production at all;
It was written by tourists we don't need to name,
For they're persons already too well known to fame.
The reader can probably name them himself,
For he already has all their books on his shelf.
The sad thing is not just that "words simply fail."
What's sad is the fact that in tale after tale
The authors have not put one thought of their own,
They manage to pile up cliché on cliché
But how it gets printed remains quite unknown,
Yes, *this* is what words simply fail to convey!

2 × 2 = ?

Vladimir Mass and Mikhail Chervinsky

He best of all verse writers did contrive
To show that two times two is four, not five.

He did not dot his "i" 's or cross his "t" 's,
But one and all were able to divine
His thought, for he had learned with practiced ease
To spell it out in vivid, pithy line.

Convinced he'd found the weightiest theme of all,

He felt that mere verse cycles were too small;
Now full-length poems he wrote and still did strive
To prove—but more profoundly than before—
That two times two can never equal five,
Nor three nor seven—but precisely four.

And since of course this viewpoint none could blame
Nor raise objections, in a short, short time
He won among the critics wide acclaim!
They held his verse a model of good rhyme.

He started then the rest to criticize
For imitation, for anemic verse.
Their narrowness of theme our friend decries,
Their superficiality or, worse,
Their having failed to vividly express
That two times two is four—no more, no less.

He lately published a two-volume work.
Disciples he can number by the score.
Everywhere his influence seems to lurk,
And that is what we most of all deplore.
In drama you can find him and—beware!—
In music, painting—in fact, anywhere.

But still one can't object, for—sake's alive!—
It's true that two times two is four, not five!

[Sergey Mikhalkov (born 1913) is a well-known Soviet dramatist and poet, whose fables and verses for children are particularly popular. He happens also to be one of the co-authors
of the lyrics for the new nationalistic Soviet anthem (1944)
that replaced the "Internationale."

The anecdote told in "Three Portraits" about the Stalinesque
one-eyed, one-armed monarch (Stalin actually did have a de-
formed arm and a pockmarked face, which were always concealed in portraits or photographs) was circulating orally on
the Soviet grapevine at least as early as 1955. In some of
these "folklore" versions the identification of various practices
in the Soviet literary world is made even more explicit. The
first painter is a "varnisher of reality" (a recurrent bugbear
of Soviet literary criticism), the Pollyanna man or "singer of
hallelujahs"). The second painter, who shows things as they

are, is a "naturalist," who fails to understand the principle of portraying reality in its revolutionary development. The brilliant solution of the last painter, of course, is possible only from a socialist realist.

Mikhalkov produced the following effective versified (and publishable) version of the anecdote. It appeared in *Literaturnaya Moskva,* Vol. II.]

THE THREE PORTRAITS

S. Mikhalkov

He had one arm, he had one eye,
    Akhmet, the Khan, the Great.
He to three painters order gave
    To paint him his portráit.

"This picture of me you shall paint"—
    'Twas so the Khan decreed,
"Shall show me in the battle fierce
    Amounted on my steed."

The day is come. The trumpets sound,
    And forth two painters stand;
Each bears before the awesome judge
    A picture in his hand.

The Khan looks at the first portráit
    Gives forth a wrathful cry:
"That is not me! You've painted there
    Some other khan than I!

"I have one arm, I have one eye—
    But here this khan astride
Grasps in two hands his bow and has
    His both eyes open wide!

"Let he who painted me so false
    Now answer for this deed!"
They chased the painter from the court:
    'Twas so the Khan decreed.

The Khan looked at the second portráit;
    His wrath was dread to see:

"This is a base and cunning plot
    Directed against me.

"You'd wish my foes, who're all around
    And wish me nought but harm,
To see that Mighty Khan Akhmet
    Has but one eye and arm!"

He spoke. Straightway the naturalist,
    Right in his prime did die. . . .
Then, trembling like a wind-blown leaf,
    The third man, he drew nigh.

But since in profile, not full-view,
    His picture had been done,
You couldn't see there was no right arm
    And eyes he had but one.

The sound left arm, we clearly see,
    Right firmly grasps the shield,
And with eagle stare the sound left eye
    Surveys the battlefield.

So to this artist, as I hear,
    Came wealth and rank and fame,
And decorations, when he died,
    To glorify his name.

And I've met other painters too
    Who had this self-same guile;
They don't paint life head-on, full-view,
    They paint it in profíle.

[Evgeny Evtushenko emerged about 1955 as one of the most
popular young Soviet poets. He was born in 1933. His poems
have the virtue of directness and sincerity, and the autobio-
graphical "Stantsia Zima," portions of which are translated here,
is a memorable documentation, despite its sentimentality, of a
young Russian's soul-searchings in the period after Stalin's
death.

  "Stantsia Zima" was first published in *Oktiabr'*, No. 10
(October 1956).]

STANTSIA ZIMA

ADAPTED EXCERPTS

Evgeny Evtushenko

True, twenty years on earth is not so long,
but I reviewed, reweighed the life I'd led:
the things I'd said when saying them was wrong,
the things I didn't say but should have said.
With prudence as my motto—watch and wait!—
too little I had thought, wished, felt my needs,
and in a life too simple, smooth and straight,
there'd been more noble impulses than deeds.

To find new strength, to find in life new aim,
with life once more to feel you're reconciled—
go back and touch the soil from whence you came,
where once you ran barefooted as a child.
So in my mind was always to the fore
the heartening thought (quite common at first sight)
of Stantsia Zima and Baikal's shore:
I would go home and things would be all right . . .

[At this point the poet recollects the story of his great-
grandfather, a Ukrainian peasant banished to Siberia for
participating in an uprising. He and others like him had
settled down there and spent their lives wresting a meager
living from that inhospitable land, to which, however,
they had finally become attached. We then jump to 1919,
when the Civil War swept across Siberia. The poet's
mother was then a nine-year-old girl; she remembered how
to the fighters of those days everything seemed so simple
and clear: push the *burzhui* into the sea, unfurl the red
banner over Russia, and the road to communism would be
lined with flowers.]

How could he know, this shaggy-headed lad,
who thought all questions settled once for all,
how many painful problems *we* have had,
how many difficulties, great and small?

[As late as 1942, when the Germans were threatening
Moscow, the poet was still a carefree Siberian child who
troubled himself little about the problems of the world.]

For there I lived and rambled as a child,
there I grew up and there I learned to love
the peaceful homes, the hills and fields, the wild
Siberian bush, Siberian skies above.
Life never brought me trials it sometimes brings,
seemed simple then——I took it in my stride——
because those other not so simple things
not I but others for me would decide.
To all the questions——how and what and why——
Came chorused answers——ready-made, well known;
but suddenly I somehow found that I
must answer all these questions on my own . . .

[The poet first visualizes his return to Stantsia Zima as
an allegorical confrontation of Childhood and Youth.
After a somewhat mutually suspicious face-off, Childhood promises to help Youth solve his pressing moral
problems.]

While homeward bound at last I'd wondered whether
I'd find unchanged the once familiar scene;
I'd figured that Zima, if not much better,
would also be no worse than it had been.
But for some reason——why I don't quite know——
the place just didn't look the same at all
as it had looked to me nine years ago——
main street, the park: it all now seemed so small.
I wandered here and there and roundabout——
it couldn't change——only my memory lied——
the streets had not grown shorter——so, no doubt
'twas I had changed——I'd grown a longer stride.
Again——maybe time changes——anyway,
everything seemed to catch and shock the eye——
I found that now I looked with some dismay
at what I used unseeing to pass by.
Yes, now my eyes were hurt by what they saw:——
the tavern drunk lying with limbs a-sprawl,
the quarrel in the line down at the store,
the lewd words crudely scribbled on the wall,
the boy chasing a cat with lifted stick,
the beggar with the artificial limb.
I lingered there no more——it made me sick——
but headed homeward, melancholy, grim.
To see such sights in any other place

I'd shrug my shoulders, not be much concerned,
but here in my Zima such things to face
where now for strength, truth, courage I'd returned!

I hurried on among my own to find
that something new which would refresh, revive,
and calm and pacify my troubled mind.
I stand before my doorway: I arrive!
"You've come!" "Hi! welcome home!" "You should have
     sent
a wire!" Kisses, hugs, shouts and running feet!
I had been right—at once I felt content,
my heart at peace, my doubts were in retreat.
"Wash now! You must be dirty from the train,"
and "Right away we'll light the samovar"—
I was at peace for I was home again,
yes, home again in Stantsia Zima!
And soon I sit with kinfolk all around,
the wanderer returned, the Muscovite—
laughter and greetings—true heartwarming sound—
my health is drunk—toasts other toasts invite.
I couldn't eat the way I could before,
the heaped Siberian dishes just appall—
"Come on and eat—you'll surely have some more?
Don't you people there in Moscow eat at all?"
That was my aunt. My uncle took in hand
the vodka bottle, poured and then replaced:
"Now that you're used to drinking Moscow brand,
tell us—drink up—how does our home-brew taste?"
We sat and joked as years before we'd done,
we drank and talked and talked and drank and ate;
then came a sudden hush on everyone:
had I seen Stalin, when he lay in state?
And, with this sudden change of atmosphere,
we talked of what so many talk about,
we talked of things which over the past year
had given rise to questioning and doubt.
Uncle Volodya laid his glass aside:
"They all act like philosophers right now—
sign of the times—not easy to decide,
to figure out just what and why and how.
The doctors, it turns out, were innocent.
It's an outrage treating people in that way.

And what a scandal all this must have meant
in Europe—it was Beria's fault, they say."
He spoke—without restraint, with small command
of words—of all that troubled every heart:
"Now you're from Moscow, you should understand,
explain it all in order from the start."
And eagerly awaiting my reply,
he looked at me and looked at me again;
as though I found it all quite simple, I
calmly replied: "Yes, later I'll explain."

They laid my bed—I'd asked it—in the loft.
I bedded down, lay listening to the night:
dancing somewhere—the accordion, loud then soft—
but for myself I saw no help in sight.
No mattress—it was prickly—and the floor
creaked, the hay rustled—soon the day would break—
and Kolka, my young brother—the last straw—
seemed all intent on keeping me awake.
His flashlight—foreign-made—he must show off,
his questions were the sort that wouldn't wait:
had I ever talked in person with Bobrov?
had I seen a helicopter climbing straight?

Next morning. In the streets cows rolled along
through the sun-shafted mist for milking time—
the world again seemed solid, healthy, strong,
and thinking seemed a folly and a crime.

No time to sit and talk and eat—instead,
indifferent to Aunt Liza's reprimand,
a truant schoolboy, pockets crammed with bread,
I ran to the river, lay down on the sand.
Before me lay the steady-flowing Oka
and logs swam past, together and alone,
unhurried—sirens sounded from afar
from time to time—gnats whined—upon a stone,
with trousers rolled, an old man, gray-haired, stood,
with rod in hand. He looked at me and frowned,
as though to say: "Fish or go home. You should
at least let others fish. Why hang around?"
He looked me over closely, then he came
wading toward me, shouldering his rod:
"It can't be! Wait! Yes, now I've got the name.

You're Zina Evtushenko's boy, by God!
From Moscow? Staying here a while no doubt?
Forgotten me? Well, that is not your fault.
I'll sit with you." He sat by me, spread out
his newspaper with bread, tomatoes, salt.
His questions tired me out, but he was not
put off, the old man had no inhibition—
he must know all: what salary I got?
would they reopen soon the Exhibition?
Caustic and sharp old man, his tongue was keen,
and guilefully he turned the conversation:
the Komsomol was not what it had been,
and neither was the younger generation.
"I well recall your mother's friends aflame,
when they were young, with yearning to create.
Yes, I remember them, their noble aim,
their passionate ideas and fierce debate.
They were ridiculous sometimes, it's quite true,
their theories sometimes harmful, we all know,
but I'll be frank, it worries me that you
or youngsters like you lack their drive and go.
And worst of all—maybe I'm wrong, my friend—
young thoughts with you are mighty hard to find;
and after all a man is in the end
the same age as the thoughts that fill his mind.
I say we've got young people, but no youth.
Take my nephew—he's typical, I guess,
he's not yet twenty-five and that's the truth—
but he looks thirty plus—at least no less.
He was straightforward once—sure it's a pity—
lately he's just forgotten how to live;
a member now of the *rayon* committee,
he bumps and thumps like an executive,
he's changed his walk, his eyes have turned to steel,
by his own speeches he's so deeply stirred:
the word is not to speed the job, you feel,
rather the job exists to speed the word.
And so, a master of the measured phrase,
he doesn't do the things he did before—
a solid citizen in all his ways,
he's given up football, goes with girls no more.
A solid citizen afraid to err!
But youth should set its limits in the sky!

No, the young people are not what they were,
nor are the fish (he added with a sigh) . . .
And now we've eaten, let's just try a cast.
Is this the sort of day the fish will bite?"
He cast his line and—not one minute past—
hauled in a carp, a big one, full of fight.
He beamed in admiration at the carp:
"Hooked him, eh? Lucky. That was quite a haul."
"You said the fish were bad!" But he was sharp:
"You can't hook me! I said so—but not all" . . .

When we'd gather as a family to eat,
I found that now I'd nothing much to say;
I'd sit and, silent, to myself repeat
the old man's words that I had heard that day.
Aunt Liza grumbled: "What's got into you?
You're gloomy, moody, like a sulky brat.
We're going berry-picking—you come too,
and try and be more simple." That was that . . .

Out picking. Just the womenfolk and I,
and in a barn we settled for the night.
I could not sleep. Turning, I could descry
the women's faces—patches of dull white.
A woman's voice came whispering through the dark:
"Liza, I can't go on—you'll never know
just what my life is like—so bare and stark.
So many things we have—a good Dutch stove—
our roof is good—everything in control—
everything clean and spic and span and nice—
children—a husband—but I have a soul!
And my soul is cold and empty, cold as ice!
My mother tells me: "Well, he doesn't beat you!
Were you marrying an angel, did you think?
He doesn't go for other women, or ill-treat you.
Of course he drinks—but then who doesn't drink?"
Oh, Liza, when he's drunk with vodka, reeking,
he grunts and growls—it's no use disagreeing—
and roughly pulls me close and . . . without speaking,
just as though I weren't a human being.
I used to cry and lie awake before,
but now I sleep—you've got to stay alive.
Look at me—I look forty, maybe more,
but, Liza, I am only thirty-five.

What can I do? I can't go on this way!
If only I had someone truly dear!
I would be glad to slave for him all day,
and even if he beat me, I'd not fear
as long as love was there; and then I'd stay
at home and try to make myself look nice,
and when I'd washed my darling's feet, I say,
to drink that water'd be no sacrifice."
Yet this same girl—I knew her voice again—
had sung that day a happy peasant song,
bareheaded, dancing in the wind and rain.
I'd envied her—so carefree, open, strong . . .

Out in the fields I met a young man—small,
merry, malicious, open, without fear,
resentful and rebellious at it all;
he told of many wrongs—angry, sincere.
He spoke with rage. Pankratov, so he said,
the chairman, was just ruining the farm—
he never tried to put things right—instead,
he feathered his own nest, he did the harm:
"I will not curry favor, and be still.
This way or that—but justice will be done.
And if Zima won't help, then Irkutsk will,
but I will finish what I have begun."
Screeching of brakes—and in his car,
Chairman Pankratov upright at the wheel,
looking just like a bureaucratic czar,
complete with brief case, symbol of all zeal:
"So you came to play the hero in Zima?
Felt brave to leave and see your mother weep?
Well, hero, you'll be sorrier than you are,
when I'm through with you!" He roared off in the jeep.
Jeep or no jeep, it surely wasn't there
I'd find unbending faith and sturdy roots,
but in the other, angry and sincere,
who to save leather carried his own boots . . .

The fly-catchers hang limply specked with flies.
The harried waitresses thrust through the din.
A teacher scans the menu with weak eyes.
A woman grumbles that the soup is thin.
A heavy-handed logger tanned with sun
taps on his glass for service, with a knife . . .

Here suddenly I bared my heart to one
whom I'd not seen before in all my life.
The journalist—such was my table-mate—
wore glasses, had a heavy, fleshy face.
His newspaper, he told me as we ate,
had sent him here to write about the place.
I told him everything right from the start,
I spoke of all the problems that defied
solution, filled with honest doubts my heart;
and helpfully my new-found friend replied:
"Once I was just like you, young and naïve,
I too was going to set the world on fire,
probe to the depths, uphold what I believe,
and mold my life close to the heart's desire.
Once I had courage too, a heart of flint—
I'd never strike my flag, admit defeat:
but then—a story that they wouldn't print—
I had a family—we had to eat!
Now I'm a newsman. Well, so what? Folk say
I'm gloomy, drink a bit more than I ought.
I don't write now. So what? Writers today
are watchdogs, not creators of our thought.
There are some changes, yes, but I don't doubt
there's something more behind all this display;
what yesterday kept quiet, we talk about,
but we keep quiet our deeds of yesterday!"
The way he weighed and scrutinized the rest,
the way he said that everything was bad:
his mien a bilious lack of faith expressed—
not faith, for faith is love and love is glad.
The fat-faced pessimist with satisfaction
chewed, smacked his lips, and griped. I understood:
by his self-satisfied dissatisfaction,
from faith in our great cause he's barred for good.
"Hell! I forgot my sketch. Now I must go
down to the saw mill—what a rigmarole.
Ye gods, the cooking here is lousy, though
what more can you expect in such a hole?"
He wiped his mouth, pushed backward on his chair,
then saw me look at him with jaundiced eye:
"Oh, yes, I quite forgot! You come from here!
Born in Zima! Excuse me. Well, good-by." . . .

"I'll take a stroll," I said. To be alone

was all I wished. My uncle, eyes ablaze,
snapped back: "Why go out always on your own?
Shameful the way you treat your folks these days!
We just don't understand you—woebegone,
you're never home, for days you hardly talk.
Is it some love affair you're carrying on?"
What could I say? I went and took my walk . . .

Some lovers in the loved one see no wrong;
however grievous may be her offense,
they still forgive, forget—and rush headlong,
blind and unthinking, to their love's defense.
We all of us have drunk but yesterday
so many tear-filled cups of bitter hurt:
blind love can be no help to us today,
we need a love that's thoughtful and alert.
Let us then take a longer, deeper view—
not live just anyhow—evaluate;
that which is great can never be untrue,
but we could be untrue to what is great.
I'm not for weak inaction, indecision,
I'm not for those of us who seek to trade
Russia's great destiny, prophetic vision
against the small change of gossip, lower-grade.
Leave these things to the weak and let them be,
they ease their lot by putting all the blame
elsewhere; not weakness Russia asks of me,
but deeds to add more greatness to her name.
I am ready, I will go, fight the good fight,
but from the heat of battle there must rise
the flame of that one truth, that single right,
which holds me fast and brooks no compromise.
Where'er I go—through whirling snow by sled—
across the waves of sun-scorched desert sands—
there must be a banner overhead
and I must feel a standard in my hands!
Some soul-searchings spring, I know, from doubt;
but ours spring from a love that never dies;
in the sacred name of truth we wrench them out,
in the name of those who fell that truth might rise.
We do not wish to live as the winds may blow,
nor can we wander blindfold down the trail;
our what and how and why—this we must know;
the great cause summons—grant we shall not fail! . . .

Doves overhead. Not overcool the shade.
The sun not hot. It could be any day.
I felt so very young, I felt new-made,
and full of goodness. I was going away.
I drank the farewell vodkas with my own
and went for the last time to view the scene—
it could be any day—I walked alone—
casting flecked pools of shade the trees stood green—
some children playing up against the wall—
the heavy trucks move past in line ahead—
and in the market place the women call,
trading their stock and produce. Onward led,
I walked before me feeling sad and free.
The last house was behind me now and I
climbed a small hill. From here the eye could see
Zima below. I stood and time passed by.
There lay Zima—the station building there,
barns, houses, roof tops: all below me lay—
and through the stillness of the evening air
I heard Zima speak to me, heard her say:
"With us today you're not the only one
in these your aspirations, searchings, strife;
don't grieve that you've not answered yet, my son,
that question which was put to you by life.
Abandon not the search, seek night and day;
and if you do not find, seek nonetheless;
truth's good, but happiness is better—so they say,
but without truth there is no happiness!
March forward with your head held high and proud,
with the good earth beneath, the sky above,
through all the world, my son, fearless, uncowed,
through good and bad go on. And people love,
and you will understand them, you will see.
Remember too, I have my eye on you,
and if the going's hard, come back to me."
And so I went, my courage born anew.

1953–6
Stantsia Zima—Moscow

[Semyon Kirsanov (born 1906) is a well-known and prolific
Soviet poet, a disciple of Mayakovsky, whose style he to some
extent imitates. The allegorical "Seven Days of the Week,"

for all its sentimentality, is one of the most forthright protests
against the heartlessness and inhumanity of the Soviet bureaucracy to appear in print in the U.S.S.R.

It was published in *Novy Mir*, No. 9 (September 1956).]

THE SEVEN DAYS OF THE WEEK

Semyon Kirsanov

All doors open wide,
        if within it's stifling!
Land of the Soviets,
        great-hearted land,
your every being, your core
        is Freedom's self.
So cancel too the passes at the entrance
and, Soviet land,
        in your kind hands accept
this our complaint
        against those whose hearts
        are stone.
And speak these words:
        "I'll not reject a plea,
though this should mean
        I must defer
        my feast.
Dear to me,
        immeasurably dear,
is every dreamer,
        weary, parched, a-thirst,
and I, like you,
        the stifling air abhor!
Lest it once more
        hang heavy overhead,
I'll not refuse protection to one soul!
Think your free thoughts,
        go ponder,
          search,
            reflect,
I will not greet you with a tight-barred door,
and, as a pledge,
        here, friend,
          you have my trust!

And may our future
          justify your day!"

Thus, Country, will you speak,
          and this is truth.

First Day

In the gloomy autumn
in the weariness and slush
after Sunday's done with
all this was written.
When you're thinking
you mustn't oversleep
you must wake up
in the early dawn
when the Institute walls
have a queer-looking frown
and the charwoman wanders
through the mess in the hall.

At just such a dawning,
sullen and forbidding,
came the swift desire,
for a new and fresh beginning.
Just to plunge into my work
like an armor-piercing rocket,
the wish to bring new boldness
of thought
      and sound
          and color.

And though plenty has been said
about everyday affairs
(of how "the greatness of our future
is made up of little things")
I wanted my idea
to be grand and oversized
that everything should seem to us
like love's first glorious rapture,
that we should have our fill
of faith and trust and confidence,
not stand as suppliants outside
the silent tight-barred door.

The wish was for a meeting,
open, light as sunshine,
the rare long conversation
stretching on to midnight,
and that everywhere the talk
at last be open, unafraid,
and that no one whisper darkly:
"Better to be careful . . ."

The wish was for the genuine,
unqualified
      opinion,
and that Monday should become
a day of true high worth.
The wish was too that everyone
whose hearts were weary, wilted, wan,
be allocated fresh new hearts,
dependable, reliable,
for their old hearts now were beating
feebly and unevenly,
and the danger always threatened
that they soon might cease to beat. . . .

But the seconds moved so slowly,
through the wearisome minutes,
and the people moved slowly,
horribly slowly, till evening came,
they eyed each other sharply,
glancing sideways with mistrust,
as though no one cared at all,
no one cared about the heart,
the closest thing they knew
was the furniture they sat on.

And their speech seemed artificial,
and their words not to the point.
For the work I did on Monday
very little could I show.
But in Monday's closing minutes,
through uneasy bitter dreams,
came the threatening thudding
of my heart's uneven beat.

Second Day

For seven days my friend has lain,
breathing heavy, hardly breathing.
His lips grow drier still and bluer,
his pressure-reading rises higher.
Soon his pulse will flicker, stop.
Who, who will come to save my friend?
"Only a new heart could save him,"
the doctor said resignedly.

On Tuesday from the very start
the same scene was repeated.
Like yesterday, the entrance door
opened just the same.
Such Tuesdays I know well by now.
The boy brings in the paper.
I saw before
     upon our floor
the self-same boy
     last Tuesday.
No great discoveries today,
no cause to get excited,
and Tuesday Tuesday greets and says,
"I'm just the same as you are."

But previously a second heart
in draft form I'd projected
and to the Ministry my plan
marked "urgent" had submitted,
that they, at once, without delay,
my life-giving plan might ratify.
Through the guichet they said to me:
"You can come back next Tuesday."

My friend by now with sweat and pain
through narrowed lids was reading
an article: "Solicitude
for the Soviet Common Man" . . .
And so once more I stand before
the entrance to the Ministry.
The doorman hands me a command,
"Just wait your turn," it says.
It is signed by Comrade Tuzdikin.
"Appropriations are reduced,

your Institute is ordered
not to produce a single thought
henceforth without directive!"

Plans and estimates require,
as good chiefs know, strict discipline,
but for my friend can be no hope
without a living heart.
I quickly to the Party turn,
they'll tell me:
        Go and build it!
And night and day without relief
I'll work at my machine!

My sleepless thoughts now follow me
with roar and loud vibration
and over the stars of night I run
from Tuesday into Wednesday.

Third Day

It's Wednesday, middle of the week,
a day the whole wide world is busy
and yesterday's blue sorrows are
as distant as the Middle Ages.
I'm pulled toward the center of the day,
and by this Wednesday I am borne
into the human stream, cascade
of urgent matters' swift advance.
And in the maze of shafts and arcs,
of bores and drills and other tools,
I too am busy: here is my work.
A heart I'm making here among
the vessels beating in the breast.
Here then the model of a heart
made for swift-footed future weeks!
Here on earth it's made to serve
for contact, like a relay team.
With someone else you can hook up
as if there were a wire between,
and it enables you to share
your joy, excitement, sorrow, pain,
and, above all, to share your love.
And if we wish, we can attach
to this one heart all human beings,

and this one heart will work for all,
ward off attacks on living heads,
attacks from without and from within!
And it will save my friend and take
upon itself the pressure of his pain.

This my discovery, this my find!
The locked-up breast I've opened wide,
replaced with this new heart my own,
and a new person have become.
Now, without need of phrase or word,
the message of the eyes I read.
I've learned to see men through and through
know who is weak,
        who sick,
            who tired,
whom overstrain has made that way
and who has learned to counterfeit,
who deserves an outstretched hand,
to whom one dare not give one's hand.
Here is my heart.
          I fondly gaze
on this pulsating thought of mine.
It's built to beat and not break down
in games a tiger might enjoy.
Such hearts as these I shall not give
unto the cunning or the proud!
On, upward, on, tomorrow come,
for now I know: on Thursday I
will finish what I have begun,
and there'll be happiness
              on Earth!

Fourth Day

So Thursday's come and from the very start
a cold sobriety possessed me.
For even as the clock was striking nine,
I felt, I knew:
           it all must be redone.
And, sure enough, this day I did discover
some defects in my beating apparatus.
What I had thought the quivering of emotion
turned out to be quite simply some loose parts.
And what had seemed like blood that filled the veins

turned out to be some sort of salt solution.
And what had seemed a real heart's vital force
was just a set of opening-closing valves
which by their lifelike movements could create
the illusion of a real heart's sympathy.
And what had seemed like friendship from the heart
was only skill at hiding savage claws.
And he who gave a friend his loyalty
now stood betrayed by that same loyal friend.
Beneath its cloth, beneath its leather cover,
this product really looked more like a lock.
It gave no sound when pain cried out in pain,
and when a hand knocked at the iron door . . .
I must begin again right from the start.
This time no dead experimental model;
no, this time it must be a real live heart.
And every detail, every valve and part:
they all must be immersed in hot red blood,
and then the heart, dependable, perhaps
will help my comrade in his sorry plight.
And so to work! Before the week is over
we'll have an apparatus of true worth.
Now everyone that's in our Institute
works with me—

         searches,

             sketches,

                argues,

                   works.

It's a good thing, analysis saved the day;
we didn't know,

        we tested,

           we found out!

Thursday's a vast day,

           made of opinions,

of errors and corrections, proofs and doubts.
A painful day, the hardest weekday this.
And so I sleep,

        exhausted, lost in sleep.

Dream on Thursday Night

I saw an exhibition
in a marble palace hall,
and there I tested, sounded out
new and shiny hearts.

Their beat is strong, dependable;
they are not wound mechanically,
and they can be inserted,
inserted in the chest.

To count the hearts and number them
there came in His Nonentity,
the local chief himself
as if he'd come to shop.

"In whom are you inserting them?
The weary? And the backward ones?
Those who've made no mark on history?
Not been leaders in our work?"

He lined them up and counted them
and moved them to one side.
Among them was my friend who breathed
as haltingly, as chokingly,
as these same lines I write.

And in their place *another* comes,
someone's favorite, so it seems.
He gives no explanation of
his merits or deserts.

The weary ones he thrusts aside,
but he's no common suppliant,
he has a ticket, invitation.

Merry, cunning, slightly bald,
a touch of fox, a touch of rat.
He looks like Comrade Tuzdikin . . .
But he does not come alone.

Enter the unfeeling ones,
holding folders in their hands
and lists they've checked through carefully,
checked and marked with ticks.

Enter next the double-faced,
the masters of duplicity,
files marked "secret," "personal,"
holding in their well-groomed hands.

Enter the false witnesses,
those who scribbled lies.

All of them have passes, permits.
Stand back and let them pass!

All enter. Each is carrying
a stone in his right hand,
the stone they used to carry
right up there in their chests.

These people can't be ranged in line.
These people can't be thrust aside.
Approach them with respect and care.
They've influence. Replace their stones . . .

"Get out of here, the lot of you!"
But, thank the Lord, it's night and this
is just an evil dream, no more!
I waken. I am saved.

Fifth Day

This the fifth day. With Friday here
no time to dally or delay.
The table's heaped with different parts,
the pulse beats make the floor vibrate.
The entire Institute pulsates
no slowing, lagging will there be,
all for one and one for all!
Party members and non-Party!
How crowded Friday is today!
No dallying and no delay!
Right now we could gladly use
seven Fridays in one week!

And now this is no idle game
of mere sensational ideas;
two thousand cardiograms already
we've administered to hearts.
All passes we'll abolish now,
heartlessness shall be a crime!
Now all petitions we'll be able
through the heart to pass.

Everywhere this heart is needed—
committees, offices and courts;
henceforward none shall be allowed
to serve as juror with no heart.
This heart will not mislead, let down.

It will not lie, nor will it vent,
like some wild animal, its wrath
upon the weak, the unprotected.

And now the test; we raise the pressure
and find to our surprise that steadily it rises higher
with no unevenness (success!)
and, like a rheostat, drops back.
No unexpected burst of feeling
can blow the valves, destroy the heart.
We test it at a quicker rate
for quarrels,

> sorrow,
>> and for pain;

the living heart beats smoothly now,
now that a second heart's at work!

But why does the whistle shrilly blast?
Why does the belt-drive slow and stop?
Only this morning we had vowed
to work right through without a break!
The little hammers cease their work.
Something unexpected's happened!
Our calculations are astray?
But look there! Through our workshop door
enter the men, the very same
I'd seen in dream the night before!

Some significant commission!
With some most important mission!
The Double-faced one there I see:
how he weighs each cautious word!
And the Unfeeling one strides in,
imposing and self-confident,
and at his side with measured stride
his personal assistant.
Resistance would be vain!
They poke and prod the artery,
their fingers knead the hearts
like fabric for a suit.
A brief report at once they write:
"Unsuitable. Won't do. That's that.
For general consumer use
we don't want such hearts at all.
And furthermore our market needs

no novelties of any kind.
What we need is useful hearts,
hearts like iron locks,
simple, handy, capable
of executing all commands:
Blacken? Blacken!
Admire? Admire!
Attack? Attack!
Roar loud? Roar loud!
Keep quiet? Keep quiet!
Destroy? Destroy!
Or love? Then love!
No cardiograms! To set things right
just take two hundred grams of vodka!
And for unauthorized research
henceforth we'll levy fines."

The paper's signed. Their work is done.
Our workers all are ordered home.
Before the paper's awesome power
we're helpless. Let each make his way
back to his respective street.
But just one street away from here
my friend lies flat with pulse gone still.
This was the knife-thrust in the back.
Still one day left. Can we, perhaps,
in one short day bring back my friend?
Stooped is the cleaning woman's shadow,
everything in the workshop smashed.
It's true, there's still one day to go,
but oh, the work there is to do.
We stand. Our eyes are blurred with tears.
So that is what this Friday brought.

I leave the lab and on my heels
the lab-assistant girls go out.
They hold their hearts as though they felt there
aching, gaping wounds.

Sixth Day

It's Saturday. The sixth day's come,
the day creation's work was done.
All was created,
                    Earth—Light,

and Man alone remained to make.
But on the sixth day Man appeared;
he turned a reed into a flute,
and only Love is lacking now.
But tenderly the man embraced
his woman, first-created woman,
beneath the tree in Paradise.
But one thing yet: they did not know
what was Evil and what Good. . . .
But then the apple tree revealed
that the Earth is round, not flat,
and in vain the Neutron pleaded:
do not smash me, touch me not. . . .
The planets' courses now are known,
but still our aspirations draw
Man ever on and up to solve
the riddles of the universe.
His thought he plunges, like a knife,
probes atoms, cells, probes death and life,
seeks not to take, he seeks to *give!*
He seeks to push creation further,
he must, he must pound on the door
and beg his Country to believe:
"Believe! Don't let those others sway
your judgment. Check on us yourself.
For no good cause our Institute
was closed. Take off the waxen seal.
You of all people know one can't
forbid the beating of the heart.
Return us to our Institute,
believe that there we have a heart
will take upon itself all pain . . ."
Through ministries' long corridors
I run, I knock at office doors.
Here the Lofty Thoughts Committee!
Here the Urgent Matters Section!
The Department of Humanity!
"Let us back into our shop,
for there we worked for one and all.
Comrade Tuzdikin is wrong.
We ask for truth, we ask our rights . . ."
And sudden in the solid wall
opens halfway a small guichet.
The wall has yielded to my knock!

The Country's heard my anguished cry!
And now in two large careful hands,
as large as two wide continents,
the Country takes my application,
bears it aloft into the clouds,
still higher where the sun's rays beat,
and scrutinizes there my plan.
I watch. I see the Country smile.
No, now I see the Country frown.
No, now from out the sullen clouds
flashes the radiance of her smile.
Surely her answer will be yes,
I see agreement on her face!
But no, once more the sullen cloud
conceals the Country from my eye.
It's not a cloud. It's just the faces,
the bureaucratic faces of those
who from the Country gladly would
all living hearts eliminate!
I waited hour after hour.
The clock strikes. It is getting late.
The buzzers sound from room to room:
Work is over! Let's go home!
Saturday is past and gone.
Chisel, pen and ax and verse,
see you Monday, good-by till then.
And this is right:
                        it's time to rest
for those who've worked since early dawn.
And yet with no days off the heart
must unresting thump and ache.
We cannot after all close down
the First Aid Station just like that!
The blinds are lowered one by one,
the tops are on the lenses screwed . . .
One understands: they've done their work.
But people used to volunteer
to work on Sundays and at night.
I think of Lenin carrying
a heavy beam upon his shoulder. . . .
What shall I do about my friend?
Thrombosis sets in:
                        things are bad!
A friend in need's a friend indeed.

Will my friend till Monday last?
His heart's in trouble,

                       losing blood . . .
I must go in the shop *right now*
and all night long work overtime,
work overtime to save my friend . . .

All is over,
rhyme no more.
The blinds come down.
No hope is left.
I whisper:
         "Comrades . . ."
But my comrades
are heading homeward,
because, perhaps,
they're not agreed
that a miracle could happen:
"Comrade Tuzdikin again
will pass the buck, defer, postpone."
But I must repay
to people all I owe!
"You've talked too much and you're upset.
Relax, forget it all, get drunk!"
Don't you see my tears?
They answer:
         "Don't you see,
this is now our day of rest.
You shall to the Rest Home go,
play games and get yourself a date.
It's too bad,
        but . . .
            so long . . ."

They're right!
        They speak the truth,
and the truth cannot be faked.

Seventh Day

Came Sunday like some gay housewarming party,
day for the swimming pool, the carousel.
The sky was blue, it almost smelled of blue,
of ultraviolet, of blinding quartz.
A fairy tale adorns the calendar;

its figure "7" smells of fresh red paint.
The postman's knocked, the alarm clock shrilled,
the refrigerator has a hundred times
switched on and off, folk rattled at the door;
but still we lay, still we did not awake.
And when at last at ten we sprang from bed,
before we even pulled the curtains back,
before to Sunday breakfast we sat down,
already in my thoughts there was tomorrow,
yes, Monday!
        Hurry, week, to your quick end!
This agonizing idleness cut short!
This comfort's an offense, since in my brief case
lies ready the required, correct solution!
O how I longed to burst into the shop,
to argue, curse—
        at last to win my point!
Into the stream, the cauldron of true-life events!
The newspapers!
        The mailbox!
        Action! Speed!

I seized the Sunday newspaper. I looked,
and horror-stricken brought it to the light.
Of Comrade Tuzdikin a photo there I saw
congratulating warmly, beamingly
a man who wears
        a rather crafty smile.
"Renowned Inventor!": thus the caption reads.
Beneath it an announcement states that hearts
at the department store are on display.
I understood those crooked, leering smiles:
my project, which the Country had approved,
had been exploited by this bureaucrat
and by this other posing as its author!

Down to the store. I press up to the counter.
There boxes and pin cushions shine and glitter
as slow they turn the better to display
their bright array of multicolored hearts.
Everywhere the stores had put on sale
hearts made of tin and hearts of rubber made,
inflatable, with press-button equipment,
and stuffed, inscribed: "For Luck."

Heart bottles contain sweet-smelling scents.
Heart albums filled with sugared verse.
A heart money box designed for thrift.
And macaroni heartlets for the soup.
And picture frames heart-shaped to please the ladies.
My plan's been turned into monstrosities of velvet.
Will these contraptions save my comrade's life?
'Twas thus that acrobats—in days gone by—
broke children's bones to make them hunchback dwarfs!

A lie they offer, served up like a heart,
and yet the public trustingly believes.
And there the heartless one to his poor girl
presents a heart-shaped brooch, of copper made.
The stand of cut-price knickknacks glitters bright,
the center of a thousand eager eyes
which stare with animation and believe
that these poor trinkets have a genuine worth,
so splendidly, attractively they shine!

"Don't buy these baubles!
                    This is just a fraud!"
But so to shout is petty, and not done,
and people may suspect some personal feud . . .
And, citizen, don't sniff like that or pout,
you have no cause, no reason to complain,
for everywhere there now are hearts on sale! . . .
But Monday comes tomorrow, it will be
a day of grand and genuine designs.
And, Country, you will weigh the pros and cons
high in the air, there where the sun's rays beat,
and thus you'll speak:
                    "Go forward, onward go.
Deceit I know and the heart's truth I know.
True aspirations shall not be confined,
Like Cinderella, in a darkling closet.
Invention and opinion I'll not have
denied, turned down and brought to nothingness.
I'll not permit the flowers on May's field
to be replaced with lifeless paper flowers.
I shall destroy on earth, like pox or plague,
the soullessness which numbs,
                    which smells of death.

For it's in me
                    all living hearts are beating
and, should they break, do not I feel the pain!
Go calmly forth; a New Week lies ahead.
Show what it is by which you really live,
the future soon will vindicate your day."

Thus, Country, will you speak,
                              and this is truth.

May-June 1956

[Robert Rozhdestvensky (born 1932) is a talented young
Soviet poet of whom more will probably be heard in the
future. "Morning," from *Den' poèzii*, 1956, is an eloquent
expression of a young Russian's yearning for a new era of
truthfulness, of recognition of existing evil, and of moral
responsibility.]

MORNING

Robert Rozhdestvensky

There is a time between the night and morning,
between the darkness and the shifting dawn,
between the transparent stillness
and the wise wind . . .
Lo, the aspen leaf trembles,
soaked through to its fibers in the night.
It waits
          for the sun to appear . . .
Inside the windows can now be discerned,
distinct,
separate
from the rest of the room.
Asleep,
          its streets spread out,
                              lies the city.

Everything in it—
                    from antenna wires
to door locks,
to posters on the walls—

everything is alive with anticipation:
Soon!
Soon!
        Soon!
                Do you hear?
                        Soon!!
The birds thunder out an avalanche of sound,
the mists dissolve and die . . .
Darkness creeps into the cellars,
out under the gates,
into empty pockets.
Darkness bends low over her watch,
looks with her faded eyes
(this will not help her now!)—
and she speaks
                with the voices
of those who cannot stand the light.
Speaks calmly at first,
but then gurgling with rage:
"You people! What is the matter?
Even under me you managed
to figure
        a few things out.
You walked, not quarreling with my truth,
slowly, it's true, and with care.
I made myself
            darker
                on purpose,
so that conscience might not torment you,
so that you would not see the dirt,
so that you would not reproach yourselves. . . .
Were things so bad for you then?
Did you ever talk about it
then?!"
Be silent, night!
Anyway you cannot outshout
the swelling dawn which now fills half the sky.
Be silent.
        Morning will give you answer!
Morning will speak with you.
Stay with your flatterers,
and do not come to us with such advice!
In the end

          man perishes,
if he
          conceals
                    his sickness!
We will look back and remember now
those whose songs were cut short
                              before morning came.
You say in your presence we couldn't see dirt?
We want to see dirt!
Do you hear?
It is time!
We want to know in what corners it lay hidden,
to look into the contorted faces of our foes,
that we may twist their arms,
that we may wring their necks.
The alarm clocks on the tables have sounded,
and—as always reluctantly—
the corridor fills with the creaking of doors,
in the pipes
          gurgling and rumbling
                              the water comes to life . . .

Good morning!
Are you still asleep?
                    Get up at once!
Put on today a gay dress!
Get up!
For you I'll command the birds to sing . . .
The day is beginning.
The day is beginning!
I love this hour.
I
love
life!

[Konstantin Murzidi (born 1914) is a minor Soviet poet,
endowed, it seems, with more sincerity than talent. The following piece, taken from *Literaturnaya Moskva,* Vol. II, though
no poetic masterpiece, has the ring of authenticity in its cry
for a rebirth of Communist sincerity and idealism and in its
indignation against official time-serving and hypocrisy.]

THE LINDENS ARE BLOOMING

Konstantin Murzidi

The lindens are blooming outside;
The apple trees smell of the spring;
Yet I and my friends here beside,
We sit here pontificating.
Now I shall stand up, frank and bold,
I'll speak what I feel through and through!
Our true Party Law is pure gold;
It calls us to deeds brave and true.
But another code rules in this land,
Not written—but there, a dead weight—
I'll never accept *its* command,
The code of committee debate,
Where nothing is left up to chance,
Where everything's fixed in advance:
It infuses my spirit with hate.
To hell with canned rodomontade!
By whom is it needed today?
By those who are making the grade
To a life of soft ease and cool shade
And are aiming to keep it that way.
A jibe? An objection? Or, better,
A smile? . . . There might be a mistake.
They want you to stick to the letter.
And the spirit? . . . Now, Comrade, beware . . .
The spirit? And why should you care?
No, better just talk for form's sake!
Yes, people there are who have paid
For having been over-sincere!
Of what is the chairman afraid?
No strangers or enemies here;
By this land of ours we were made,
Grew up in this land, hold it dear.
Thus the apple tree grows every year
Still higher beneath the sun's rays.
It blooms and it strengthens its root,
It spreads to the sky its green maze,
And it doesn't give off bitter fruit.

Let this to our chairman be told!
Bring him, Party, the bard's vibrant plea!
No, poetry just leaves him cold,
So make it an urgent decree!

CRITICISM

[Konstantin Paustovsky (born 1892) is a much respected Soviet novelist of the older generation, a specialist in nature stories (*Kara-Bugaz*, 1932; *A Story of the Woods*, 1948; *The Birth of a Sea*, 1952, etc.). The speech presented here was delivered on October 22, 1956, at a meeting of the prose section of the Moscow Writers' Union. The meeting had been called as a public forum for discussion of Dudintsev's *Not by Bread Alone*. This novel had created a sensation in Russia, and public interest in the discussion was enormous. According to reports, the crowds were so great that some students, unable to get into the room where the discussion was being held, placed ladders against the outside walls and listened through the windows. Paustovsky's speech was inadequately and somewhat misleadingly reported in *Literaturnaya Gazeta* (October 27, 1956). But a stenographic report was smuggled out of the country, translated into French, and published in *L'Express* (March 29, 1957). Our translation from the French appears here by permission of *L'Express*.]

THE DROZDOVS

A SPEECH

Konstantin Paustovsky

I don't intend to speak here of the novel's qualities and defects as a work of literature. But I do think that the time has come to speak out, loud and clear. For me, comrades, Dudintsev has depicted a very important social phenomenon. Dudintsev's novel is the first attack on the Drozdovs, against whom our literature must pit all its forces until they are entirely destroyed in our country.

But there are thousands of Drozdovs and it is of this that I wish to speak. One thing gives me pleasure: those people who to some extent align themselves with the Drozdovs have not found it possible to put in an appearance at this meeting. In a way, I find this fact gratifying. The writer's conscience must be in every respect the conscience of his people.

Dudintsev has expressed that profound anxiety which all of us feel about the moral character and purity of Soviet man and about our culture. Dudintsev's book is the merciless truth—the only truth which our people needs on its uneasy progress toward a new social regime. Dudintsev's book is the merciless truth, and it is also a very serious warning. For the danger does exist: the Drozdovs are no fewer in number than they were; they are still with us.

Not long ago I had occasion to spend a considerable amount of time among the Drozdovs and to see a good deal of them. It was aboard the *Pobeda*. Half of the passengers (intellectuals, painters, writers, workers, people connected with the theater) made up one social stratum, occupying the second- and third-class accommodations. The de luxe and first-class cabins were occupied by another social stratum: deputy ministers, very high-placed administrative officials, and other very exalted personages. We did not and we could not have any contact with these people. For, in the opinion of the second- and third-class passengers—that is, half the total number of passengers— these people were not content merely to make themselves unbearable by their dismal arrogance, their total indifference to everything except their own position and their personal vanity. They also amazed us by their crass lack of culture. (Applause.) To allow such people to cross the borders of our country is, in my opinion, simply a crime. (Applause.) A crime because they—the Drozdovs—and we have completely different conceptions of our country's prestige and of the dignity of Soviet man. I need only give two fairly classic examples of the type of question which these people addressed to our guides and interpreters. You know that the Sistine Chapel contains Michelangelo's masterpiece "The Last Judgment." One of the Drozdovs who some time ago attained a very high position asked the guide: "What's that painted there? The judgment of Mussolini?" (Laughter.)

In front of the Acropolis I heard another Drozdov ask: "How is it that the proletariat allowed the Acropolis to be built?"

In general, everything good in the West was condemned by the Drozdovs. When one of my neighbors, a Leningrad writer, exclaimed: "The sea has a magnificent color!" one of the Drozdovs made the remark: "Well, does the sea look worse back home? This comrade should be investigated." It's a small incident, but it does serve to throw light on the mentality of the Drozdovs.

I have been speaking of the anxiety which is growing in all of us, the anxiety which Dudintsev feels so deeply. Where does it spring from? Why should Dudintsev, a man of great courage and high conscience, feel such misgivings? The problem is not merely the portrayal in literature of a few careerists. It's not simply a matter of careerists. The whole affair is much more complicated and much more serious than that.

The problem lies in the fact that in our country there exists—unmolested and even to some extent prospering—an entirely new social stratum, a new caste of *petit bourgeois*.

This is a new group of acquisitive carnivores, a group which has nothing in common either with the Revolution, or with our regime, or with socialism. (Voice in the hall: "Quite right.") They are cynics, black obscurantists, the same people who aboard the *Pobeda*, without any embarrassment or fear, quite openly carried on anti-Semitic talk of a kind worthy of pogrom-makers.

There are thousands of these Drozdovs and we should not close our eyes to their existence. Dudintsev's great merit lies in the fact that he has struck a blow at the most vital link in the chain. He speaks of the most terrible phenomenon in our society, a phenomenon to which we cannot at any price close our eyes, unless we are willing to allow these Drozdovs to overrun our entire country.

Where did all this originate? Where do they come from, these profiteers and boot-lickers, these men of intrigue, these traitors, who claim the right to speak in the name of the people—of a people whom they really despise and hate, though they continue to speak in its name? They know the opinion of the people. Each and every one of these Drozdovs can—freely and with impunity—go up onto the platform and hold forth on what and how the people thinks. (Applause.)

Forgive me for speaking so brutally. But I consider that in this context veiled allusions would be quite out of place; for all this is too sad and too dangerous. Where did these people spring from? They are the result of the cult of personality—a term, by the way, which I consider extremely euphemistic. This is the fertile soil on which these people have sprung up—from 1937 on,

They have survived until today, strange though this may appear at first sight. The prevailing atmosphere has accustomed them to thinking of the people as dung. They have been educated and encouraged to gratify man's basest instincts. Their weapons are betrayal, calumny, moral assassination, and just plain assassination. If these Drozdovs had not existed, our country would still have such great men as Meyerhold, Babel, Artyom Vesyoly, and many others. It is the Drozdovs who destroyed them. And why were these men destroyed? They were destroyed to preserve the stinking well-being of these Drozdovs. We cannot imagine what an infinite number of talents, minds, and remarkable men have disappeared. But if they hadn't disappeared, if these men were still living, our culture would be in full bloom! We are just oblivious to this fact.

Dudintsev has described the particular case of an inventor who exposed the monstrous picture of the "activity" of the Drozdovs. But the Drozdovs are many. Don't we in our own milieu know some Drozdovs? These are not empty words. Look at the story of the Ministry of the Fishing Industry. Quite knowingly, because of servility and, perhaps, stupidity, enormous damage was caused to our economy. Ruin is brought upon the country—and this without any reason, foolishly, stupidly. There are no more fish in the Sea of Azov. The Black Sea has been almost entirely drained of fish. And all this is the work of the Drozdovs, who do it in order to carve careers for themselves.

What brazenness enables them to refrain from answering to the people for having devastated the country? Take the Oka banks from Aleskin to Tarusa. (I've published several articles on this subject.) The forestry protection belts have been laid waste. The water has been polluted. The Drozdovs don't give a damn. They want to fulfill the plan, so down go whole forests.

One other thing which must be fought with every possible weapon: dishonest profiteering. The idea of profit has begun to dominate many people—people who are money-grubbers. This profiteering could ruin and destroy the country.

These people, these Drozdovs—we see them every day about us. They are so much of one piece, even to the way they dress, that they all, in the same ignoble manner, with the same complete disdain for the Russian tongue, employ a dead language, a language of red tape. This is a force which weighs heavy upon the country. And all this is camouflaged by empty words about the happiness of the people! In their mouths these words are a sacrilege and a crime. These men dare to claim the right to represent the people—without the people's consent. They dare to dispossess our country of its human and material wealth for their own personal interests—and to dispossess it with no small amount of brazenness!

But I think that the people, which has now come to feel the dignity of our way of life, will before long firmly sweep away the Drozdovs. We must fight this battle to the end. This is only the beginning! (Applause.)

[Leonid Sobolev (born 1898) is a minor Soviet novelist, a former naval officer and author chiefly of stories about the navy. Since 1956 he has become one of the leading Soviet literary "McCarthyites."

The speech translated here (from *Literaturnaya Gazeta,* May 22, 1957) was one of the highlights of the third plenum of the Board of the Writers' Union, held in Moscow in the second half of May 1957. The main—perhaps the sole— purpose for convening the plenum was to crush the literary "opposition" and to elicit admissions of error from such people as Dudintsev and the editors of *Literaturnaya Moskva.* At a March meeting, Dudintsev and others had defended themselves openly—an unheard-of proceeding in the Soviet literary world. The novelist Venyamin Kaverin, one of the editors of *Literaturnaya Moskva,* even threatened to institute legal proceedings against his opponents for slander and intimidation. But by May the situation had hardened. On May 13 and 19 Khrushchev met groups of writers and addressed them in person. Open defiance was no longer possible. The "erring" writers took refuge in silence—in itself an act of defiance and high courage. It was this "heroic silence" that inspired the wrath Sobolev displays in this speech.

Sobolev was commended for his attitude by Khrushchev and rewarded by being made chairman of the newly formed R.S.F.S.R. Division of the Writers' Union. A similar threatening and whip-cracking speech made by Sobolev at the Constituent

Congress of the R.S.F.S.R. Writers' Union in December 1958
appeared in English in *Soviet Literature,* No. 4 (April 1959).]

MILLIONS ARE LISTENING

L. Sobolev

[*Literaturnaya Gazeta* (May 22, 1957) prefaced its transcript
of Sobolev's speech as follows:]

In his impassioned and principled speech, which drew a
lively response from those present at the plenum, L. Sobolev
dwelt on shortcomings in the work of the Moscow Writers'
organization, on the harm that had been inflicted on the organization by the factional struggle undertaken by certain comrades.

In the Moscow organization, Sobolev noted, there are people
who defend their blatantly false attitudes on grounds of principle. In the present instance they are shielding themselves with
the notorious catchword "the whole truth"—which they have
been using with no small success for their own purposes.

It is perfectly true that the Twentieth Party Congress
made many of us aware of the evident need to write
straightforwardly and honestly about those bad, harmful,
and backward things that interfere with the great cause
of the people and the Party. And it is perfectly natural
that there should be errors of exaggeration, that criticism
should at times get out of hand. But the important thing
here, in my opinion, is not the errors, natural enough for
the passionate mind of the writer, but the attitude we
take toward these errors—our own and those of others.

And here we are all to blame: the top leadership of
the Writers' Union and all of us men of letters.

Last fall I was in the Baltic area and did not therefore
take part in the notorious discussion of V. Dudintsev's
novel. The novel itself I read considerably later, after
the first *Literary Gazette* article. But the surprising thing
is this. In Tallin, where I was staying at the time, neither
in the library nor among the public, naval or civilian, did
this novel produce the tremendous sensation it created
in Moscow literary circles.

It is well known that for certain people this novel has
become a sort of banner. And though it grieves me to

have to say this, a section of our men of letters aimed to make the *Literary Moscow* anthology into just such a banner. But, after all, a banner should be defended. And I am surprised that the writers who are making this collection their banner, who have been expressing their views by publishing in it stories, articles, and verse—I am surprised that these writers are not defending their attitudes here at the plenum. There's something strange about this.

But it is very much their duty to speak up! We must not forget that this rostrum is a very lofty one. On it we writers are being watched from all sides, the length and breadth of our broad Motherland. Millions of people who read our books are listening with great attention to what we are saying on this rostrum. From the rostrum of this plenum we express what we failed to say in our books, or we correct those things which were written in error. And these proceedings are being followed with especial eagerness by that most ardent and trusting part of our readers: our youth.

We brought enough confusion into the heads of our youth with those works of the past literary year which allegedly told this notorious "whole truth." And what of the effect on our youth! Of youth's reaction to this! So why no explanations from those who are responsible for confusing these young minds? Without doubt they ought to explain to our youth what it's all about.

There are two possibilities. Either the authors of these works and those who have been supporting them understand that the reproaches addressed to them are justified— in which case they ought to come out and say so. Or they consider the reproaches unjustified and believe that they are right—in which case they should rally to their banner and defend their literary convictions.

But they do neither. Whether these comrades wish it or not, they are by their own behavior bringing upon themselves extremely serious accusations of factional interests—camouflaged with the pompous banner of "principle" and "artistic convictions."

We are grown-up people and it should be understood that what is looked for here is not that you beat your breasts in contrition. What is asked of you is simply that you carry out your duty as members of the Writers' Union

and as servants of the people. This duty is to serve the
people by your books and by your lives. And if your book
causes confusion, if your story is ambiguous, if it produces an effect other than what you intended, then it is
your duty to state just *what* you intended to say and how it
happened that you were not properly understood. This is
hard to do, I agree, but it is necessary for the cause we
serve.

Our duty as writers is in general a very difficult one
and, other things apart, it is difficult because every word
we say goes directly into the souls and minds of our
readers.

How can one remain silent? How can I leave even the
smallest cloud of uncertainty between myself and my
reader? This is a dangerous cloud. Because of it we could
lose the confidence of the people.

As you know, in music a pause sometimes conveys
more feeling and thought than a melody or a chord. Your
silence is dangerous. It is disorienting the readers. What
does it mean? What lies behind it? A proud disdain for
the opinions of others? A contemptuous confidence in
your own infallibility? An insulting "How could I expect
you to understand me"? A spirit of self-sacrifice? What
does this silence mean? Forgive me, we do not understand. Nor will the people understand.

But this is what's amusing. In a year or two these
works of "genius," these "un-understood" stories, novels,
and poems will be completely forgotten. Yes, they will be
forgotten. This is a bubble of froth on the wave that
rolled through our country after the Twentieth Party
Congress. And froth, as we all know, disintegrates.

Do you know what I learned yesterday; what amazed
me because of the deadliness of the enemy's aim, its
gangsterish calculation, its Jesuitic far-sighted scheming;
and what actually made me get up on this rostrum and excite myself against doctors' orders?

Did you know that the Western press is giving hypocritical encouragement to you who should have spoken
today but remain silent; that to you is extended the hand
of "friendship," a hand that contains poison, that arms
are opened wide to embrace you, an embrace that—should
you trust it!—will strangle you; that a lasso has already

been cast over your shoulders which will drag you far from your people?

Did you know that you are being called upon to maintain a *heroic silence?*

Heroic silence!

What terrible, envenomed words! Remain silent: you have recognition, you have friends, your heroic silence will go down in history.

But who is it who is to remain silent? A writer? A poet? Then what good to him are his talent and his mind? Of what use his impassioned conscience? Of what use is life if he is to spend that life maintaining a heroic silence before his own people?

I do not believe that you will follow this devilish advice. I do not believe so. If not here, if not from this rostrum, then in print you will speak out honorably, as befits a Soviet writer. You will speak out because on our planet there is something more serious than the minor squabbles in the Moscow organization; there is the long-standing dispute between the two systems, a dispute which has again become acute, and for our enemies there can be no greater joy than to divide and to corrupt a detachment of true Communist warriors—the Soviet writers!

[Aleksandr Kron (born 1909) is a prominent Soviet dramatist, author of several successful plays produced both before and since the Second World War. He has also written a considerable amount of criticism on the theater and drama. Kron is a good example of the sincere, idealistic Communist writer struggling with the moral problems posed by the corruptions and tergiversations of the "system." He has shown considerable courage and independence on several occasions, even during the worst of the anti-cosmopolitan campaign of 1948–9. The article translated below, taken from *Literaturnaya Moskva,* Vol. II, is probably the frankest and most searching discussion to appear in Russia of the effects of the "cult of personality" on literature (i.e., the rule of Stalin).]

A WRITER'S NOTES

A. Kron

The historic achievement of the Twentieth Party Congress was the repudiation of the cult of personality, which had caused tremendous harm, material and spiritual, in all spheres of our society. It is extremely important to note that the Party condemned not only the cult of the personality of J. V. Stalin but that it condemned the cult of personality in general. Cults of all sorts are alien to Marxism-Leninism, the scientific world outlook of the proletariat. In areas where a cult exists, scientific thought must give way to blind faith, creativity to dogma, public opinion to arbitrary power. A cult breeds a hierarchy of its votaries—the deity needs his bishops and his saints. A cult is incompatible with criticism; the healthiest criticism easily turns into heresy and blasphemy. A cult is essentially anti-popular; it degrades the people and forces them to accept as gifts from above things which they have paid for dearly with their own labor and blood. Even the cultist deification of the People, with a capital *P*, has its reverse side—it debases the individual. The leader was a servant of the People, but when millions of masters stood up at the mere mention of the name of their servant, there was something in this utterly alien to those democratic traditions in which we have been educated by the Revolution and the Soviet social order.

People are now used to saying that the cult of personality has caused incalculable harm to our society. Incalculable, immeasurable, limitless, unprecedented, boundless—such words used in large quantities produce an unpleasant flavor of irrationality. It is not by chance that they were very fashionable a few years ago. If our riches are incalculable, our forces inexhaustible, our confidences limitless, our authority boundless, then there is no need for us to be economical or careful, to study and listen; it is easy to lose all conception of reality, forget one's sense of moderation, and abandon oneself to the most unrestrained gigantomania. No, no matter how great the harm caused by the cult of personality, it *is* calculable, and indeed it must be calculated. At the same time we must soberly evaluate our strength and our opportunities. If we do so, we shall see that our strength is quite sufficient to enable us finally and completely to overcome the consequences of the cult in all phases of our economic, political, and cultural development. It will not help us to say immeasurable instead of numerous, invincible instead of powerful, wise instead of intelligent, great instead of large.

The cult of personality is, first of all, an ideological distortion. Literature and art could not escape its pernicious effects. Artistic creation cannot exist without initiative, the search for innovation. And the innovator, no matter what historical period he lives in, is always in advance of the perceptions of his contemporaries and is not always immediately understood. When the taste of one person becomes indisputable, the unavoidable result is standardization and crude interference in the creative process. A harmful tutelage is established which is injurious to real talent but quite comfortable for mediocre craftsmen. Under these conditions, not to be understood means to be condemned. When truth is the absolute possession of a single man, artists are left to serve only the modest function of drawing illustrations and composing odes. One cannot look forward with one's head bowed.

About modesty. During recent years there have been cases when members of our literary and artistic world did not behave with sufficient modesty in their daily lives.[1] Of course, this is disgusting. Lack of modesty in daily life is most frequently a disease of people who play a very modest role in their particular branch of art. In other words, their modesty appears just at the point where modesty is by no means a virtue. Let us recall what Marx wrote on modesty:

> Truth has as little modesty as light; and with respect to whom would it be modest? With respect to itself? *"Verum index sui et falsi."* ("Truth is the measure of itself and of falsehood.") In other words, with respect to Falsehood?

If some work of science or scholarship has modesty as its outstanding feature, it is rather a sign of fear of the truth than of fear of falsehood. Modesty is an instrument for fettering one's every step forward. It is a fear of drawing conclusions, a fear imposed from on high on one's investigations; it is a prophylactic against truth.

Further: truth is general. It does not belong to me alone.
It belongs to everybody. It possesses me; I do not possess
it. My property is the *form,* which constitutes my spiritual
individuality. "The style is the man."

The administrative style of supervising art has not
contributed to the development of the artist's own individual style. The emphasis has been placed not on style,
but on method. But in architecture and the graphic arts
there did develop after the war a peculiar style—crudely
ornamental, official, pompous.

It is no longer a secret that our theatrical art is going
through a serious period of stagnation. Thoughtful people
have often spoken of this before, but in the period when
it was customary to regard our development in every sector
only as an uninterrupted victory march without halts or
retreats, they were quickly called to order. Specifically,
criticism of our academic theaters[2] was declared an un-
patriotic act. Now even non-specialists can see that this
did not do the theaters any good. It is only a step from
inviolability to untouchability. People used to draw lots
for the right to buy a cheap ticket at the box office, but
now the theaters play to half-empty houses—an ominous
symptom. It is impossible to explain it away by the inva-
sion of television. And perhaps the most alarming symptom
is the lack of demand for cheap tickets especially. It is
very comforting to explain this fact by the increased prosperity of the spectators, but still the real reason probably
lies elsewhere. Audiences cannot be regarded as a kind
of amorphous mass. New generations of theatergoers are
formed after certain intervals of time. October opened
the doors of the theaters to the people, and with every
passing year the theater became a larger and more permanent part of the everyday cultural experience of the
worker. There is considerable reason to suppose that the
present difficulties have been caused, not by the caprice of
a bored public, but by a considerable decline in the number
of people who attend theaters regularly. The generation of
theater-lovers which has either grown old or turned away
from the theater has not been succeeded in sufficient
numbers by enthusiastic young people who would regard
the theater primarily as a school of life. Sad as it may
seem, at present our theaters appeal much more strongly

to that section of the public which goes to the theater to rest and be entertained while sitting in a comfortable armchair than it does to those who used to be ready to stand in the gallery through an entire play in order to feel the pulsation of a vital new idea or experience a thrill of joy from an actor's skill. The picture that emerges at first seems strange. During recent years we have spent a great deal of time talking about the rich ideological content of our plays: we have struggled to attain it, given awards to those who displayed it, and censured those who lacked it; but what we have achieved is a decline in the ideological influence of our theater.

Three basic and closely related causes, all stemming directly from the cult of personality, produced this stagnation: disregard for the objectively existing laws of artistic creation, hypertrophy of the editorial function, and the creation of a bureaucratic hierarchy in art.

It is profoundly untrue that the so-called "no conflict" theory originated among the writers and artists themselves.[3] One might just as well argue that the effort to outlaw Darwin's theory originated among biologists. There is not a single playwright who would not understand that conflict is the necessary foundation of any dramatic work. The conflict of a drama is based on the life of human society, with all the contradictions inherent in it. Dramatic conflict is a reflection of these contradictions, which exist objectively. Consciously or unconsciously, the playwright follows the laws of the dialectic. The notorious theory of the "struggle between the good and the still better" proved to be just as unfounded, and it served as a theoretical prop for those who sought to falsify and prettify reality. It becomes clear who needed these theories and for what purpose if we recall that they arose during the years when even such an exact science as statistics was used by the hallelujah singers for creating all sorts of falsifications. If this was true of statistics, it is all the more true of the theater.

Not nearly all these bureaucratic delusions became an accepted part of our theory. That does not make them any less tenacious of life. The conviction has become deeply rooted that the subject matter of an artistic work is not the invention of the author, and that therefore "themes" can be planned from above as easily as industrial output. That the plot of a play is like a Gospel parable, necessarily embodying a moral lesson. That the spectator's most immediate need is to imitate and that he only awaits an opportunity to copy in life the outline he has seen on the stage. That whenever a negative character attempts to justify his base actions, the author is yielding the rostrum to the enemy. That every work in which evil remains unpunished is a sign of pessimism. That the second, or connotative level of meaning—the hidden, unspoken undertones and overtones which determine to a great extent the ideological and emotional effect of a play and a performance—is a crafty subterfuge, hard to evaluate and control; and that therefore characters should express their thoughts unambiguously and distinctly. Lastly, thoroughly distorted conceptions prevail concerning the relation between the individual and the "type."

One of the most pernicious delusions, which even recently was no less current than the "no conflict" theory, was expressed approximately as follows: "Works of art may be bad, mediocre, or good. Our Soviet reader (spectator) works tirelessly, he does not have the time to read (see) everything that comes out. It is in our power to excise everything poor and mediocre and to give the Soviet people a limited number of model works." As a result of this theory, which was practiced most widely in the motion-picture industry, a country of 200 million people, which had created its own magnificent and original cinema art, was at one time producing fewer motion pictures than Poland or Belgium.[4] The number of theaters and literary magazines decreased. But the number of outstanding works did not increase, even percentagewise. They continued to loom up in their solitary way against a background of mediocre and poor works. Moreover, the effort to create at all costs a perfect work that could serve as a model or standard, an artistic document that would give an exhaustive and uniquely correct elucidation of a certain subject, reduced even important artists to schematism.

About editing. It would hardly enter anyone's head to deny the need for well-trained editors or to minimize the actual contributions of our best editors. But lately the number of people and organizations which claim the right to perform editorial functions has multiplied so rapidly, their rights and powers have become so grossly inflated,

that it has become a calamity. Nobody is surprised now
that magazine reviews carry the name of the editor next
to the name of the author of the book. It looks as if the
book (like the old civil-war army units) had a command-
ing officer and a commissar both. If the reviewer does not
like the style of the author, he frequently reproaches the
editor for it, even when the author is no fledgling, but a
mature, established writer. Things are even worse in the
theater. In all the contracts concluded between a playwright and a theater there is a clause stating that the
author undertakes to make any changes and corrections demanded by the theater; refusal involves economic sanc-
tions against him. Recently, the stage manager E. Krasnyansky published an article in the magazine *Teatr* demanding that the title page of every play indicate the name of
the theater that had edited it.[5] And some years ago, the
critic A. Makarov published a theoretical justification of
this established practice on the grounds that "the experience
of life of the collective is always broader, richer, and fuller
than the experience of an individual." [6]

There is no question that theater people can be very
useful to a playwright. First of all, because of their stage
experience. As for life experience, it is a debatable point
whether a writer's life experience represents only the experience of a single individual and whether it is legitimate
to equate the life experience of a theatrical group with the
experience of the people as a whole, their collective wisdom.
I am firmly convinced that it is a mistake, equally disastrous for the playwright and the theater, to regard a play
as a semi-manufactured product. Interference by the
theater is harmful, not only when the author objects, but
often even in cases when the author professes his gratitude.
As a rule, gifted and original works are made worse by such
interference, while vapid and feeble works are improved.
This is the way ersatz products acquire the right to exist.

When they encroach on a territory not their own, directors and actors often become less exacting toward themselves. They begin to circumvent and evade complicated
problems, and they tamper with the text of a play in
order to justify the comfortable solutions they are used to.
Everything that does not succeed immediately begins to
seem unattainable, and everything controversial seems
mistaken, something to be corrected. Thus belief in the

play and respect for its basic ideas disappear and are
replaced by an irresponsible attitude toward the text. When
this attitude encounters no resistance from the contemporary public, it is even extended to the classics.

In addition to the theaters themselves, there are many
other echelons of authority which have the power, if not
the right, to dictate their will to the author, either directly
or through the theater. As a result, a play is edited by
everyone who feels like taking the trouble, and any current propaganda drive, like the campaign against drunkenness, for example, can serve as a pretext for demanding
changes in a play that is already being performed. Even
the mimeographing bureaus that duplicate plays for distribution in very limited numbers of copies—even they have
their editors. Even the publishers' proofreaders arbitrarily
delete from plays dashes which they think unnecessary
and replace them with commas; only Gorky is permitted
frequent use of the dash. It is useless to argue that Gorky
actually was responsible for a reform of the Russian
punctuation system and that in direct discourse the dash
has taken on much broader functions. There is a book
of regulations.

You cannot help mentioning the devil once in a while;
but here again you run up against the book of regulations.
The word for devil (*chort*) must be spelled with an "e"
(*chert*). Maybe it's right, but the flavor is no longer the
same.[7]

Producers have somewhat similar experiences. Those
who have had occasion to be present at the preview of a
play ready for public showing know the peremptory tone
the numerous preceptors and inspectors are wont to use
when giving their instructions. (Incidentally, there are perfectly good Russian words, *nastavniki,* and *nadzirateli,* for
designating these functionaries, but they are nevertheless
known as *instruktory* and *inspektory.*)[8] Nowadays this
procedure is gone through in a somewhat more liberal
form than it was, but the substance is little changed. As
for theater criticism, the behavior of the newspapermen
remains virtually unchanged. The system still prevails
whereby people who write worse and know less have complete freedom to correct people who write better and know
more. It is considered quite a normal proceeding for editors
to delete or insert whole paragraphs. This is the source

of the common attitude toward newspaper reviews: it does not matter who writes them; what matters is where they are published.

In art there is only one legitimate hierarchy—the hierarchy of talent. It is established by time and by the people. But when it is set up hurriedly and in small committees, the result is essentially nothing but the well-known rank chart, unjust in the eyes of contemporaries and ridiculous in the eyes of posterity. You do not have to be very daring any more to talk out loud about how little good was done and how much damage caused by the Stalin prizes.[9] They introduced into the theater a spirit of intrigue and speculation, set writers to gambling on the choice of subject, and produced far from socialist forms of competition. They confused writers, directors, and actors on the one hand and audiences on the other by canonizing shams and placing them on a level with authentic works of art, and sometimes even higher. The same may be said about the countless competitions and contests. In general, a profusion of ranks and regalia does not increase the number of talented people. Diplomas are like treasury notes; when they lack sufficient gold backing, they drop in value.

Read carefully an ordinary playbill of the present-day Moscow Art Theater. After the words "performers" a new paragraph begins with a list of People's Artists of the Union who are winners of Stalin prizes; just below, or indented, are the People's Artists of the Union who are not winners of Stalin prizes. On the next line are the People's Artists of the Republic who are winners; below them, plain People's Artists. Then follow, with an appropriate space between, Honored Workers in the arts and Honored Artists of autonomous republics, and finally, at the very bottom, ordinary artists of the Art Theater, as such, including the performers of the leading parts.

One cannot help recalling Chekhov. Not the author of the lyrical *Sea Gull,* which spreads its wings over the upper corner of the playbill,[10] but Chekhov the satirist, author of the story "Vint." Remember the deck of cards invented by the bored officials.[11]

K. S. Stanislavsky[12] would hardly have approved of a playbill in which an actor is ranked as a deuce or a collegiate registrar.

There were good reasons for instituting the system of honorary titles. The rank of People's Artist used to be awarded only to a few actors who had truly been recognized by the entire people—Nezhdanova,[13] Chaliapin,[14] Yuzhin,[15] Stanislavsky. . . . The rank of Honored Artist was awarded to those who, by long years of work, had earned the special gratitude of their contemporaries. Nowadays the people cannot possibly remember who all the People's Artists are, and as for the rank of Honored Artist, a promising young actor expects to achieve it in the first five years after he graduates from school. Honor has nothing to do with it. It is a question of position, salary, and fees for appearances at concerts. In the last analysis it all boils down to a classification and nomenclature of a series of civil-service ranks.

Among playwrights, the hierarchy is determined somewhat differently. For this purpose there are survey articles. Usually these articles are signed by completely unknown individuals, but this is immaterial, since these people write in the name of the people: "The people know and love such writers as . . . ," "Such writers as . . . are not fulfilling their duty to the people," "Popular recognition has been given to plays like . . . ," "The people have rejected plays like . . ." This magic formula, which completely frees the writer from the obligation of producing supporting arguments, is followed by a list of names or titles. In the "long live" list it is best to be near the top, and in the "in memoriam" list, at the bottom. And again one is reminded of Chekhov—this time of "Spun Out." [16]

But who is responsible for the existing situation? So far, we have spoken of mistakes made in the supervision of the theaters. These mistakes are grave. But this does not imply that art should not be supervised at all. It is not guidance, but tutelage that is harmful. The actors and directors of our theaters and all Soviet writers have been educated by the Party and instilled with Lenin's doctrine of party spirit in literature.[17] It is just for this reason that most of them have shown such moral stability during all the sharp turns of history. They did not break away from the life of the people, and they welcomed the decisions of the Twentieth Party Congress with enthusiasm.

The fact that the difficulties we are now experiencing are after-effects of the cult of personality does not relieve

writers and actors of personal responsibility for the fate
of the theater. Even during earthquakes people behave
differently—some courageously, others cravenly, some
nobly, others basely; some hurry to help casualties, others
rob deserted houses. There can be no denying the fact
that in that difficult period honest and talented people
behaved better than careerists, and people of party mentality better than apathetic time-servers. Therefore, there
is absolutely no sense in continuing the old argument about
which guild is responsible for the present sad situation—
the playwrights or the actors, the producers or the critics.
This internecine squabble is utterly fruitless and can only
breed mutual irritation, of which we have plenty as it is.

The most popular version, one that has become almost
official—is that the chief culprits are the playwrights.
They are ignorant of life, and as a consequence our drama
is always in arrears. Before accepting or rejecting this
version we must determine more exactly the meaning
given to the term "our drama," and whom or what it is
lagging behind.

It is just as hard to write a good play as to write a good
novel. A. M. Gorky thought it was even harder. But it
is much easier to write a bad play than even the poorest
novel. That is probably the reason why so many bad plays
have been written in all periods of history. The old
Aleksandrinka, though an excellent theater, produced a
surprising amount of trash.[18] However, when we speak
of the Russian drama of the nineteenth century, we do
not mean these forgotten plays, but our real dramatic
literature, the creation of writers who left a vivid imprint
on the intellectual life of their contemporaries. For some
reason, when we talk of the contemporary drama, we first
of all haul out dusty lists of the members of the drama
sections, add to them lists of prose writers and poets who at
some time or other have written for the theater, dissolve
the whole in a vat containing ten parts of the natural
product which overflows the brief cases and shelves of
the repertory committees, and sort the resulting mixture
according to subject. Then, without troubling to analyze
the works concretely and operating chiefly with statistical
data, we take note of the recurrent fact that our playwrights are not up to par. In survey articles and stocktaking lectures it is reported that "writers such as . . ."

continue to maintain their silence, while others produce "swarms" of plays on uniform topics, ignoring the diversified requirements of their audiences, who have matured immeasurably.

It is long since time to understand that in the drama, statistics are of little use; that real plays by their very nature cannot come in "swarms"; and that it is an utterly useless occupation to draw conclusions about processes taking place in the sphere of art on the basis of statistics about works that lie entirely outside of art. A man who does not know life is neither a playwright nor a writer. Besides, there are all sorts of playwrights; they cannot be approached with the same measuring stick. And if the comrades who are so enthusiastic about statistics would undertake the task of Plutarch and would trace the careers of at least two Soviet playwrights such as Arbuzov[19] and Sofronov,[20] instead of discussing generalities, they would understand much more.

If one examines the drama as compared with Soviet literature as a whole, there are no serious grounds for driving it into the lock-up. Soviet playwrights have created quite a few plays that have stood the test of time. We are not so very poor if *An Optimistic Tragedy* could wait twenty years before being performed on the Leningrad stage.[21]

Perhaps the plays that are written are not as good as the theaters that produce them? The theater cannot develop in isolation from the drama. The directors are not a bit better than their repertories. There are hardly any new names. Instead of training worthy successors, many masters of the older generation have preferred to keep "assistants" who go on doing the dirty work for their maestro until their hair turns gray. Now the results are being felt. Things are not well with the art of acting. Of course, we have not run out of talent, and we have some good actors. But not all we need, not by any means. Even our best companies lack actors for many of the roles of the classical repertory. The average is fairly high, but few rise above it. The companies are overloaded with second-raters, capable of playing any part competently in a second-string play. The opening nights are brilliant, but there are few theaters able to display in an ordinary performance such a galaxy of stars as could once be seen every day on the stage of the former Korsh Theater,[22] to say nothing of the Academic theaters, and the Korsh Theater used to be much vilified and is now almost forgotten. No sooner does a promising actor appear in a lower-category theater than he is taken away by the big theaters in the capitals, even though every large theater has its own school, in the direct figurative meaning of this word. All this is worth thinking about.

Perhaps the plays are inferior to the audiences? One can agree with this only with one important reservation. The expectations and tastes of the audiences depend to a large degree on the state of the theater and of the drama. Read the letters from the theatergoers and the stenographic reports of the spectators' conferences and you will see, alongside competent, meaningful, and sincere opinions, attesting to the culture and civic maturity of the audiences, some very sad human documents, which testify to the serious damage done by shamelessly varnished plays and hypocritical writings of people who will praise anything.

The trouble lies not in the fact that we playwrights have lagged behind life—a defect that we usually try to overcome by means of seminars and official trips, meetings, and other techniques. And the trouble is not that plays are often written by people who have no talent and even no honesty—this has happened, is happening, and will go on happening. The trouble is that the creative ties between the theaters and the writers have weakened and have started to disintegrate. Many writers have stopped writing for the theater altogether. Reproaches and exhortations will not help; it is just as impossible to force a man to write as to forbid him to write. The theaters now do not care whose plays they produce, and the playwrights do not care where their plays are produced.

Among the causes of the dissolution of creative bonds between the writers and the theaters, the playwright's utter lack of rights plays an important part. This does not happen because of the tyranny of the producer, as it sometimes seems to the authors. The era of the "producer's theater" is long past. The theater now is not a producer's and not an author's theater; if we have to give it some name, it is rather a manager's theater.[23] The inequality in the positions of the playwright and the manager is that the manager represents a state institution, writes on official letterheads, and has a round seal, whereas the writer, if he does not hold some important public position, is considered a purely private individual because he writes on ordinary paper and does not have a seal. The theater has no obligations at all toward the playwright except financial ones. The literary rights of the playwright are not protected at all; he must make any changes in the play the theater demands, and he cannot even withdraw the play in the event of insuperable disagreement with the theater. As long as the contract to produce has not been signed and the manager and the chief producer are trying to persuade the author not to give the play to another theater, the writer can still maintain his own viewpoint. During this period he is given all kinds of promises which, as a rule, are never fulfilled. If the author were an institution, nobody would dare to behave this way; if the director or the chief producer were private individuals, they would be ashamed. But in this case they do not feel uncomfortable at all. Behind them stand the collective, the plan, the budget; they are accustomed to identifying their own interests with the interests of the state and regarding the interests of the author as a private matter. Of course, there are exceptions, but they are not numerous.

All this is not said to condemn the theaters wholesale. Their position is not easy. A writer can stop writing plays, but the theater cannot stop giving performances. The writer has to account for his work only once in several years; the theater does so every quarter. Sometimes it seems as if the theater had two souls: one seeks the congenial soul of the writer, dreams of bringing something new into art, and is looking toward tomorrow; while the other lives in the present, in the box office and on speculation, hunts for fashionable plays, and gloomily and haughtily abuses playwrights. Everything depends on which soul has the upper hand. Theaters that are on the up-swing usually do not complain about the repertory; they create it. Nobody stopped the Central Children's Theater from entering into a mutually fruitful creative collaboration with V. Rozov.[24] On the other hand, nobody forced the ultra-refined Yu. Zavadsky to throw himself into the somewhat rough but seemingly very reliable arms of A. Surov.[25]

Without creative collaboration between the playwright

and the theater there can be no flowering of dramatic literature and, consequently, of theatrical art as a whole. It is in our power to achieve, not just individual successes (they exist and have existed even in worse times), but a true flowering; not a return to the past, even a brilliant past, but a new upsurge, before which the forces of television will have to retreat. Instead of being a competitor, the television set must be turned into a promotion agent.

In order to achieve this new up-swing, we must first of all honestly and fearlessly reckon up the damage we have suffered and count our losses. Otherwise neither truth nor justice can be restored. Some people believe that there is no use in raking up the past. There has been, they say, much that was bad, but now everything is getting better; therefore let us let bygones be bygones. But there is no way out of it; art is not a game of solitaire, where the old score can be crossed out and the game begun anew. Just as military art cannot progress without re-appraising many facts of the history of the Patriotic War in the light of the decisions of the Twentieth Party Congress, theatrical art cannot develop normally until we have done once and for all with the falsification of the history of the Soviet theater, with myths and inflated authorities, until we rehabilitate reputations of people and works that have been unjustly defamed.[26] Specifically, we must state openly that no group of anti-patriotic theater critics ever existed in reality.[27] Individually, the "members of this group" have long ago been exonerated, the Communists have been reinstated in the Party; but the myth is still alive.

The truth must be restored, not for the sake of settling old scores—nothing more harmful could be conceived—but in the interests of truth itself. An attempt is sometimes made to justify our glossing over existing contradictions by claiming that we need to "consolidate all our creative forces." But it is a bad consolidation. Illnesses should be treated, not concealed.

It is imperative that once and for all we abandon all attempts to revive the policy of the carrot and the stick in art. The artist is equally harmed by both head-spinning ascents and head-smashing falls. We should not be hasty about passing judgments; we should not add up scores or give grades too often. There is no need to replace broad public criticism with "organizational decisions," orders, and categorical articles which are followed by a 180-degree turn of all the criticism in the press. There was hardly any need to sound the alarm and stop the performances of N. Pogodin's play *Three Went to the Virgin Lands*.[28] It probably did not contain any basic defects, but merely mistakes the author might easily have remedied. Otherwise how can one explain the success of I. Kalatozov,[29] who produced the movie *The First Echelon* with the same plot and basically with the same characters? The vigilant comrades who have discovered a leaning toward all kinds of satirical and denunciatory plays have created a panic unnecessarily: this leaning, which arose as a natural reaction to "no-conflict" and varnished productions, was not in the least dangerous. Nobody planned to libel Soviet reality. Equilibrium would have been restored in a few months without any alarm sirens.

The time is ripe for a substantial reform of the entire organization of theatrical affairs. Decentralization, sharp reduction of the echelons of command having the right to influence, in one way or another, the life of the theater and its repertory. A review of the system of paying people who work for the theater, to the end that people of equal qualifications should be paid equally, no matter where they work. Then official considerations will not take precedence over artistic considerations. And this happens often. Here are three examples of what has happened in Leningrad theaters:

A few years ago the producer N. Akimov[30] was removed from the managership of the Comedy Theater and transferred to the same position in a lower-category theater. It was supposed that it was Akimov who was being punished, but actually the ones who really suffered were the quite innocent theatergoers. As before, when setting out for the Comedy Theater, they would say: "Today we are going to Akimov's." Then they stopped going. It turned out that the theater had disintegrated and it was necessary to restore the unrepentant Akimov.

An example of the contrary: G. Tovstonogov,[31] who in recent years has developed into an outstanding producer, has turned the Lenin Komsomol Theater, which he managed, into one of the best theaters in the country.

Instead of using administrative measures to make permanent the success achieved by the theater, it was decided that the producer was ready to be transferred—from a theater under city jurisdiction to a theater under republic jurisdiction. Now Tovstonogov is chief producer of the Bolshoi Drama Theater, in which the style of acting is very far removed from that of the Komsomol Theater.

A third example: For over a quarter of a century there existed the Baltic Fleet Theater, a collective with a heroic biography and many honors to its credit. It stood fast during the most difficult years of war and blockade. Now it has been destroyed by a stroke of the pen; in some routine reorganization no suitable rubric was found for listing it.[32]

This ossified structure must be reformed and made more flexible. What has become obsolete must be allowed to die a natural death, to be replaced by something new. Ministerial red tape impedes both these processes. It preserves theatrical corpses, but interferes with the birth of new theaters. And young theaters are needed, like air, not only for themselves but also to make their older brothers bestir themselves. There is no doubt that youthful theaters will have no trouble acquiring repertories.

The theater cannot live without criticism that expresses public opinion. We need broad discussions, both in the press and at public meetings. Not the kind of discussions where the truth is known to the presidium even before the debate starts. Each participant must be sure that his opinion will be objectively represented in the press. The newspapers must revive a forgotten genre—the refutation. The honor of the uniform must not be placed above the honor of the man and the artist. We must have real polemics in the press, make it possible for authors and directors to defend their positions. There is much to argue about.

All this is realizable. Therefore, there are no grounds for pessimism. The Soviet theater is young; it will come out of all its trials with renewed strength and vigor.

NOTES

1. This is probably a veiled reference to an episode widely publicized in 1954. The veteran writer Fedor Gladkov

published an article in *Literaturnaya Gazeta* (April 6, 1954) denouncing certain prominent writers, especially the playwrite Anatoly Surov, for "violent drunken sprees," "fist fights" (one with his chauffeur), and "hoodlumism." A few days earlier the playwrite and novelist Nikolay Virta had been similarly castigated in *Komsomol'skaya Pravda* (March 17, 1954). As a result, Surov, Virta, and two others were expelled from the Union of Soviet Writers "as persons who had committed amoral and anti-social acts incompatible with the calling of a Soviet writer" (*Pravda,* May 6, 1954). There is further evidence of Kron's antipathy to Surov later in this article.

2. The word "academic" is an honorific term applied to the oldest and most famous theaters in Russia. It is part of their official titles and has no connotation of sterility or conservatism. The academic theaters include the Bolshoi, Maly, and Moscow Art theaters in Moscow, and the Pushkin Theater of Drama (the former Aleksandrinsky) and the State Theater of Opera and Ballet (the former Mariinsky) in Leningrad. This is a reference to the denunciation in 1948–9 of a group of "anti-patriotic" theater critics. See below, note 27.

3. The "no-conflict theory" was one of those excesses which the Soviet system of controlled art is apt to produce. Reduced to its simplest form, it runs as follows. Conflict in drama is normally a reflection of conflict between classes. But in the Soviet Union "antagonistic contradictions" between classes have been eliminated, and Soviet society is officially classless. Therefore, it follows that in a drama depicting present-day Soviet society no genuine acute conflict is possible. The action of a play could be based on a new conception of conflict: conflict between "the good and the better," mentioned here by Kron, conflict between "the better and the excellent," or even on mere "misunderstandings."

This "theory" or its variants circulated in the years 1947–52. It never received official recognition. In fact, it was from time to time refuted. Kron himself denounced it in an article entitled "A Dramatist's Reply" in *Teatr,* No. 9, 1948. It was finally declared a heresy in a *Pravda* editorial on April 7, 1952. The article blamed the no-conflict theory for the wretched state of Soviet drama, maintaining: "The political and moral unity of the Soviet people, the elimination in Soviet society of antagonistic class contradictions, have led to the extinction of many old conflicts. But this by no means signifies that the playwright can portray the life of the creator-people in serenely idyllic, sugar-sweet tones. . . . . A play must show life's conflicts; without that there can be no play."

Following a time-honored Soviet practice, responsibility for the no-conflict theory was laid on individuals, notably the playwright Nikolay Virta, who, to his misfortune, had been one of the last to express views of this sort. The point that Kron is making here is that this absurd rationalization was not primarily the work of men of letters. It was inspired by the over-all atmosphere prevailing at that time. The extreme xenophobia of the anti-cosmopolitan campaign and the mandatory glorification of all things Soviet had made it almost impossible to depict conflicts in Soviet life without incurring the charge of "slandering Soviet reality." Virta himself explained his onetime acceptance of the "theory" in these words: "I must say frankly just how the 'theory' of conflictless drama arose in me and certain of my comrades. It arose as a consequence of 'cold observations of the mind' on the manner in which those of our plays which contain sharp life conflicts passed through the barbed-wire barriers of the agencies in charge of the repertory. As I have already said, everything living, true to life, sharp, fresh, and unstereotyped was combed out and smoothed out to the point where it was no longer recognizable. Every bold, unstereotyped word in a play had to be defended at the cost of the playwright's nerves and the play's quality." Speaking of one of his own plays, *Our Daily Bread,* Virta goes on: "No one knows what agonies the author of the play had to go through before it finally saw the footlights. It is hard to describe the tempestuous attacks of some of the members of the [Arts] Committee when this 'slander against the collective farms' reached their hands." Needless to say, Virta was rebuked both for his frankness and the "theory." Not till after Stalin's death did it become possible to suggest, as Kron does here, that the blame for the no-conflict theory should be laid elsewhere than in the theater itself.

4. Soviet film production was astonishingly low in the period following the Second World War. The number of feature

films produced between 1948 and 1952 averaged less than ten per year. In 1951, for example, the U.S.S.R. produced nine feature films, compared to 102 for Mexico, 260 for India, and 432 for the United States. Cf. Joseph Anderson: "Soviet Films Since 1945," *Films in Review* (February 1953); Dwight Macdonald: "Soviet Cinema: A History and an Elegy," *Problems of Communism* (November-December 1954; January-February 1955); Paul Babitsky and John Rimberg: *The Soviet Film Industry* (New York; 1955).

5. E. Krasnyansky: *"Opyt, zhdushchiy svoego osmysleniya"* ("An Experience Which Awaits Recognition"), *Teatr,* No. 7 (July 1956), p. 151. Krasnyansky feels that the "life experience of the whole creative collective," incorporated into a play in the form of revisions made during rehearsals, should receive some recognition in print.

6. A. Makarov: *"P'esa i spektakl' "* ("The Play and the Performance"), *Teatr,* No. 4 (April 1954), pp. 79–89. In this reference Kron archly conceals the fact that Makarov's article had been concerned with Kron's own play, *Kandidat Partii (A Candidate for the Party)*, which was produced by the Vakhtangov Theater in 1953. The play had been severely criticized in 1950, when it was to have been produced by the Moscow Art Theater. Kron subsequently revised it thoroughly, apparently profiting by the "creative experience of the theater collective" as well as by the wise words of the party critics. However, the playwright's appreciation of this generous assistance seems to have diminished in retrospect. See below, note 19.

7. Russian spelling, though generally very consistent, has vacillated in certain minor respects, one of which is referred to here. By a decree that went into effect on September 1, 1956, the phoneme /ó/, when it occurs after the "hushing" sibilants and affricates in the roots of words (not inflectional endings), is to be spelled with the letter "e" (optionally written "ë"), and not with the letter "o," as formerly. Thus the famous *chort* ("devil") must now be spelled *chert*. The pronunciation, of course, remains the same.

8. The last dress rehearsal of a Soviet play is attended by these censorship officials, who have the power to authorize or forbid public performance and to prescribe any changes, deletions, or additions which they think are politically

necessary. The "perfectly good Russian words" for these officials were the titles of certain supervisory officials in the old czarist school system.

9. The Stalin prizes were abolished, without public announcement, in 1953. In 1956 it was announced that *Lenin* prizes would subsequently be awarded, but that the literary standards would be much more exacting. In April 1957 awards were made to Leonid Leonov for his novel *Russkiy les* (*A Russian Forest*), and posthumously to the Tatar poet Musa Jabil, executed by the Nazis in 1944. In 1958 no awards were made for literature at all. In 1959 the Lenin prize for literature went to the Kazakh writer Mukhtar Auezov for his novel *Abai's Path* and to the dramatist Nikolai Pogodin for his trilogy *A Man with a Gun, The Chimes of the Kremlin,* and *The Third Pathétique*. In 1960 the winners were the Ukrainian poet Maksim Rylsky for two volumes of verse and Mikhail Sholokhov for the two complete volumes of *Virgin Soil Upturned* (*Seeds of Tomorrow*).

10. Chekhov's *Sea Gull* was the first production of the Moscow Art Theater in 1898, and a representation of the bird is used as the theater's emblem.

11. "Vint" (the name of a card game) is a short story published by Chekhov in 1884. A group of government clerks have invented a new pack of cards in which ranks and suits are represented by various government institutions, officials, and their wives.

12. Konstantin Sergeevich Stanislavsky (1863–1938), the famous founder and director of the Moscow Art Theater.

13. Antonina Vasilyevna Nezhdanova (1873–1950), a great coloratura soprano at the Bolshoi Theater in Moscow.

14. Fedor Ivanovich Chaliapin (1873–1938), the famous bass. Though made a People's Artist in 1922, he nevertheless refused to return to Russia after a singing tour in Europe in that year and spent the rest of his life as an émigré. His reputation has recently been posthumously rehabilitated in the Soviet Union.

15. Aleksandr Ivanovich Yuzhin-Sumbatov (1857–1927), a famous actor and playwright.

16. "Spun Out" (*"Kanitel"*), another short story by Chekhov, published in 1885. An old woman is negotiating with a priest to have him mention the names of a long list of her relatives during the Mass. For some of these the priest

is to pray for their "long life," and for others, being dead, he is to ask peace for their souls. There is an impossible mix-up as to which names belong on which list.

17. This word *partiynost,* or "party-ness," usually translated as "party spirit," is bandied about a great deal in all Soviet literary discussions. It is derived from an article entitled "Party Organization and Party Literature," written by Lenin at the height of the 1905 Revolution. The essential burden of this article was that under the new conditions of freedom then obtaining, any "literature"—by which he meant mainly journalism, not belles-lettres—that claimed to sympathize with the socialist cause ought to come out openly, declare its allegiance to the Party, and submit to Party discipline. He never dreamed that this little article would one day be used as a scriptural foundation for the doctrine that all the writers of belles-lettres in all Russia, whether members of the Party or not, must steep themselves in party-ness. In practice it has come to mean: stick to the Party line, or else.

18. The Aleksandrinka was the prerevolutionary nickname of the Petersburg Theater founded in 1832 by Nicholas I. It is now officially known as the A. S. Pushkin Leningrad State Academic Theater of Drama.

19. Aleksey Nikolaevich Arbuzov, a prominent Soviet playwright. A volume containing six of his plays written between 1934 and 1954 was published in 1957. Arbuzov appears to be as much exercized about the state of the Soviet theater as Kron. The August issue of *Novy Mir* in 1956 carried a report on a discussion session held in its editorial offices on the subject: "The Playwright Must Return to the Theater." Incidentally, in one passage in his speech Arbuzov criticizes the Moscow Art Theater for its disloyalty to Kron: "More than ten years ago the theater produced *Glubokaya razvedka* (*Intelligence in Depth*) by Aleksandr Kron, undoubtedly the Art Theater's best production dealing with contemporary Soviet society. The basis of its success was unquestionably the fact that the theater had acquired a dramatist *of its own,* in the very best sense of the word. Why, then, when rehearsing *A Candidate for the Party,* did the theater not help its friend during this period which was so painful and difficult for him? Why did it not support him at least to the extent that it was obligated to support him? Frivolously and forgetting its quon-

dam raptures, it exchanged him, in Renard's neat expression, for 'a writer very famous last year.' "

The last is a reference to the abandonment by the Moscow Art Theater in 1950 of its production of Kron's play *A Candidate for the Party*. The "writer very famous last year" is probably Surov. See notes 6 and 25.

20. Anatoly Vladimirovich Sofronov (b. 1911), a prominent Soviet playwright of a rather "official" Stalinist stamp. Since the war he has produced about a play a year, two of which won Stalin prizes: *V odnom gorode* (*In a Certain Town*, 1946) and *Moskovsky kharakter* (*The Muscovite Character*, 1948). Other notable productions are *Serdtse ne proshchaet* (*The Heart Does Not Forgive*, 1954), produced by the Moscow Art Theater, *Den'gi* (*Money*, 1956), and *Chelovek v otstavke* (*A Man in Retirement*, 1957). He is probably an enemy of Kron's: in 1948–9 he was one of the instigators and leading spokesman of the anti-cosmopolitan campaign and in particular of the assault on the drama critics. In 1957 he delivered a blistering attack on the editors of *Literaturnaya Moskva*. In 1956 Sofronov visited the United States along with two other very "official" Soviet writers, B. Polevoy and N. Gribachev.

21. This play by Vsevolod Vishnevsky (1900–51), a heroic drama of the Civil War, is regarded as a Soviet classic. It has been translated into English in *Four Soviet Plays*, ed. Ben Blake (New York; 1937). Written in 1932, it was given a brilliant production in Tairov's Kamerny Theater in 1933 and was performed elsewhere in the Soviet Union, but for some reason not in Leningrad. A recent (1956) production by G. Tovstonogov (referred to later in this article) at the Pushkin Theater of Drama in Leningrad was extremely successful. See A. Maryamov: *"Vstrecha s istoriey,"* ("A Meeting with History"), *Teatr,* No. 2 (February 1956), pp. 51–60.

22. A commercial theater in Moscow, founded in 1882 (when permission was first granted for the establishment of private theaters in Russia) by Fedor Adamovich Korsh (1852–1921). It somehow survived down to 1932, when, as the *Great Soviet Encyclopedia* puts it, "It failed to respond to the new requirements of its audiences and . . . ceased its existence."

23. In Russian theaters the highest artistic authority is the *rezhissyor* (from the French *régisseur*), who combines the

functions of director and producer—i.e., has general supervision over the selection, interpretation, and staging of a
play. The *direktor* is more like the English manager—i.e.,
he constitutes the financial and administrative authority.

24. Viktor Sergeevich Rozov, a young Soviet dramatist, author
of several plays produced by the Central Children's Theater
in Moscow, among them *V dobry chas!* (*Good Luck!*
1954). He is the subject of a special laudatory article by
Kron himself, *"Rozhdenie dramaturga"* ("The Birth of a
Dramatist"), *Teatr,* No. 5 (May 1955), pp. 83–96.

25. The full meaning of this allusion can only be guessed at.
Yury Aleksandrovich Zavadsky (b. 1894) is a famous
Soviet theater director of the prerevolutionary generation,
a disciple of Vakhtangov, later associated for many years
with the Moscow Art Theater. After 1932 he became chief
director of various theaters, since 1940 of the Theater of
the Moscow Soviet. Obviously an esthete by nature, he
has several times been called to order for "formalism."

Anatoly A. Surov (b. 1910) is a Soviet playwright who
came to prominence in the postwar period. He is apparently
a rough-and-tumble careerist and opportunist, who made
his way by writing made-to-order propaganda plays on
approved themes. One of these, *Rassvet nad Moskvoy*
(*Dawn over Moscow,* 1951) received the Stalin prize. This
play was produced by Zavadsky.

One may surmise that Zavadsky, feeling his position
shaky in the years of terror just before Stalin's death,
hoped to display his loyalty by collaborating with such an
impeccably true-blue Communist writer as Surov. In 1954,
however, as pointed out above (note 2), Surov was publicly
denounced for drunkenness and expelled from the Writers'
Union; thus his undoubtedly "rough" arms proved to be
only "seemingly reliable."

26. In the period since Stalin's death and in particular since
Khrushchev's denunciation of the "cult of personality"
at the Twentieth Party Congress in 1956, it has become
possible to rehabilitate, often posthumously, the reputations
of some (though by no means all) of the victims of the
purges of the 1930's. In the sphere of literature this has
meant new editions of the works of writers whose very
names had long been utterly taboo, among them the short-
story writers Isaac Babel, Ivan (not to be confused with
Valentin) Kataev, and Artyom Vesyoly, the dramatist

Vladimir Kirshon, and the journalist Mikhail Koltsov. In the theater the most notable manifestation of this tendency is the restoration to the Soviet pantheon of the great director Vsevolod Meyerhold, who was purged at the end of the thirties. A recent editorial article in the magazine *Teatr* illustrates this yearning for the restoration of history as it really was: *"O nekotorykh voprosakh istorii sovetskogo teatra"* ("On Certain Questions of the History of the Soviet Theater"), *Teatr,* No. 7 (July 1956), pp. 49–57. It must be acknowledged, however, that this restitution of history is only a halfway affair. In the sphere of politics Khrushchev, though admitting that many of the victims of the purges had been accused unjustly, still did not go so far as to repudiate the purges themselves or to rehabilitate the reputations of the major Bolshevik leaders, such as Kamenev, Zinoviev, or Bukharin, who had seriously opposed Stalin. So, in the arts a really truthful history is still quite impossible, and many ghosts still wait vainly in the limbo of history.

27. The campaign against the "anti-patriotic" theater critics was one of the Soviet "cultural" sensations of late 1948 and early 1949, one in which Kron himself was indirectly involved. The campaign against "cosmopolitanism," "kowtowing to the West," and similar dastardly crimes was already in full sway. Soviet officialdom was looking for scapegoats to blame for the doldrums in which the Soviet theater found itself after the Zhdanov decrees of 1946, and in particular a way of tracing this unfortunate situation to the ultimate source of all evil, the capitalist West. The link between the two was suddenly discovered to be a group of theater critics, many of them Jews, who had viciously attacked patriotic Soviet plays and insidiously endeavored to infect the Soviet theater with the noxious microbes of bourgeois decadence and formalism. A violent campaign was launched in the press, and meetings were held at which one speaker after another got up to express the universal indignation of the Soviet people against these cosmopolite villains.

The campaign was apparently initiated at the Twelfth Plenum of the Writers' Union in December 1948, where the report on dramaturgy was delivered by none other than A. Sofronov, then Secretary of the governing Board of the Union. Sofronov, who had himself been attacked by the critic A. Borshchagovsky, delivered himself of a violent diatribe against a whole group of prominent drama critics who, he said, were guilty of promulgating "apolitical provincial-esthetic" theories which had done immense harm to the Soviet drama. Sofronov's remarks were supported and amplified by Fadeyev at the same meeting, and shortly thereafter, in January 1949, received the imprimatur of editorials in *Pravda* and *Kultura i zhizn'*. The campaign against the "rootless cosmopolitans" was under way.

As usual after such an event, meetings of professional groups concerned with the new policy were held, at which everyone, including the victims of attack, had to stand up and thank the Party for the wisdom of its guidance and promise to toe the new line with increased devotion. One such gathering was a meeting of the Communist Party members of the Union of Soviet Writers on February 9 and 10, 1949, presided over by the same Sofronov. One of the featured speakers was Comrade A. Surov, who made a patriotic denunciation of the homeless cosmopolitan J. Altman. The meeting criticized those Communists in leading positions in the Writers' Union who had failed to recognize the danger and take measures against it. One of these was the "former chairman of the Commission on Dramaturgy of the Writers' Union," A. Kron. Kron spoke at the meeting, but evidently made some attempt to defend the cosmopolites and himself into the bargain, as the content of his speech is not reported; it is only stated that it "had an insincere ring."

As Kron points out here, the victims of this campaign have gradually drifted back into their former positions, but no formal admission has been made that the campaign against them was mistaken.

28. Kron gives the title of this play somewhat inaccurately; it is actually *We Three Went to the Virgin Lands*. Nikolay Fedorovich Pogodin (born 1900), real name Stukalov, is probably the leading Soviet dramatist, a prolific producer of competently written plays, mostly on topical propaganda themes, but not devoid of literary quality. Three of his plays have been translated into English: *Tempo* (1928–9), in Eugene Lyons, ed.: *Six Soviet Plays* (Boston and New York; 1934); *Aristocrats* (1934), in Ben Blake, ed.: *Four Soviet Plays* (New York; 1937); and *Chimes of the*

Kremlin (1941), in Alexander Bakshy, ed.: *Soviet Scene. Six Plays of Russian Life* (New Haven; 1946).

In the December issue of *Novy Mir* for 1955 Pogodin had published a new play on a most timely subject: the resettlement of young people from the cities to the "virgin lands" of Central Asia, a program initiated by Khrushchev himself in an effort to solve Russia's perennial agricultural crisis. The official propaganda sought to represent the people involved in this campaign as an army of dedicated young patriots who with high hearts and exalted spirits had volunteered to devote all their youthful strength and enthusiasm to making the desert bring forth an abundance of grain for the Fatherland. Pogodin, in an ill-timed burst of true (as distinct from socialist) realism, had chosen three most unsuitable characters to represent the noble pioneers: a young "hooligan" who had signed up only to escape prosecution for his misdeeds; a lonely and unattractive girl hoping to find romance amid the vastness of the steppes; and a youth who volunteered in a fit of pique when his girl failed to show up for a date. Moreover, Pogodin had made no attempt to conceal the physical squalor and misery in which the pioneers were obliged to live. This was pushing the new freedom too far, and Pogodin was called to order in the familiar manner of the Stalin era. A thunderbolt was hurled from on high in the form of an unsigned article in *Pravda* (January 5, 1956), entitled "The Serious Mistake of a Dramatist." Besides his failure to show a single character who had gone forth to the wilderness "at the command of a patriot's mind and heart," Pogodin was reprimanded for his use of "realism turned inside out," his naturalistic photography of details of violence and sex (very mild, may we say, by American standards). He needed a socialist-realist filter for his lens. And, as usual, any poor critics who had made the mistake of praising the play before the gods had expressed their disfavor were rapped sharply over the knuckles. The Central Children's Theater, which had included the play in its repertory, was likewise guilty, as were those responsible for its performance on television. The ghost of Zhdanov walked again.

29. An elaborately produced color film entitled *The First Echelon* was produced by the Mosfilm Studio in 1956, based on Pogodin's play. The producer was Mikhail Kon-

stantinovich Kalatozov (b. 1903), whose initial Kron gives incorrectly. Kalatozov is incidentally the author of a book entitled *Litso Gollivuda* (*The Face of Hollywood*), in which, according to the *Great Soviet Encyclopedia*, he "unmasks the reactionary character of American cinematography." On *The First Echelon*, see *Iskusstvo kino*, No. 4 (April 1956), p. 124.

30. Nikolay Pavlovich Akimov (b. 1901), a talented and distinguished stage designer and director. His leanings toward "formalism" and "estheticism" had got him into trouble before. He worked in the Vakhtangov Theater in Moscow in the early 1930's, where he produced a "de-psychologized" *Hamlet* that made a great stir. From 1935 to 1949 he was in charge of the Leningrad State Theater of Comedy, apparently with much success; but, as the *Great Soviet Encyclopedia* puts it, "In the post-war years there was exhibited in the work of the Leningrad State Theater of Comedy a tendency toward superficial entertainment, and the ideological and artistic level of its repertory declined." Akimov was kicked downstairs to the Leningrad Soviet Dramatic Theater. Akimov seems to have been restored to the Theater of Comedy in 1956.

31. Georgy Aleksandrovich Tovstonogov, a prominent director, originally from Georgia. As Kron points out, he had been chief director of the Leningrad Leninist Komsomol Theater, apparently rather small potatoes as theaters go, but was promoted to the A. S. Pushkin Leningrad State Theater of Drama. There he successfully produced in 1956 Kron's own play *Second Wind* (*Vtoroe dykhanie*). In 1958 he received the Lenin Prize for his production of Vishnevsky's *Optimistic Tragedy* (see above, note 21).

32. The Theater of the Baltic Fleet was founded in 1930 as a center for amateur productions by the sailors themselves. It gradually became professionalized, and in 1934 A. V. Pergament became its permanent director. During the war it was one of the few Leningrad theaters to remain open. One of its productions in 1942 was a musical comedy, written in collaboration by Vishnevsky, Vsevold Azarov, and Kron, and entitled *Raskinulos' more shiroko* (*The Sea Flung Wide*). It was apparently closed down in 1955, but we have not been able to find any public statement to this effect.

FICTION

[Aleksandr Yashin (real name Popov; born 1913) is a prominent Soviet writer, known chiefly as a poet. He is of peasant origin, having been born in a village in the Vologda region, and since becoming a writer he has specialized mostly in peasant themes. His epic *Alyona Fomina,* concerning the life of a woman collective farmer, won the Stalin prize in 1950.

Yashin's short story "Levers" is a good illustration of the nature and limits of the "protestant" spirit that came to the fore in 1956. For all its vivid demonstration of the stagnation and bureaucracy that hang heavy over Russian village life—the contrast between the genuine and the official meeting of the Party members in the collective farm is especially telling—"Levers" is essentially a demand for reform *within* the "church," for renovation of Soviet government and Party institutions that touch the peasant and recognition of the importance of spontaneity and initiative in the lower echelons of power. The Twentieth Congress is hailed at the end of the story as a promise of regeneration. But Yashin's demonstration of evil was too graphic for the Party stalwarts, and "Levers" was one of the most severely attacked pieces in *Literaturnaya Moskva,* Vol. II.]

LEVERS

Aleksandr Yashin

One evening in the administration building of the collective farm the kerosene lamp was burning, and the battery radio crackling as usual. The radio was playing marches, but you could hardly hear them. Four men were sitting and talking at a square pine table. Just as at big meetings, there was so much tobacco smoke in the room that the lamp barely flickered. Even the radio seemed to be crackling because of the smoke. There was a large clay jar for cigarette butts standing on the table, and it was already full. Every now and then a fire would break out in the jar from one of the butts thrown there, and then the bearded Tsipyshev, who was in charge of the animals on the farm, would cover the jar with a piece of glass which had broken off the table top. And every time this happened, someone would make the same joke:

"If you burn off your beard, the cows won't be afraid of you any more!"

To this Tsipyshev invariably replied: "If they're not afraid, maybe they'll give more milk." And everyone laughed.

They knocked the ashes from their cigarettes onto the floor or the window sills and threw only the butts into the jar.

They had sat there talking for a long time, without hurrying, talking a little bit about everything, and confidentially, without reservations, like good old friends.

In the dim light you could just make out on the log walls various posters and slogans hung there at random, along with a list of the members of the collective farm, indicating by the month how many work days each one had earned,[1] a fragment of an old wall newspaper,[2] and a blackboard divided into two equal parts by a white line: on one half was written in chalk the word "black" and on the other "red."[3]

"You know, the co-op[4] got some more sugar a few days ago," said the warehouseman Shchukin, the youngest of the group. From his clothes you could tell that he had been to a city school: he was wearing a shirt and tie, and a fountain pen and comb protruded from the breast pocket of his jacket.

"Somebody told on him, is that it?" slyly asked the third person at the table, a man with his left arm missing, corpulent and a bit flabby, with a dilapidated raincoat that looked as if he had worn it at the front flung over his shoulders.

"Nobody told on him. Mikola himself sent a woman to my house with a couple of kilograms. He said we'd settle for it later."

"And you took it?"

"Sure I did. If you don't take it when you can, you'll spend your life without sugar. You would have taken it, too."

"But he won't send *you* any, Petr Kuzmich." Tsipyshev laughed behind his beard, squinting sideways at the one-armed man. "He's got a grudge against you. But Serega is a pal of his," he said, turning to Shchukin. "Serega did not kick him out of the warehouse, even though he took over his job."

Until quite recently Shchukin had been a rank-and-file collective farmer. When he joined the Party about a month ago, he had started hinting that all the leading positions in the collective farm should be held by Communists, and that now it was awkward for him not to get some sort of promotion. People agreed with him. They recalled that the farm's warehouseman had been reprimanded several times for pilfering; and so they assigned Shchukin to the warehouse. At the next general meeting no one objected to this decision. Shchukin bought himself a fountain pen and began wearing a tie. His predecessor went to work for the co-op. He was the person they had been talking about.

"What if I did take it?" Shchukin said after some thought. "Where is there any justice, anyway? Where does the sugar go to, and the soap, and everything?" After saying this he took out his comb and began smoothing down his thick, young, unruly hair.

At this the fourth man spoke up: "What do you need with justice? You're a warehouseman now!"

The fourth man was middle-aged, prematurely gray, pale, and apparently not in very good health. He smoked incessantly, more than anyone else, and coughed a great deal. When he stretched out his hand toward the jar to throw away a cigarette butt that was burning his fingers, you could see his big thick nails and the earth under them—not dirt, but earth. He was the field-work brigade leader[5] Ivan Konoplev. He had the reputation of being a fair-minded but ill-tempered fellow. He spoke little, but when he did, his words had a bite to them. Still, as a rule nobody took offense at his cutting remarks; apparently people did not feel any personal animosity in them. Shchukin was not offended, either.

The one-armed man, whom everyone called by his first name and patronymic, Petr Kuzmich, replied: "Well, as for justice, we do need it. It's what holds us all together. But, friends, there is still something I don't understand. I can't understand what is going on in our rayon.[6] First they issue a statement that the plan should be drawn up from below, that the kolkhoz should decide what is profitable to plant and what isn't. But when we do it, they don't approve our plan. This is the third time now that it's been returned for corrections. Apparently they collected all the kolkhoz plans, added them up, and found they didn't agree with the rayon plan. And the rayon plan is given from above. There's not much room for discussion there. It's like the scythe that hits the stone: the sparks fly, but there's no sense to it. Again there is nothing left of our plan. There's justice for you! They don't trust us."

"In our rayon, justice is only elected to honorary presidiums so that it won't feel slighted and won't open its mouth," said the pale Konoplev, throwing a cigarette butt into the jar.

Shchukin too put in a word: "Justice is only needed at meetings, on holidays, like criticism and self-criticism. It's of no use in real life, isn't that right?"

An expression of cautiousness and of some feeling of embarrassment suddenly crossed Tsipyshev's face, as if he had become displeased with this confidential conversation.

"All right, hack away, but look out where the chips may fall," he said harshly to Shchukin, but immediately changed his tone, as if regretting his rudeness. "Justice, brother, is justice. And if somebody put you on an honorary presidium, you too wouldn't be able to see the ground any more," he said, and burst out laughing, blowing out his mustache and beard.

Tsipyshev's beard grew not merely on his chin, but also on his cheeks and in back of his ears, and merging with his reddish eyebrows, it overhung his eyes; and when he laughed, his whole face and beard laughed too, and his eyes twinkled from somewhere in the depths of all this hair.

"A few days ago I went to the rayon committee and saw the big man himself," Petr Kuzmich continued, referring in this way to the first secretary of the rayon committee.[7] " 'And what,' I said, 'are you doing to us? The kolkhoz members won't agree to change the plan a third time, and they'll be offended. We need flax. The best land should be given over to flax. We've already experimented with rabbits and with grass-crop rotation.[8] We wore out a lot of people to no purpose. There was no grain, and to the state's loss. Let's take,' I said, 'say, ten or twenty hectares at the most to start with, not a hundred or a thousand. When we get used to it we will increase the amount ourselves, we'll be asking for more. Let's not try to do it all at once.' 'No,' he says, 'it has to be at once. We must overfulfill the plan, and we must promote innovations actively.' 'Actively is a fine word,' I said, 'but this is the North: there aren't many people here, and the earth demands its own. People have to be persuaded. As Lenin said, we must actively try to persuade people.' But he says: 'So you go ahead and persuade them! We persuaded you before, when we organized the collective farms: now you persuade the others, uphold the Party line. You,' he says, 'are our levers in the village now.' While he was talking, he waved his arms as if to say that things weren't so nice for him, either. But he's too inflexible. He doesn't understand what the Party wants, he's afraid of understanding."

"A red-hot atmosphere," Shchukin said as if in explanation of his statement, and once again reached for his comb.

"Things won't be so nice. Anyway, he won't last long here," Tsipyshev said. "He didn't take the right attitude here. He's too strict. He doesn't listen to people, but decides everything himself. For him people are only levers. And the way I see it, friends, this is just what 'bureaucracy' means. Let's say we go there to a meeting. Well, he ought to talk to us like a man, straight from the shoulder. But no, he can't get along without acting tough, he always sticks to this toughness of his. He looks everybody over condescendingly and then growls: 'Let us begin, Comrades! Is everybody present?' Well, everybody's heart sinks: we sit and wait to be raked over the coals. If he would only tell us frankly what is wrong—people will move mountains if you talk to them straight. But that's something he can't do."

"He thinks that the Party will lose its authority if he talks simply, like a human being. He knows very well that in the kolkhoz we get a hundred grams per work day,[9] but he keeps on saying the same thing: every year the value of the work day rises and prosperity increases. There are no cows left in our kolkhoz, but he says: every year animal husbandry in the collective farms is expanding and growing stronger. If only he would say, there are such and such reasons why you're not living too well, but we're going to live better. If he would say that, people would be more willing to buckle down to work."

"A red-hot atmosphere!" Shchukin said again, as if concluding Petr Kuzmich's impassioned speech.

Ivan Konoplev was finishing another cigarette; he was

nervous and seemed eager to say something—probably
something sharp and cutting. But a severe fit of asthmatic
coughing suddenly gripped him, and made him get up
from the table. By the entrance Konoplev lifted up a
broom and spent a long time spitting into the corner.
Meanwhile the cattleman, Tsipyshev, scolded him sym-
pathetically: "You must have changed your tobacco again.
Don't smoke anything but the cheapest tobacco, with only
stems in it, and you'll feel better."

Feeling somewhat relieved, but still bent over, Konoplev
raised his head and said hoarsely: "Our rayon chiefs
have forgotten how to talk to peasants: they are ashamed
to. They understand what needs to be done, but they're
afraid to take the leap. What business is it of theirs to
persuade? They are counting on us levers. They see houses
in the village all shut up, but they don't want to talk about
it aloud. All they care about is that the figures in their
accounts should be in round numbers. And as for real
people, who cares about them? What are they left with?"
And Konoplev once again began coughing painfully.

"All right, all right, keep still, or you'll cough your
soul right out of your body." Tsipyshev got up from
behind the table and started toward the door, where
Konoplev was. "Wait a bit, Ivan, and we'll wangle you
some travel order through the rayon committee. You'll
take a trip to the seashore for the fresh air, and at the
same time you'll take a look at how people live there,
you'll study them a bit and tell us about it. You'll bring
us back some extra cheer."

Konoplev waved away impatiently, as if to say: "Sit
down, what are you wandering over here for? Go away!"
But because of his coughing he couldn't say a word.
Tsipyshev went back to the table.

"His wife will write him such a set of travel orders
that he won't know what hit him," said Shchukin. "She
keeps a close eye on him. He can cough and smoke and
drink as much as he wants, but she won't let him go a step
away from her."

"Our air is as good as it is at the seashore," Petr
Kuzmich observed dreamily. "Air is one thing we do
have! In the old days to cure a cough people used to go to
work for a tar or resin distillery. A man would live in
the pine woods for three or four weeks, collecting this

resin from little cups into barrels, and before you knew it he would have earned some money and found it easier to breathe at the same time. Do they buy up this resin anywhere nowadays? For some reason I haven't heard anything about it. They used to make a kind of turpentine out of it, and the resin for violinists. I'll bet they play without resin now."

"They've replaced it with plastic. Look here!" Shchukin held up his comb. "It's made of plastic, too."

No one looked at Shchukin's comb.

"Look, boys, our lamp is going completely out," said Tsipyshev, lifting his beard upward.

Konoplev replied from the doorway: "You would go out too if you didn't have any air. A lamp needs air too."

For the last time Konoplev rustled the dry broom and came back to the table. His face was pale, and he was breathing heavily. "This is the way I see things," he said. "As long as they have no confidence in the ordinary peasant in the collective farms, things won't be really right, we'll have a lot to put up with. They keep writing that a new kind of man has appeared. It's true, he has! The collective farms have transformed the peasant. It's true, they have! The peasant is really a different man. All right! Then this peasant must be trusted. He has a mind too."

"The wolves haven't eaten it," Tsipyshev agreed slyly.

"That's it! So they shouldn't just teach us, they should listen to us too. But everything comes down from above, always from above. The plans are sent down from above, the kolkhoz chairmen come from above, and so does the size of the harvest. They haven't got time to persuade people, and why should they, it's easier without! All they have to do is pass the word down, know what's happening, and make recommendations. As for educational work, they've given that up: it's too much trouble. The reading rooms and clubs exist only on paper, and there is no one to give lectures and reports. The only thing left is the campaigns for various supplies and collections—the five-day campaigns, the ten-day, the month-long ones."

Konoplev stopped for breath, and Petr Kuzmich took advantage of this to get in a word: "Sometimes things happen this way. When you can't get a wedge in somewhere, you blame it on the wood; you say the wood is rotten. Try and disagree with them in the rayon center. They say they're giving advice, recommendations, but it isn't advice, it's an order. If you don't carry it out, it means you have let the reins slip out of your hands. And if the collective farmers don't agree, it means you have failed politically."

"Why failed?" Konoplev almost shouted. "Aren't we working for the same cause? Are our interests any different?"

"Well, the rayon committee too doesn't exactly get a pat on the back if something goes wrong. They have demands made on them too, God knows.

"God knows indeed!" fumed Konoplev. "Next to us, in Gruzdikhin rayon, things are different. My brother-in-law was here a few days ago and told me that their chairmen don't shake in their boots every time they are ordered to report to the rayon center. There isn't any of this fear. The secretary comes to the kolkhoz without any fanfare and talks with people without reading from notes."

The radio on the shelf in the front corner began to sound louder. It was still crackling and hissing like an exhausted fire extinguisher, but now through all the hissing and static it was no longer music that one heard, but a voice talking hesitantly and in a northern accent. They were broadcasting letters from people in the virgin lands. Some fellow was telling about his feats of labor in the Altai region. The four men began to listen.[10]

"They call us all Muscovites, even though we come from various towns. We get along together well and don't let anyone push us around. Last year we got an extraordinary harvest. You walked into a wheat field as if it was planted with reeds. Even the old men don't remember grain like this. There wasn't any place to put the grain; that was the trouble."

The boy was speaking to his dear mamma, but he talked as if he had never called her that before. He was obviously microphone-shy.

"Just listen to that," said Petr Kuzmich. "Even there they have their troubles: nowhere to put the grain." He waved his hand in the direction of the radio, and his tarpaulin raincoat slipped off his armless left shoulder.

"Everybody can't go off to the Altai!" growled Konoplev,

and started coughing again. He got up from the table, took the jar with the cigarette butts in both hands, and went toward the doorway. There he kicked back the broom with his foot and emptied the butts into the corner.

Then it was discovered that during this whole conversation there had been a fifth person in the room. From behind the big tile stove there came an imperious old woman's cry. "Where do you think you're dumping those butts, you old carcass? You're not the one who has to clean up in here. I just got through cleaning the floor, and now you've made a mess of it again!"

Taken by surprise, the peasants started and exchanged glances.

"Are you still here, Marfa? What do you want?"

"What do I want! I'm keeping track of you. If you set fire to this office, they'll try me for it. That broom is dry, and if, God forbid, there were a sudden spark . . ."

"You go on home now."

"When it's time to go, I'll go."

The friends' conversation was cut short. It seemed as if they felt guilty toward one another for some reason. For a moment you could hear the noise of the wind in the street outside and a girl singing a long way off. Sergey Shchukin turned off the radio, and the voices of the virgin-land pioneers fell silent abruptly.

Again they began tearing off bits of newspaper, pulling it out little by little from beneath the broken table top and rolling themselves home-made cigarettes. For a long time they smoked in silence. When they began exchanging short remarks again, they talked in phrases, about nothing in particular and concerning nobody in particular. About the weather—the weather is lousy, the kind that makes your bones ache. About the newspapers—there are different kinds: when you roll a cigarette out of some of them, they are so bitter that you can't even taste the tobacco. Then something about what had happened the day before—somebody should have gone somewhere, but didn't. Then something about the next day; somebody had to get up early because for once his old woman was going to make pancakes. They were empty phrases, and even they were uttered somehow quietly, in subdued tones, with constant glances to one side and the other and at the stove, as if it was not the office charwoman Marfa who was hiding there but a stranger, an unknown person of whom they had to be wary. Tsipyshev grew serious, stopped talking and smiling, and only asked three times or so, without addressing anyone in particular: "Why is that schoolteacher so late? It's time to start the Party meeting."

Shchukin was the only one who behaved rather queerly: he couldn't sit still, his stool kept squeaking, and his mischievous and sly young eyes had a gleam in them. He looked challengingly at everyone. Shchukin seemed to have seen something that no one else had seen yet, and therefore he felt superior to the others. Finally he couldn't restrain himself and burst into guffaws.

"Whew, that damned woman has given us a scare!" Shchukin said, roaring with laughter.

Petr Kuzmich and Konoplev exchanged glances and also burst out laughing.

"She really did, the she-devil! Suddenly she bellows out from behind the stove. . . . Well, I thought . . ." Ivan Konoplev had trouble finishing his sentence. "Well, I thought that the big man had come and caught us red-handed."

"We were as scared as boys caught in their neighbor's bean patch."

Laughter released the tension and restored the men to their normal state of feeling.

"What are we so afraid of, fellows?" said Petr Kuzmich suddenly in a thoughtful and somewhat mournful voice. "We've got to the point where we're even afraid of ourselves."

But this time Tsipyshev did not smile. He hadn't seemed to notice it when both Konoplev and Petr Kuzmich had started laughing, but he looked sternly, like a superior officer, at Sergey Shchukin.

"You're too young to make fun of such things. When you've lived as long as we have . . ."

But Shchukin was not to be squelched, especially as Petr Kuzmich and Konoplev were clearly on his side. They gave him encouraging winks and went on laughing.

"That's how scared we are," said Konoplev.

Behind the stove Marfa was silent.

Two lads of Komsomol age burst into the office.

"What do you want?" said Tsipyshev, turning his whole body toward them.

"We want to listen to the radio."

"You can't. There's going to be a Party meeting here right now."

"Where can we go? There are a lot of us here."

"You can go where you like."

Saying this, Tsipyshev glanced at his friends, as if he wanted to find out whether they approved of his behavior. Petr Kuzmich did not approve of it. "Look here, fellows," he said to the young boys. "We'll polish off this Party meeting, have a talk, and then you can take over the field."

Finally the schoolteacher, Akulina Semenovna, arrived, a short young woman, almost a little girl, looking tired. She unwound her gray wool scarf and took it off her head, then buried herself in the corner under the wooden shelf where the radio was. When she came in, Tsipyshev became more animated. But he expressed this animation by addressing the teacher in an exaggeratedly strict and authoritarian tone.

"Akulina Semenovna, why do you keep us all waiting?"

Akulina Semenovna looked guiltily at Tsipyshev, at Petr Kuzmich, and then at the jar with the cigarette butts and at the lamp, and lowered her eyes.

"I—I got delayed in the school. Look, Petr Kuzmich," she said to the one-armed man, "I would like to settle one thing before the beginning of the meeting. There is no firewood in the school."

"We'll talk about business later," Tsipyshev interrupted her. "Now we must hold our meeting. The rayon committee has been insisting for a long time that we hold two meetings a month, and we can't even get together and agree on the minutes for one of them. How are we going to account for it?"

At this Ivan Konoplev gave a snort, and for a brief moment Tsipyshev again seemed to feel awkward and unsure of himself. He looked timidly around as if apologizing for what he had said. But everyone kept still. Then Tsipyshev's voice took on real firmness and authority. What had happened? His beard was straightened out and grew longer, his eyes became stern and lost the lively twinkle that had gleamed in them a few minutes before during the unaffected friendly conversation. Tsipyshev now addressed the charwoman Marfa in a peremptory tone. "Marfa, you get out of here! We're going to have a Party meeting here. We're going to be talking."

Even Marfa seemed to sense the change that had taken place; she made no attempt to argue and didn't even grumble. "Go ahead and talk. I understand. I'm going."

When the door had closed quietly behind the subdued Marfa, Tsipyshev stood up and repeated the same words that the secretary of the rayon Party committee always said on similar occasions and even in the same dry, severe, and seemingly conspiratorial voice that the secretary used at the beginning of meetings.

"Let's get started, comrades! Is everyone present?"

When he said this it was as if he had turned the switch of some magic machine. Everything in the room began to change, so much so that it became unrecognizable: people, things, and even the air seemed to be transformed.

Shchukin and Konoplev moved noiselessly back from the table. Petr Kuzmich remained seated where he was, but he folded up the raincoat, which had half slipped from his shoulders, and put it to one side on the bench. Akulina Semenovna, the schoolteacher, shrank still farther into the corner under the radio. Everyone's face became set, tense, and bored, as if they had prepared themselves to perform an extremely familiar but nevertheless solemn and important ceremony. Everything ordinary and natural disappeared, and the scene seemed to shift to another world, a more complicated world, to which these unaffected, warmhearted people had not yet fully grown accustomed or come to understand.

"Is everyone present?" Tsipyshev repeated, looking around at the people in the room as if there were at least several dozen of them there.

Yet, as we already know, there were only five of them all told. The herdsman Stepan Tsipyshev turned out to be the secretary of the Party organization. On the recommendation of the rayon committee, he had been recently elected secretary. Flattered by this, Tsipyshev was trying to carry out his duties as best he could, and being inexperienced, without knowing it he began imitating in everything the "rayon boss." To be sure, he sometimes made fun of himself, but every directive from on high he carried out so zealously and so literally—for fear he might make a mistake—that at times things would have gone better if he hadn't tried to fit all the spokes into the wheel. The zonal instructor of the rayon committee, who had been present at Tsipyshev's election, had joked that comrade Tsipyshev had many virtues, but that he had a few defects as well, and that his chief defect was his beard. Tsipyshev had taken this joke seriously, as a directive, and had made up his mind that he would certainly remove the beard and all other hair from his face; but so far there had not been an appropriate occasion for doing this.

Petr Kuzmich Kudryavtsev, the one-armed man, proved to be the chairman of the kolkhoz. Ivan Konoplev, as we know, was a field-work brigade leader. Sergey Shchukin was the warehouseman. When Shchukin had been made warehouseman, his predecessor had been stricken from the Party rolls at the same time as he was transferred to work in the co-op; since then there had been no rank-and-file collective farmers in the Party organization. Akulina Semenovna was a full-fledged member of the intelligentsia, though she was no outsider, but had been born in the village. She was completely dependent on the kolkhoz administration.

"According to the agenda, I first turn over the floor to the chairman of our kolkhoz, Petr Kuzmich."

Petr Kuzmich Kudryavtsev stood up. Tsipyshev sat down. The Party meeting had begun.

And the meeting was marked by just what these members of the Party organization, including the secretary himself, had just been talking about and criticizing with such frankness and perspicacity—official routine, bureaucracy, and pedantry of word and deed.

"Comrades!" said the chairman of the kolkhoz. "The rayon committee and the rayon executive committee have not approved our production plan. I believe there are certain things we have not taken into account and have allowed to drift. This is unbecoming of us. We have not carried out explanatory work among the masses and have not convinced them. And people must be persuaded, Comrades. We here are the levers of the Party in the kolkhoz village. This has been pointed out to us in the rayon committee and the rayon executive committee."

The schoolteacher, with careful, stealthy movements of her hands, so as not to disturb anyone, again tied her kerchief on her head. Her face could no longer be seen, and no one could tell what she was thinking about.

But Shchukin began to smile again. He took his fountain pen out of his pocket, spun it in his hands, then took out his comb, looked through it at the lamp, blew lightly on its teeth, and put it back without using it on his hair. His face grew broader and broader, and a sly, mocking twinkle began to sparkle in his eyes. It looked as if Shchukin might burst out laughing any minute. But he did not do so; he only poked Konoplev in the side and whispered: "Did you see what is happening? Do you recognize him now?"

Konoplev smiled too, but wryly and unpleasantly. "All right, now, don't hinder him from saying his say. That's the way it has to be. Petr Kuzmich is speaking officially now. That's the way it is in the rayon committee, that's the way it is here. As the priest is, so is the parish."

"And what about justice?"

"Justice—it will make itself known. Soon it will even reach us; it will come like thunder."

"But we'll come to the end of our rope."

"No we won't."

And Konoplev reached for the jar on the table, pulled it toward him, and went on smoking, smoking. He didn't dare cough and held himself in, even though everything in his chest was clattering and whistling.

Petr Kuzmich Kudryavtsev did not talk long. The gist of his speech was that the rayon would begin to doubt the militance of the Party organization unless the kolkhoz plan for crop rotation was corrected immediately and unconditionally according to the specifications of the rayon committee and the rayon executive committee. With this all those who took part in the discussion agreed. It was impossible to do otherwise.

Those who took part in the discussion were Akulina Semenovna, and Shchukin and Konoplev. No differences of opinion were revealed, just as there had been none during the friendly conversation before the beginning of the Party meeting; to be sure, the agreement and unanimity were now manifested in a different way—one might even say, exactly in reverse.

Tsipyshev was satisfied by the solidarity of the Communists and took the floor himself on the second question. Once the zonal secretary of the rayon committee had called attention to the fact that political education work in the kolkhoz was inadequately developed. He had accordingly presented a memorandum on this subject to the first secretary of the rayon committee.

"We are not encouraging the better elements, comrades," Tsipyshev said in this connection. "We are not punishing the laggards; there is no competition. Take a look at our red-and-black board: the picture is clear. We must lead the masses, comrades! This is what I think: we should select several projects for awards, and pick one or two persons for each project. And a few people should be fined so that things will be balanced on both sides. We will be commended by the rayon committee."

The meeting unanimously decided to select five persons for awards and three for fines. The only discussion was about which projects should be used for the awards and which for punishments.

They did not have time to compose a single resolution, for Marfa came back to clean up the office and lock up. Petr Kuzmich proposed that the drawing up of resolutions be left to the secretary.

"You know how to write it up," he whispered, pleased that the meeting had come to an end. "In an atmosphere of great enthusiasm for work, there is spreading over the whole kolkhoz—"

"Over the whole country . . ." Shchukin prompted him.

They quickly got ready to go home, and it looked as if everyone had a feeling of having done his duty and yet at the same time a certain embarrassment and dissatisfaction with himself. But on the porch there was already a tramping of boots. A lot of young people appeared at the door.

"Have we come at the right time?" asked one of the two boys who had been in the office before.

"Right on time," replied Petr Kuzmich. "Just right. Come in, boys, all of you."

A draft of cool air from the street filled the room. The lamp burned brighter, stools were moved around. A window was opened.

"It's awfully smoky in here," clamored the girls.

When the young people appeared, Akulina Semenovna straightened up and took off her kerchief. These were people of her own age, and with them she felt freer. Sergey Shchukin too began circulating; he tightened his necktie and attached himself to the girls' company.

The radio was turned on. Unexpectedly, it emitted loud, clear tones. The announcer was giving a report on the preparations for the Twentieth Party Congress. Everyone listened to it.

Petr Kuzmich seemed to soften up. As he was going out, he said to Akulina Semenovna: "Don't worry, there will be some wood. I'll take care of it."

And Tsipyshev came up to Sergey Shchukin and squeezed his arm above the elbow. "Are you staying here?"

"Yes."

"Well, watch out that nothing . . ."

When Kudryavtsev, the collective-farm chairman, and Konoplev, the field-work brigade leader, emerged from the office into the dark, muddy street, they resumed their conversation about life, about everyday doings, work—the same conversation that had been going on before the meeting.

"Now let's see what the Twentieth Congress will say!" they kept repeating. And once again they were clean, warmhearted, straightforward people—people, and not levers.

NOTES

1. In Soviet collective farms, account is kept of the number of "work days" contributed by each peasant. This is not simply a measure of time worked, but varies according to the nature of the work. Thus an actual day's work may be worth anything from half a "work day" in the case of an unskilled field hand to as many as seven "work days" for an experienced tractor driver. The "profits" of the collective farm, in money and produce, are distributed among its members according to the number of "work days" each member has earned.

2. Handwritten or typed "wall newspapers" have been an institution in Soviet factories, farms, etc., since the early twenties. They are supposed to serve as a means of spontaneous self-expression on the part of the workers or peasants, but, like so many Soviet institutions, they have become thoroughly bureaucratized, with permanent "editorial boards" carrying out propaganda assignments issued from above. If the factory or farm is too small or poor to support such an enterprise, its "wall newspaper" may, like this one, become a relic of the past.

3. The blackboard was evidently used for keeping score of the various forms of "socialist competition" among the collective farmers, who were divided into teams and urged to compete with one another in the quantity and quality of work performed. Later in this story there is evidence that a good deal of this "socialist competition" had become an empty formality.

4. The *selpo,* or village co-operative society, is the main source of household and farm supplies in the Soviet countryside. As this passage shows, its stocks of basic supplies are often a good deal less than adequate.

5. Permanent teams of collective farmers for certain kinds of work are called "brigades." Their leader is naturally called a "brigadier."

6. A geographical division roughly analogous to the American county. In most areas the hierarchy is: republic, oblast, rayon.

   According to law, the general assembly of the members of the kolkhoz has the right to approve or reject or suggest changes in the annual production plan. In practice, however, the collective farms have simply had to accept the plan as dictated from above by the centralized planning authorities. However, the failure of the planners to take local needs and conditions into account has drawn repeated criticism, and pious statements are made about "planning from below." But the regime clearly will not go far in the direction of allowing the peasants to manage their own economic affairs.

7. Every rayon has its Communist Party Committee, which is the major center of authority in the area, and its first secretary is the most powerful individual known to the average collective farmer.

8. There have been periodic campaigns in Soviet agriculture to induce the peasants to sow part of their land in industrial crops or undertake other agricultural experiments. There is often a tendency, as this passage shows, for these changes to become compulsory regardless of local conditions, and for local administrative officials to force them through ruthlessly, in the name of immediate fulfillment of production goals, despite considerable losses suffered by the peasants themselves.

9. That is, 100 grams of grain. By contrast, the *Great Soviet Encyclopedia* gives the following figures for a model kolkhoz in the Ukraine in 1951. The average number of work days earned was 431; per work day each peasant received 7.50 rubles in cash, 3 kilograms of grain, .2 kg. of sunflower seeds, and .2 kg. of potatoes.

10. The big program for cultivation of virgin lands in Central Asia as a solution to the agricultural crisis was announced by Khrushchev in February 1954, and received a great deal of attention in the propaganda media.

[Nikolay Gavrilovich Zhdanov (no relation, apparently, of the late unlamented Andrey Zhdanov) is a young Soviet short-story writer. His first volume of stories was published in 1958. The story translated here, originally published in *Literaturnaya Moskva*, Vol. II, gives a vivid picture of the psychological bureaucratization of a Soviet official and incidentally of the poverty and frustration of Soviet-village life.]

A TRIP HOME
Nikolay Zhdanov

Returning to his office after a long, wearisome meeting, Pavel Alekseyevich Varygin began sorting the official papers that had accumulated in his absence and that his secretary, Nonna Andreyevna, handed to him in a calico-covered folder. He glanced over several questionnaires and started on the telegrams, which were usually sent from outlying areas and dealt with various reminders and problems. While reading, he marked the telegrams with a blue pencil and laid them aside one after another. Now only one was left, for some reason unopened: probably Nonna Andreyevna had been careless. Varygin himself tore off the paper band and unfolded the sheet.

"Marya Semyonovna died Wednesday, twenty-fourth. Funeral Saturday," he read.

He left for the country the same night, on an inconvenient train, which necessitated changing twice on the way. The express ran only every other day, and that would have meant waiting another whole day.

Varygin's wife said good-by to him at the door of their apartment. She kissed him on the cheek with a mournful face and said she thought she would not say anything to the children, as they had not yet received their grades for this quarter.

"Do as you please," he replied. But as he walked down the stairs in the yellow light of the bulbs, he thought: "For her it is just a vexatious annoyance, nothing more."

In the railroad car he sat near the window and looked out through the dim pane at the grayish strip of land and the dark silhouettes of trees flying past.

Varygin had seen his mother for the last time about six years ago. She had come from the collective farm for some "millet," as his wife, who had a somewhat ironic attitude toward his village relatives, had later said.

It now seemed to him that those six years had gone by without his noticing them at all. One fall he had planned a trip to the country, but his doctors had advised him to take a rest cure for his heart trouble, and he had gone to Kislovodsk instead.

Sometimes, very seldom, he received letters from his mother. They were dictated by her and written in a childish handwriting, usually on a sheet torn out of a school notebook.

"We are living not too well, but we don't complain," his mother reported. He felt saddened, but then reminded himself that his mother had never lived too well and that therefore the phrase "We are living and don't complain" sounded on the whole quite optimistic.

It took the train more than twenty-four hours to reach the station of Dvoriki. The sluggish November dawn had not yet chased away the gray shadows of the night. They clung to the low, cold sky and hid under the station shed, where mounds of potatoes, probably awaiting shipment, lay covered with matting.

He remembered from his childhood that immediately back of the station there began a low, marshy wood, stretching for about eight versts. Beyond it were the villages, all of them with similar names: Lozhkino, Derevlyovo, Kashino, Korkino, Lapshino, Pirogovo, and finally his village, Tyurino. But he did not see any wood. Varygin set out on foot through a swampy depression along a fence of blackened poles.

On either side rose regular stacks of peat. They evidently were extracting peat here now. Beyond the depression there was a highway, which hadn't been there in the old days, either. Varygin was picked up by a truck going his way, rode as far as Lapshino, and walked from there to Tyurino.

He learned that his mother had already been taken to the cemetery. This he heard at the first cottage from a middle-aged woman in a well-washed soldier's blouse, who was carrying water from the well in wooden pails.

"And who might you be?" she asked, glancing at Varygin's good, heavy cloth coat.

"Her son," he said.

The woman put the pails down on the ground and looked at Varygin again.

"Konstantin? Really?" she asked. "I am Anastasiya Derevlyova, don't you remember?"

"My brother, Konstantin, died long ago. I am Pavel," he explained.

"That's just what I was saying, that Konstantin was dead," the woman answered quickly. "My daughter-in-law keeps insisting, no matter what you say to her. But can you find your way to the cemetery? You've probably forgotten how to find your way around here. Klashka!" she shouted to a little girl gathering the cabbage leaves that had been left on the ground after the harvest. "Run along and show him the way to the cemetery—straight across the field."

Following the girl, who ran ahead of him, he strode over the field, already frozen hard but not yet covered with snow. He stumbled heavily at the uneven places, trying not to pant, and kept wiping the perspiration from his face.

They rounded a field of winter crops and on a crooked log crossed a tiny brook that looped among some bushes. Further on, the bank rose in a sloping hillock, and against the gray sky Varygin saw an old wooden church and cemetery crosses among sparse, leafless trees. He remembered this old church and this brook. But now they were considerably smaller than they used to be. He also remembered the pits full of water they were now walking past. People used to soak reeds in these pits, and boys said that goblins hid in them.

The cemetery had no fence around it. They saw from a distance that there was someone standing on the church porch.

"Uncle, I'll go back now, all right?" the girl said, slowing down. "There is the midwife, your lodger. She might tell the teacher that I've been to church! I'll go back, all right?"

"All right, you can go," Varygin said.

When he came closer, a young woman ran down the wooden church steps to meet him. Her face, rosy from the frosty air, was wet with tears and at the same time glowing with health.

"We had begun to think you weren't coming," she said when Varygin told her who he was. "We expected you on the night express and went to the station to meet you. We didn't know what to do. You see, perhaps you will be angry —I am an unbeliever, too—but Marya Semyonovna insisted on being buried in the old way, as a Christian."

Taking off his fur cap and without adjusting the hair that had clung to his forehead, Varygin passed in under the dark archway. Inside, three or four figures were standing in the dim light cast by a few meager candles.

The midwife followed him in and stood near the door. He moved nearer. Suddenly he saw the dark face of his mother, small as a child's, lit up by a yellow candlelight. He stopped and stood motionless, seeing only this face in front of him.

A priest with sparse gray hair and a thin cartilaginous forehead was chanting a prayer. He seemed to be addressing only the mother, who lay motionless, her thin, bloodless lips pressed together. Out of the darkness loomed the flat countenances of the saints painted on the altar screen. There was an odor of incense, and this smell, combined with the Church Slavic words the priest was intoning in the gloom, reminded Varygin of his childhood, when he used to go with his mother to this church and even sang in the choir. All this seemed so long ago that it might never have happened at all. Once the priest came quite close, and

Varygin got a whiff of garlic from his worn old vestments.

When the funeral service was over, the women who had been hidden in the darkness closed the coffin, lifted it, and carried it off.

Varygin came out of the church with the others and helped carry the coffin over the faded grass between the wooden crosses. He came to himself only when his mother had already been buried.

Then he made his way back over the crooked log across the tiny brook, from which rose a thin mist resembling incense, and walked again over the hard field. It seemed to him that he had just returned from a world he thought had long since ceased to exist.

When they had returned to the village and came to the house, the midwife ran ahead up to the porch and, fishing the key out of her pocket, opened the door. Varygin remembered the porch and the door with the iron handle. Only the gate by the house was different. It was a new one, and as he passed he saw a sign on it: "Midwife's Office."

Varygin crossed the threshold. On the left, a white stove rose to the ceiling. In the corner on the right stood a wide wooden basin and over it a clay jug—probably the same ones that had been there in his childhood. He had completely forgotten them, but now he remembered them well.

The ceiling had become much lower than it used to be. But the dark hewn beams, slightly sagging in the middle, were the same, he could vouch for that. Here were the old iron hooks for the cradles: one, two, three. His father had lived here with his brothers. There were three sisters-in-law in the house, and each rocked her own cradle. In one of them he, Varygin, had begun his growth.

"I mostly stay in the other part of the house," the midwife said. "I have an office for my patients there. Marya Semyonovna stayed here. There is her bed, and the towel is hanging just as it was."

Varygin looked at the towel, gray with age, and again, and not for the first time, the thought that his mother had been in need stabbed him painfully.

He took off his coat and cap and wearily sank onto a stool. He wanted to lay his head down on the table and drop off into forgetfulness. Long ago the whole family used to have their meals at this table. In the corner, under the wooden icon, his father had sat. Varygin remembered the smell of cabbage soup and warm bread with cabbage leaves clinging to the bottom crust. His mother often washed the table with hot water and scraped it with a knife with a broken handle. This knot there, with its dark center, had always seemed to him like the eye of a horse. Now the boards of the table had yellowed and cracked and the "eye" had turned black and crumbled.

A stack of copybooks lay on the table. "Oblast courses in midwifery. Notes of A. Antonova," he read. He had seen this painstaking childish writing on the letters he sometimes received from his mother.

A. Antonova brought in an armful of firewood, lit the stove, and put on a kettle. Then she removed the copybooks, took a clean towel from a suitcase under the shelf, wiped out a cup, and poured a cup of tea for Varygin.

"I have to hurry off to Lapshino. I have a delivery there," she said. "So please excuse me."

He did not want any tea. He sat there alone, motionless. During his childhood this house had been seething with life, but now this life had all vanished. It seemed strange that only these walls and he, Varygin, remained. But he too had nothing to do here and ought to leave. He did not want to think about leaving. He simply didn't want to move. Was there some place to lie down? He turned his head to look around.

On the bench in the corner, leaning foolishly to one side, stood an old samovar, no longer used, with a broken faucet. It seemed to be grinning slyly and winking at the bench as if to say: "Aha! You too have become broken down on the road! So lie down next to me, brother!"

Varygin pressed both hands on the table to help himself up, and the table too seemed to wink at him with its horse's eye: "So you have come back, in spite of everything!"

Varygin walked over to the bed and lay down.

When he opened his eyes, the cold red strip of sunset was burning, out beyond the fence. It was reflected in the window pane. He suddenly thought that he had fallen asleep on his mother's bed, where she had died. He got up and sat down at the table. Opposite him, on the wall, hung his overcoat; his cap lay on the bench. Beyond it, in the corner, stood the samovar, serious and sullen, as if offended at something.

Near by, probably back of the wall, someone was crying in a shrill, nervous voice: "They are not behaving like Communists, that's why I'm making a noise. If you want to know, nobody is going to push us village machine operators around. What is it, anyway, is it according to the law? People should know if things are not done properly!"

"They will go into it at the rayon executive committee," replied a reserved, remonstrating voice. "You had better go now. I told you he was resting."

The voices moved away. Apparently the disputants had gone out the gate.

Then a little later a board creaked on the porch and a stooped figure in a sheepskin coat appeared in the doorway.

"Are you awake?" came out of the dark. The switch clicked, and an electric light bulb came on over the table. Varygin saw a skinny old man looking at him with small, jolly eyes.

"And who are you?" Varygin asked.

"I? I am Ilya Moshkaryov. I'm a watchman now, but I used to be a blacksmith. It's because of sickness that I've become a watchman. Right here, at the smithy. That's where I keep watch."

He sat down on a stool by the table.

"I've brought some firewood for Antonina Vasilyevna. I saw that you were asleep. She must have gone to Lapshino: Zoya Sinyukhina is having another baby there."

"Who was that shouting out there?" Varygin asked, nodding toward the wall.

"Pelageya Komkova, the wife of the combine operator, a refueler. They used to be here with us in the artel, but now they are on the M.T.S. payroll. She kept holding on to her membership in the kolkhoz, but only as a formality, so that her personal plot would not be taken from her. They have two-fifths of a hectare. Now she has been taken off this list. The reason is that in the whole year she only earned twelve work days. You could hardly keep her in the kolkhoz for that! Their private plot is being taken away from them, and so she is screaming that the machine operators are being mistreated. She came to complain to you. Who can possibly injure her! The very idea!"

"Aren't they entitled to a plot?"

"They are. According to the law they get fifteen-hundredths of a hectare, but not out of kolkhoz land. It's going to be marked off separately, on waste land. This was decided by the village Soviet at a formal session."

He was silent for a moment and then began again. "So you came to bury your mother? The last duty. You showed respect for the aged. Thank you for not forgetting. I was assigned to work on peat and couldn't make it to the funeral."

The old man stretched out one leg and, bending backward, pulled a quarter-litre bottle of vodka out of his trouser pocket. The bottle was almost full.

"Here," he continued, becoming more animated. "If you're not too important to drink with a working man, let's drink to your mother's memory. Don't get the idea that I'm a drinking man. My niece, Marya Skornyakova, got married today to Pyotr Dezhurov, from the flax plant. They're having a celebration, but I couldn't get Semyonovna out of my head. So I grabbed up a quarter-bottle and left. To each his own."

He rubbed his hands as though they were cold, looked on top of the shelf, carefully lifted down two cups, one after the other, and poured a little into each.

"Your father and I used to be great friends. Now I hear that you're one of the leaders. That's the way things are: some people go one way and some another. But actually we are all alike. Will you have some?" he asked, passing the cup. "Wait a minute, I have something we can eat with it."

He thrust his left hand into his pocket, brought out a dark, knobby pickle, wiped off the tobacco crumbs sticking to it, and broke it in two.

The vodka burned Varygin's mouth. He puckered his face at the sight of the pickle and refused. The blacksmith also took a drink and ate his half of the pickle.

"So-o-o," he said with satisfaction, screwing up his cunning eyes under their bushy, faded eyebrows. "So you are the leaders; we are the producers. That's how it is, heh-heh. Shall we finish up what is left?"

He carelessly joggled the half-full bottle in his hand, and they drank again.

"For some it's a funeral, and for others a wedding. That's the way it is, heh-heh!" said the old man.

Varygin felt a warmth in his chest, and his spirits rose for the first time in three days.

"But how did my mother live? Fairly well, or—how?" he asked.

"Well, she had her ups and downs. She lived the way everybody else did."

"But, still . . . Well, what about food, for instance?"

"Well, there was nothing to complain about. Our own grain does not last longer than the spring, so we go to Lapshino, to the village co-op. Some people even go to the town. The village Soviet paid rent to her for the house. They set up the midwife's office here. Thirty-five a month. She didn't need much. Sometimes she had white bread and enjoyed some factory tea. This year they brought in some sugar several times, and she had some too. No, there is nothing to complain about."

Wheels rattled on the frozen road outside the gate. A cart passed the house, and you could hear the clumping and noisy snorting of the horse.

Then an accordion sounded somewhere close by, a gay crowd walked past the house, and a strident girlish voice sang, half yelling:

> "Over the spring wheat field
> Over the rayon co-op
> Over the courses for bee-keepers,
> I am parting from you."

"That's our people having themselves a good time," said the blacksmith. "Shouldn't I go out and get some more?" He stood up, pushed the empty bottle into his pocket, and vanished without saying good-by.

Varygin also got up, put on his overcoat, and went outside. It was already quite dark, and cold stars shone in the cloudless sky. He walked up and down near the gate, shivered from the cold, and looked at his watch. The luminous green hands showed only 7:10. He remembered that the express left late at night, and the few hours remaining before he could leave seemed long and tiresome.

The accordion was playing at the outskirts of the village, and he could hear the sounds of voices, girls' squeals, and laughter. Varygin turned around and went toward the house. Derevlyova, the soldier's wife, was waiting for him on the porch. She was still wearing the soldier's blouse, but now had a heavy woolen shawl wrapped around her head and shoulders.

"I came to make you some tea," she said in a singsong voice, following him into the cottage. "Antonina Vasilyevna is worrying about you. She sent a messenger from Lapshino. She can't come herself: Zoya is slow to give birth and is holding her up."

She started a fire in the front of the stove and set the teapot to boil.

"It is too bad that Semyonovna did not live to see you. How happy the old soul would have been!" Varygin heard her say.

"Did she expect me to come?" he asked.

"She didn't say anything about it this year. But the other summer, when you had promised to come, she really did look forward to it very much. She used to say: 'It will be today, today!' Then she became silent. But she was not angry, no. She understood that it is not so easy for such a busy man to get away. Out of all our village people you have gone the farthest. And Afanasy Beryozin from Korkino—he's a general somewhere in transportation."

She scalded the tea, put the cup on the table near him, and sat down.

"It's only that we haven't much to brag about. There are only women in this kolkhoz. We do what we can, but not much comes of it. In the kolkhoz named 'Struggle' people got four kilos of grain apiece, while we——" She made a hopeless gesture. "Things are not going right with us," she said apologetically. Probably she was embarrassed to speak to a man of Varygin's prominence and importance about the lack of achievements of their kolkhoz.

"This is what I wanted to ask you," she went on, untying her shawl. "Is it right, what they are doing to us? This year we planted seventy-four hectares of hemp. No sooner had it started to bloom than the spring grains were ripe. We wanted to reap the grain and leave it in sheaves, but they told us to thresh it and bring it in right away: procurements. So you see what happened? It's thirty-nine versts from here to the grain-collection station. There are two ferries, and then you have to wait at the grain elevator. Yet if you don't pick the hemp on time, it's not good for anything. But the agents keep pestering us. 'Bring in the grain!' 'Is it possible,' we said, 'that our government can't wait seven days?' We would have delivered our quota. We would have brought in the grain as soon as we were through with the hemp. Nothing doing! You can't get anywhere with them! And there's no one to appeal to. By the time we had carried the grain to the elevator and threshed it, we had missed the time for harvesting the hemp crop. The hemp we had not finished reaping had fallen to the ground. True, we were credited with delivering the grain: in fact, we were listed among the first to deliver. But again we had no bread for ourselves. So you tell me: is it right? Or isn't it?"

"She thinks that this is all within my power," Varygin thought distractedly, trying to remember what he knew about hemp. But he couldn't think of anything.

"This is a political problem," he said aloud. "The state must always come first. Everything depends on the level of consciousness of the masses."

He felt he was not saying the right thing and fell silent. But Derevlyova listened to him with an expression of satisfaction on her face. "That's just what I think—a political problem," she chimed in readily, apparently pleased that the conversation was acquiring real depth. "That is true. You put it very well. Our masses still lack consciousness."

The noise of a motorcycle came from the darkness outside.

"She must have come," said Derevlyova. "Probably the M.T.S. engineer brought her. He comes every Saturday. And she is always busy. Oh, the midwife doesn't know where her luck lies."

Antonina Vasilyevna came in first. Following directly behind her was a tow-headed young man with a weather-beaten face and prominent cheekbones.

"Well, how are you doing?" she asked briskly. Her melancholy mood of the morning seemed to have disappeared without a trace.

She washed her hands, sat down by the table, opened a package of sandwiches apparently bought somewhere in a restaurant, and, offering them around, began telling about the nice strong girl Sinyukhina had given birth to.

She made a pleasant picture with her milk-white arms, bare to the firm elbows, the gentle, feminine movements with which she swept the strands of wet hair behind her pink ears, and her brightly flushed fresh cheeks. As she talked she did not once look at the engineer, but she must have been continually aware that his eyes were fixed on her.

"No, she knows where her luck is," Varygin decided,

looking at the girl, whose eyes were shining despite all the anxieties and worries of the day. He remembered his shape-less wife, always disgruntled about something, and the way she overfed the children, as a result of which at eleven Gena already had a paunch and Sveta looked like her aunt with her childish face and heavy, thick legs. He thought: "This engineer is a lucky fellow." If, long ago, life had taken an-other turn and he, Varygin, had remained in the village, he would now probably still be a strong and healthy man, and the skin on his face would have been firm and swarthy, like the engineer's. But the past cannot be changed—nor the future either, apparently. Perhaps if a young woman with arms as white as these and a beautiful, supple, strong body would consent to love him, nothing would come of it any-way.

"Have you been here long, in this area?" he asked.

"It's time for me to get away!" She gave a laugh, but there was a hard glint in her eyes. "Everyone is eager to get away from here, from the villages into the towns, and the nearer the center, the better. Things are more civilized there, and there's more to eat. But they say we are needed here more."

She looked at the engineer as if asking for his support.

"Yes, there is lots of work here," said the engineer. "Out of the nineteen collective farms in our rayon, more than half are below par. Their crops are poor, their income is negligible. The people work unwillingly, and eat badly." Without looking, he took a cigarette out of the field bag at his side and lit it nervously.

"Why so?" Varygin asked.

The engineer shrugged. "You should know better than we do. Nobody wants to work without pay."

The midwife silently touched the engineer's hand. He got up from the table and began walking up and down the room.

Varygin sat with his back against the wall and chewed his sandwich. He had eaten nothing since morning. He thought the engineer was looking at him in an unfriendly way.

"Aren't you spreading it on a bit thick?" he asked hoarsely. "At first I thought you were an optimist."

The engineer went over to the corner and threw his cigarette into the basin.

"Optimism," he said, coming back, "is a much more complicated thing than it looks. The village would be a lot better off if there were fewer dispensers of official cheer. We have to grit our teeth and surmount the difficulties we face, not try to gloss them over. Take our M.T.S., for instance. There is so much latent potential there—but nobody really cares. Come over tomorrow: you'll see for yourself."

"I'm leaving today on the express. Urgent business!" Varygin said, and looked at his watch.

The engineer also looked at his watch. The enthusiasm he had just shown disappeared at once. "So I'll be going, Tonya," he said.

She went out into the passage with him. Varygin heard them whispering about something on the porch.

"It's probably time for me to go, too," Varygin said when she returned.

"Wait. There is still plenty of time. Mitya will tell them to send a car from the M.T.S." Looking around at Derevlyova, who was quickly washing the dishes in the corner, she began speaking with embarrassment about the house. What was to be done with it? Did he want to break her lease, or perhaps was he thinking of selling it, or were things to remain as before?

"Let everything remain as it was," Varygin said.

Some of his mother's belongings remained in the chest of drawers. He took two old family photographs from the bottom of the top drawer.

He felt that he had neither the desire nor the strength to go into all this, or into what the engineer had said, or into what he himself had seen here in a day.

"So please make the necessary arrangements yourself," he said, and pushed the drawer back.

The car came much sooner than he expected. The midwife went with him so that he would not have to bother about buying a ticket himself.

The road to Lapshino was horrible, but later, when the car came out onto the highway and with a soft rustling of tires began to speed along the gray ribbon lit up by the moonlike glow of the headlights, Varygin gradually recovered his usual calm, and the aftertaste remaining from his meeting with the engineer disappeared of itself.

"Of course," he thought. "The local Party organs are

not yet adequately staffed. Sometimes they work clumsily and crudely, and cite objective factors only to cover up their own ineptitude. But we cannot straighten things out everywhere at once. We can correct and prompt them from above, but they must do the work themselves. Themselves!

"Yes, themselves. That's right," he thought again a minute later and was angry with himself for not having said so to the engineer.

They arrived at Dvoriki almost an hour before the train came and, after buying the ticket, sat down in the buffet.

The midwife, embarrassed, clumsily drank the port he offered her and kept glancing around as if afraid of something.

"Why don't you come with me? You could be my secretary," Varygin said jokingly.

She choked, spilled some wine on the oilcloth, and blushed so deeply that Varygin too felt uncomfortable.

In the train, while getting ready for bed in the half-dark compartment, where the other passengers were already asleep, he reminded himself with relief that the disturbing and unpleasant experiences of the last few days had already been left behind, and he thought with pleasure about how tomorrow he would come to his warm, well-furnished office and would sit down in his comfortable chair at his desk.

However, some feeling of guilt remained with Varygin for a long time. He couldn't get to sleep. Through heavy drowsiness his imagination conjured up images of the wooden crosses against the gray sky, the familiar house, the long plank bench against the wall, and in the corner the old samovar, tilted sideways. His mother was sitting at the smoothly planed table; her face was small and dark, just as it had been in the church. She moved toward him and asked him, just as Derevlyova, the soldier's wife, had asked him, with hope and expectation: "Is it right or isn't it, what they have done with us?"

[Yury Nagibin (born 1920) is a very prolific writer of short stories and one of the editors of the magazine *Znamia*. The two stories translated here, both from *Literaturnaya Moskva*, Vol. II, illustrate various phases of the muckraking spirit let

loose by Khrushchev's "de-Stalinization" speech of 1956. "A
Light in the Window" is a simple "class" protest against the
gross sycophancy universally displayed toward high officials
and their hogging of the good things of life. While ordinary
citizens at a vacation resort must spend their holidays in
quarters so cramped that even a honeymooning couple have
to be separated in dormitories, a whole house, beautifully
furnished and maintained, is kept ready and empty lest some
Soviet mogul suddenly descend on the resort.

"The Khazar Ornament" shows us an interesting and unexpected corner of the Soviet backwoods. Nagibin here takes
up some of the conversation problems alluded to in Paustovsky's
speech, although he attributes the wasting of natural resources
not to bureaucratic mismanagement of careerism, but to the
backwardness and ignorance of people who have not been
reached by the Party's message and organizing will. In the
course of the story the Party and potential progress do come
to this benighted region, brought by a stock character in Soviet
fiction, the true, non-bureaucratic Communist organizer, flexible, human, and understanding, but strong and firm-willed. But
despite its official resolution, the story nevertheless partakes of
the "protest" spirit in its exposure of a reality widely divergent
from its official representation. And Nagibin makes in passing
some other notable thrusts, e.g., at the failure of the regime to
build roads in outlying areas while spending vast sums on the
ornate "Socialist Gothic" skyscrapers which now disfigure the
Moscow horizon.]

A LIGHT IN THE WINDOW

Yury Nagibin

The little bridge over the deep gully that lay between the
rest home and the highway collapsed late in March. And
on top of that the ice on the river broke up, destroying
the road across the ice—the last link with the outside
world. Deliveries of supplies to the rest home stopped.
Emergency stores kept the home going for a few days, but
eventually they were exhausted. A few cans, some sugar,
vegetable oil, and dried vegetables remained in the pantry.
Then the director, Vasily Petrovich, decided to slaughter
his own pig to feed the vacationers.

The slaughtering was done by the chief cook himself—
a former army cook, middle-aged and tough as iron—
while Vasily Petrovich helped. It turned out to be not so
easy. The enormous, immobile Mashka, who had been
overfed on warm, greasy kitchen slops till she weighed
over 400 pounds, took to flight like a bird when the
slaughterers crossed the threshold of her pen. She had
evidently guessed what they had come for, even though
the chef hid the knife behind his back. They had a terrible
time throwing her. First in turn and then together Vasily
Petrovich and the chef sprawled out on the dirty floor
boards, trying to get hold of Mashka's legs. But with an
agility inspired by her fear of death, the heavy sow, almost
blinded by fat, kept slipping out of their clutching hands and
dashing about the pen with heart-rending squeals. Finally
they managed to throw her onto her back. The chef took the
long knife and, with a neatly calculated movement, plunged
the thin, narrow blade under the sow's left leg and pulled
the knife sharply toward himself.

First Mashka was singed till she became like brown wax,
then skinned and cut up; the dark clots of blood were
scooped out with spoons. Vasily Petrovich worked as
though in a dream. He had killed pigs many times, but
now this simple, ordinary business seemed to him an act of
the most brutal cruelty against a warm, breathing, defense-
less creature. He could not forget the desperate reproach
in Mashka's half-blind, amber-colored, narrow eyes. No
pig he had slaughtered for his own use had ever looked at
him like that.

But the deed was done. The vacationers consumed
Mashka with the same unfailing appetite with which they
devoured all the other courses served them. Nor did
Vasily Petrovich expect any thanks. He found a sort of
bitter satisfaction in the very fact that his selfless action
was doomed to oblivion. But events proved otherwise.
The eyes of the members of the rest-home staff, when they
looked at the director, reflected something that had not
been in them before. Vasily Petrovich did not notice this
at once, and when he did notice it, he did not at first understand the faint but warm light that shone from the eyes
of the charwomen, waitresses, nurses, and other employees.
Nonrecognition has melancholy joy of its own, but the
approval of one's associates, even a silent approval, be-

stows much greater happiness on a man. A certain
bounciness appeared in the gait of this rotund, heavy-set,
roly-poly director.

Only one person did not appreciate the modest good
deed of Vasily Petrovich: Nastya, the charwoman of the
annex building. In her black sunken eyes the director
missed the familiar, heartwarming glow. And her approval
would have been especially pleasing to him: there was a
delicate and complicated relationship between Nastya and
the director.

When Vasily Petrovich had first taken charge of the rest
home, he and the former director had made the rounds
of all the outbuildings and land, and all the residential
premises of the main buildings and the annex. When
this was done, the former director took him to a neat
one-story bungalow with a glassed-in porch.

"In this bungalow . . ."

Breaking off, he moved ahead, opened the spring lock on
the door, which was lined with felt and oilcloth, and
gestured to Vasily Petrovich to follow him. They entered
a roomy hall smelling of dry pinewood, from which
Vasily Petrovich could see a spacious three-room apartment
worthy of Moscow or Leningrad, while on his right an
open door disclosed the dull green cloth of a billiard table.

In the first room—the living room—a television set
stood on a polished oak table; soft sofas lined the walls;
in the center of the room, an oval table covered with a
heavy fringed tablecloth was surrounded by massive armchairs, which seemed to be made of lead. Over the table a
crystal chandelier glittered in the dull reflected light.
The two doors leading to the other rooms gave a glimpse of
the starchy coolness of well-stuffed pillows in the bedroom
and the corner of a desk and the edge of a thick rug.

Vasily Petrovich, overwhelmed by this magnificence,
remained silent.

"This is our special untouchable reserve," said the former
director with playful pride. "We kept it in case he himself were to come."

"Well, I doubt that he himself would come here . . ."
Vasily Petrovich murmured with a forced smile. Not once
during his long life of hotel management had he ever had
any dealings with the higher authorities and therefore

he would not admit that such things were possible. "You know, I wouldn't be too sure," concluded the former director in the same special, vaguely playful tone which he had assumed when they had crossed the threshold of the sanctuary. "So be on your guard."

This advice had gone to Vasily Petrovich's very heart. He actually had been on his guard all the time lest the arrival of an exalted guest from the ministry catch him unawares. He assigned to the apartment the charwoman of the annex building, Nastya. Every day she had to clean the deserted rooms, scrub the untrodden floors, change the flowers in the vase, which shed their fragrance in vain, brush the green cloth of the billiard table, the pile of which seemed to be growing like a neglected lawn. Part of the responsibility fell also on the porter, Stepan: he had to chop off the ice on the steps, remove the snow piled up under the windows, have a ready supply of birch logs in case the high personage might want to enjoy the play of flames in the fireplace.

In short, everything was done to make a spur-of-the-moment guest feel that he had been eagerly awaited and that everything had been provided for his coming with great care.

And yet these rooms were a source of constant inner anxiety to Vasily Petrovich. As a manager he had difficulty reconciling himself to the fact that a splendid apartment stood vacant, uselessly wasting money and work. At times he became irked in a very human way at the prohibition laid upon these rooms. He could not forget for a long time the faces of two newly-weds who had come to the rest home right at the peak of the July season: they had almost faltered then, imagining what bliss a private apartment would have brought them. But he had controlled himself, and the young people had gone off to different buildings, exchanging a look as if they were parting for life.

Vasily Petrovich did not feel any better when a famous stonemason, who had worked on the rest home itself, came to stay. The stonemason came with his wife and three irrepressible sons; even in a two-room suite the old couple never had a minute's rest from the stormy high spirits of their unruly offspring.

The new director listened sadly to the rattle of the balls

on the broken-down public billiard tables, while a magnificent table stood useless and without purpose in the vacant apartment; the same sickly feeling came to him when he saw the waitresses with their faces glued to the windows of the television room—the cramped viewing hall could hardly hold the vacationers. The girls pushed each other and quarreled, trying to catch the fleeting images distorted by the window glass, and all the while a splendid television set was going to waste in the cottage.

All this depressed Vasily Petrovich to the point that he found it intolerable to bear the burden of his sorrows alone. He began to share them with the charwoman Nastya; he was sure that this taciturn, reserved woman with her dark, deep-set eyes would not give him away. He told her about the newly-weds and about the stonemason, but each time what he saw clearly in Nastya's dark eyes was not sympathy but censure. This made him feel even more distressed, but still he complained to her again and again about each recurring episode of this kind with the dim hope that someday she would at last understand him. But when he realized that even his sacrificial act, his little feat of martyrdom, had not extinguished the piercing reproachful light in Nastya's deep and excessively steady gaze, he knew he must bear his cross alone.

Vasily Petrovich did not understand Nastya. And it was no easy thing to understand this quiet, somewhat deaf, reserved woman with a strange, ugly, and yet attractive face. Of course, Nastya was homely; yet if anyone said: "But you know, she has something . . ." everyone was ready to agree. People only needed this kind of prompting to make them recognize suddenly Nastya's latent, rather wild charm. It is hard to say where this charm came from: perhaps from her shy, very youthful (though Nastya was long past thirty), oddly deep and penetrating gaze; perhaps in the proud carriage of her head; perhaps in something else. This second image of Nastya was ephemeral; it faded quickly, leaving after it a feeling of puzzlement; then once again there reappeared a homely woman of undetermined age with a pale, weather-beaten face and big, work-worn hands. Many years before, Nastya's strange and fleeting charm had attracted a young trainer from the horse farm, but the war came and Nastya was no sooner a bride than she became a widow. She had devel-

oped a grudge against life, and whereas the director
wanted to be thought good, Nastya feared more than
anything else that someone might suspect her of being kind.

She fiercely protected her rights: to do the rooms
between nine and ten o'clock in the morning—not a
minute sooner, and not a minute later; to bring hot water
for shaving at eight thirty sharp. She did not have to
make the beds: this was supposed to be done by the vacationers themselves. Whenever someone tried to demand
extra services, she flung in his face: "It is not my duty!"
But it somehow turned out that Nastya did make the
beds, brought hot water three times a day, and performed many other services which were not her duty. She
avenged herself for this in her own way, by refusing
categorically to take the ten- and twenty-five-ruble notes
which people pressed on her as they were leaving. At
such times her face became so cross that the vacationers,
murmuring apologies awkwardly, tried to hide the wads
of money which had grown damp in their hands.

Nastya's entire life changed when she was assigned as
charwoman for the special building. At first she took the
director's order as a gross infringement of her rights,
and even the ominous word "himself" did not impress her
at all. But she was enraptured by the magnificent furnish-
ings of the rooms and suddenly lost all desire to protest.
After that the whole purpose of her existence became
focused on these rooms.

Nastya gave herself up to her new job with all the
passion of her unexpended heart. Gradually her mind
created a marvelous, fairylike picture of the person who
was to come and reign over all this grandeur. She believed
that he was an extraordinary man, unlike anyone else, because so much effort was expended on his behalf, and even
though he remained unseen, he caused people to think
of him every day and every hour. And Nastya was never
so happy as when she was taking care of the rooms which
were to receive him. But she did not neglect her former
duties. Unfailingly conscientious as usual, she cleaned both
floors of the annex, swept the floors, emptied the ash trays,
scrubbed the bathtub and wash stands till they shone like
glass, changed the water in the carafes, shook out the
scatter rugs, and even made the beds, grumbling to herself. But none of this touched her heart; it was all part

of everyday life, a life which could have been dispensed
with. But, on the other hand, she lived fully, passionately,
tremblingly when the turn of the sacred chambers came.
Here ordinary drudgery became creative work. One can
simply wash a window, or one can perform a miracle:
make the panes so transparent, so shining, so sunny that
they seem to draw into the room the blueness of the sky,
the whiteness of the snow, and the greenness of the pines;
the walls vanish and the room becomes part of the open
spaces. It is one thing to tidy up a room, and another
when, in the whole expanse of a room, each object finds
the perfect place for itself; to place the cabinet not
quite straight but slightly at an angle, to pull the
television set a bit forward, to move the flowers from the
whatnot to the center of the oval table—and everything
becomes different; instead of mere orderliness—beauty.

Almost every passing day brought Nastya a small discovery, and the director, who from time to time inspected
the vacant premises, felt something which he could hardly
define. He did not notice any changes; everything seemed
to be as it was; but for some reason the sight of these
rooms gave him, every time, new happiness and an ever
growing sense of security.

Nastya considered blasphemous the very idea that these
rooms might be occupied by some chance person. The
waverings of the director outraged her; nobody could
dare to cross the threshold of this house except *himself*. . . .

But days, weeks, and months went by, and nobody
came. A year passed, and another quickly started rolling by
after it; still the rooms remained as before, vacant and
cold, unwarmed by human presence. The objects continued to gleam with a cleanliness appreciated by no one;
the blind and mute television set continued to stare blankly
with its whitish eye; the balls on the grassy greensward
of the billiard table seemed to have lost the knack of
rolling and were growing fatter and rounder; the beautiful
mirror in its carved frame did not reflect a single human
face except the swarthy face of Nastya with its tautly
drawn skin and black deep-set eyes; no head drugged with
sleepiness touched the tight, cool starch of the pillows.

Vain expectation, wasted effort, and ardor expended
to no purpose gradually aroused in Nastya a feeling of

hatred. She had been deceived. It was not the director—what did she care about him!—who had deceived her; it was the one for whom she had been waiting with such passionate impatience.

But to think that the long-awaited guest had not come meant that she was still awaiting him; and Nastya could not, would not, wait any longer. She stopped touching or moving anything in rooms, and it seemed to Vasily Petrovich that Nastya had begun to neglect her duties. He passed his hand over the top of the television set and over the arms of the chairs, but found no speck of dust anywhere; he touched the windowpanes with his finger and the finger squeaked on the cleanly washed and carefully wiped surface; he stamped on the scatter rugs trying in vain to raise even a small cloud of dust. There was nothing he could find fault with. And yet something was lacking, and Vasily Petrovich frowned in discontent.

Meanwhile, Nastya's contempt for the invisible tenant grew and finally mastered her whole being. It now seemed to her that a gross injustice was being perpetrated in assigning to him these large rooms full of light and air and all these beautiful and useful articles.

One night Vasily Petrovich was returning home after a lonely late walk. He loved this hour near midnight, when the entire rest home and all the surrounding buildings were deep in sleep; and when he no longer felt the constant pressure of people's importunate demands; when he could no longer be bothered by the vacationers, or the housekeeper-nurse, or the chef, or the bookkeeper, or the warehouseman, or the gardener, or a sudden inspector from the Ministry, or a telephone call from the kolkhozes, which always wanted something from him, or his wife, who could never get it into her head that he was the director and not the owner of the rest home. True, he was not often able to enjoy even this simple happiness; usually weariness laid him flat as soon as the working day was over.

The night had wrapped the rest home and its grounds in darkness, through which the greenish light of the new moon barely filtered. In this greenish darkness everything seemed elegant, orderly, appropriate, necessary, and beautiful—even the high piles of snow along the paths and walks, their tops turned to solid ice, even the plaster deer, which looked unbearably ugly in the daylight, resembling a sheep dog with horns tacked on as a joke.

It was a time when he could think of everything clearly and calmly: that the most difficult things in life were behind; that now he could fall asleep slowly and pleasantly in the warmth of his bed, without fear that he would be got up during the night; that the spirit of mutual understanding and trust among people was increasing; that without fear of ill-wishers, he could try wholeheartedly to make the lives of his vacationers more agreeable, more satisfying, more peaceful and gay, and his own life into the bargain.

Vasily Petrovich turned the corner of the house and suddenly froze, throwing his head back and a little to one side, like a horse that had run against a fence; there were lights in the windows of the vacant cottage. More exactly, there were lights in the den, the bedroom, and the billiard room, where he could hear the dry, brittle crack of balls. The living room was dark, but there was music there, and when Vasily Petrovich overcame his momentary numbness and took a step forward, he saw on the wall facing the living-room windows a fluttering, pale-lilac reflection, and he realized that the television set had been turned on.

A strange feeling went through Vasily Petrovich. For an instant he fancied that the furniture had got tired of being useless and had revolted. It had started living a life of its own without the aid of man: the lamps had flashed on, the balls had begun rolling over the green field of the billiard table, the television set had come alive to the joy of the armchairs, the whatnots, the table, and the sofas. But this queer feeling immediately gave way to another, which was more sober but just as exciting: it had happened! . . . The event he had expected with such trepidation for over a year and had almost stopped expecting—it had happened. The high-placed guest had deliberately arrived when the director was absent, when nobody was expecting him, and in some mysterious, incomprehensible way had found the rooms set aside for him, penetrated into them without a key, and with his masterly, confident authority had animated the inanimate.

But this thought, too, did not stay in Vasily Petrovich's mind for more than a flash and was crowded out by anxious perplexity; no, this could not have happened. . . .

Standing for some reason on tiptoe and moving stealthily, he stepped from the path into the wet, loose snow and went up to the window.

In front of the television set, on the screen of which glimmered a bluish spot crisscrossed by fast-moving thin lines, sat the charwoman Nastya with her large hands folded on her knees. To her right, eyes and mouth wide open, crouched Klavka, the ten-year-old daughter of the porter, Stepan, while on the other side Klavka's younger brother was sleeping sweetly in a large armchair. Through a crack in the door he could see Stepan toiling at the billiard table, lit up by the two chandeliers; he was jabbing clumsily with the cue at the balls.

Nastya had violated the interdiction! Openly, brazenly, she had entered this charmed world, set herself up as its rightful mistress, and brought Stepan into it. Vasily Petrovich felt, with a strange sinking feeling, that what he was now witnessing was something very good, very right, and very necessary. But at the same moment he raised his hand and knocked at the windows so sharply and roughly that the glass rattled. . . .

And then Vasily Petrovich shouted, threatened, and stamped his feet, carried away and intoxicated by his own screaming. He expended as much effort as if he thought that his furious indignation would reach the ears of the one whose rights had been so crudely disregarded. Whether *he* heard him or not, the violators remained deaf to the director's rage. Leading the children by the hand, they walked past the director with calm and severe dignity.

And seeing their stern, almost solemn faces, Vasily Petrovich suddenly stopped short and fell silent, listening with surprise to a strange, new, unfamiliar feeling that was rising and growing inside him, penetrating to his very finger tips—a feeling of unbearable disgust with himself.

THE KHAZAR ORNAMENT

Yury Nagibin

Last year the winter proved exceptionally snowy, and the spring floods were unusually high. Making our way from Spas-Klepinki to Lake Velikoye, we did not recognize

the road we had traveled before or the familiar Meshchera
spaces. The forests were afloat in water; the trees seemed
to grow out of tea-colored lakes. Every gully and every
hollow was brimming with water, reflecting the blueness
of the sky in the daytime and the stars at night. Dry
ditches and ruts had turned into rivers, every crack and
wrinkle of the earth was a brook, everything around flowed,
bubbled, squelched, steamed with fog, drizzled; and the
biting cold penetrated to our very bones. The last of the
snows, gray in their glassy crust, were still creeping down
the north slopes of the hills, hissing and dissolving into
meager waterfalls at the bottom.

The water had altered the configuration of the land
to a surprising degree. It had smoothed out the folds,
leveled the uneven places, sometimes covering hazel groves
and young oak spinneys; it had swallowed up all young
growth, and was unable to devour only firs, pines, and
old weeping birches. The light reflected from the water hid
from view the trunks of faraway trees. It looked as if the
canopies of firs, the clusters of birches, and the crowns
of almost bare pines were hanging in space.

On the mirror-like surface of newborn lakes, over
plowed fields and meadows, glided dories and the famous
local "oak boats," hollowed out of pines more often than
oaks. The trees and bushes over which they passed clung
to their bottoms like seaweed, and sometimes the rowers
parted the alders with their oars, as though they were reeds
or canes.

Had I been alone I would have lost my way long ago,
but my companion, Leonty Sergeyevich—an enthusiastic
hunter and fisherman, and an art historian during intervals
between hunting and fishing—strode along confidently,
not letting the spring deluge confuse him. But this did not
mean that we were progressing rapidly toward the end of
our journey. We had started in the afternoon and by
nightfall had not even covered five kilometers of real
distance, because of the endless detours. The darkness
came alive with stars. They shone over us, under us,
around us. Toward midnight, moonlight flowed downward
and upward, and one could no longer distinguish the
earth from the sky.

We looked a long time for a dry resting place for
the night and at last came upon a campfire. Several

hunters were sitting by the fire. They were drying their boots and leg wrappings and vigorously and unanimously cursing the spring, the floods, and their own restless passion for hunting, which had driven them out of their homes into this confounded mud hole.

We somehow managed to find a place at the fire, which was constantly threatening to go out and gave more smoke and fumes than heat, and passed a troubled night lying on some spruce boughs. In the morning, two of our group turned homeward, and five of us continued on our way.

Now we no longer cursed the spring, but rather the two men who had turned tail, and this cheered us up. Nevertheless, two more dropped out after we crossed Lake Svyatoye in oak dugouts, over small, nasty waves, which constantly shot icy, penetrating spray at us from the bow. We somehow dried ourselves in a forester's hut, which was awash on all sides, and the three of us who were left set out again. Our companion was a tall, sturdy lad with a round, rather womanish face covered with the light soft down of a young beard. He strode on stubbornly without picking his way or looking for paths, sloshing water into the tops of his rubber boots, crashing through thickets that showered him from head to foot with water from the branches, and it was hard to decide whether this recklessness came from courage or despair. Everything became clear toward evening, when we stopped for supper in a tiny café in one of the little villages on our way.

The hunter drank a glass of vodka and began telling us that his wife was deceiving him with the local veterinary. The story was long, detailed, unnecessarily candid, and we saw that this companion had resolved to turn back. This proved correct. After paying for his supper he rose, nonchalantly picked up his gun and knapsack, and went out without saying good-by, as if he meant to return directly. We waited for half an hour, but he did not come back.

"So much the better," Leonty Sergeyevich remarked. "We'll get all the ducks."

"No, someone else passed through here before you," said the waiter, a slight, sharp-featured lad, raising his eyes from the check.

"What kind of man?" Leonty Sergeyevich asked, surprised.

"Also a hunter," the waiter replied. "He left before you came."

"Amazing!" Leonty Sergeyevich exclaimed, his eyes shining with excitement. "What a man! Alone, with night coming on, and he's not afraid!"

Frankly, I would not have minded in the least if all the ducks had fallen to the share of this lonely hunter. I was tired, chilled, wet; the endless streams of water had long ago extinguished any hunter's flame in me, but I knew that neither complaints nor arguments would have any effect on Leonty Sergeyevich, and so I only sighed.

"Never mind, the day will come when I shall think of this campaign in the past tense." I fell back on this favorite consolation and followed Leonty Sergeyevich out of the warmth of the café into the wet darkness.

Naturally, we lost our way, but were slow to realize this because the roads in the area did not differ much from the surrounding land; the same bumps, the same puddles, the same mess underfoot. Once I suddenly felt the earth give way under me, and I seemed to be stepping into a fluid, sticky mire. I tried in vain to find any kind of footing around and with every step sank deeper into the repulsive mixture.

I stopped. The lopsided moon, dimmed by thin ragged clouds running in different directions, threw yellowish spots of light on the bog. Looking closely at these spots, I decided that the yellow color came from grass and that therefore the ground must be firm there, and that the dark patches were peat, muck. Measuring with a glance the distance to the nearest yellow spot, I wrenched myself loose from the clinging mire, took two stumbling strides, stepped on the yellow place, and sank up to my waist. Bewildered, I tried to grasp at the nearest yellow islet with my hands, but became stuck in the peaty mixture. I managed to pull my arms free, but the effort pushed me even deeper into the morass. The moonlight had shifted the light and shadows so treacherously that I had taken bog for solid ground. It was my own fault, by the way; how could I have failed to realize that the moon's reflection on the water overpeat would give a yellow look to the boggy part and that the grass islets would look dark?

Strangely enough, I had never attached any importance to the primeval perils of Meshchera. I did not believe that

people died in the ways about which the local people love
to tell. Meshchera is so close to Moscow, to all the
customary stability of Moscow life, that I simply could
not believe that one could lose one's life here. But now,
surrounded on all sides by the vast yet oppressive night,
I felt isolated from the rest of the world. I felt hopelessly
cut off from everything dear, familiar, and safe, and for
the first time I was really scared. I had just enough self-
control left not to shout "Help!" in panic, but "Leonty
Sergeyevich!" instead.

"Give me your hand," came a voice from close by, and
I immediately felt ashamed. I should have known that my
reliable companion was right here and that he would have
come to my aid without waiting for my call.

Gropingly, I thrust out my hand and grasped his fingers.
With one powerful pull Leonty Sergeyevich jerked me out
of the liquid trap.

"Follow in my footsteps," he said.

"I don't see any footsteps."

"Step on the dark patches."

It wasn't so easy; each dark spot looked to me like a
terrifying slough. To step in one meant to drown. But I
had to go on. . . .

The darkness before us became more solid, and this
dull blackness, blacker than the rest of the night—probably
bushes—was surrounded by a weak, flickering outline of
light. It did not seem as though we were approaching this
blackness, but rather as though the blackness was floating
toward us. And it was already quite close to us when unexpectedly something gave way underfoot, and Leonty
Sergeyevich suddenly became very small in stature. A
moment later our sizes were equalized: I too had fallen
into the bog up to my waist.

"It's all right, it's all right," Leonty Sergeyevich said
briskly. "Give me your hand, we'll get out right away."

Something like a beam from a miniature searchlight
slipped over the bog. It colored the reeds emerald green,
curled through the bluish miasma of the morass, and,
leaving it, made a wide circle of light around us.

"Take hold of the stick," came a voice from the spot
where the cone of light originated. "There is firm ground
right next to you. . . ."

The next moment Leonty Sergeyevich suddenly rose up

over the morass: his fingers gripped my hand like a vise—
a jerk, and we stood on firm ground with the tall wet
bushes tickling our faces.

"The road is right here, back of these bushes," said
our unseen deliverer.

"Are you from around here?" Leonty Sergeyevich asked.

"I have a map," the stranger replied, squeezing a ray
of light out of his flashlight and showing us a map under
the cellophane cover of a case.

We started out through the bushes single file and soon
came on a broad stretch of land shining with numerous
puddles and stretching out into the distance, into the
darkness. But walking along this road was almost as difficult as walking through the bog. Apparently, at one time
it had been paved with cobblestones, but the paving had
been broken up by wheels, and some stones remained only
at the edges of deep, water-filled pits.

We went on for a long time, an unbearably long time,
slipping in the clayey, uneven ruts, falling into holes,
getting water in our boots, and stubbing our toes against
cobblestones. Finally we came to a hamlet.

We were admitted to the very first house where we
asked permission to spend the night. Hunters are never
refused shelter in Meshchera, no matter how small and
crowded the dwelling. And one could hardly imagine a
place more crowded than this cottage. A cradle hung in
the middle of the room. It was being rocked by an old
woman, her face disfigured by lupus. With her monotonous
humming she kept lulling herself, not the baby, to sleep.
Whenever she dozed off, the baby started howling. The
noise did not bother the numerous other people in the
cottage at all, who were sleeping side by side on the floor.
In addition, two pairs of bare feet showed over the edge
of the stove. However, our sleepy host confidently and
without looking moved some benches around, tossed a
sheepskin coat and a coverless calico pillow into a corner,
raked up some hay, covered it with a towel, and the result
was a bed large enough to accommodate three persons.
Then, without saying a word, he climbed back up on the
stove shelf, and instead of four feet now there were six.

While Leonty Sergeyevich and I were washing up in
the passage, our companion carefully studied his map by
the weak light of a night lamp.

"Yes, this actually is the very road!" he said when we had returned to the room. "Here are the marshes, the bushes, here is Perkhushkovo, where we are now, and there is the line of the road. And look at the note: the road is designated as paved!"

"Yes," Leonty Sergeyevich agreed, glancing at the map. "And why are you surprised?"

"But this is not a road: it is the devil's own mess!" the man burst out. "And they have the nerve to mark it on a map! Furthermore, there are similar so-called roads all over the rayon. Not only over the rayon—over the entire oblast! . . ."

I knew Leonty Sergeyevich abhorred sharp discussions. So now, to draw the attention of the stranger away from dangerous subjects, he asked:

"Are you from Moscow?"

"No, from the town," he answered casually—in the local idiom that meant the rayon center—and resumed as heatedly as before. "Roads are the face of the country. And what kind of roads do we have? All the unnecessary suffering a Russian endures because of this accursed lack of roads! . . ."

"Be patient—you can't have everything at once," Leonty Sergeyevich murmured. "We have built so much! . . ."

"Don't say it!" the man angrily interrupted. "Built! . . . And how much useless junk has been built? All those columns, arches, little balconies, curlicues, all those ginger-bread houses, all those palaces! And that's not all! They took it into their heads to drag a palm tree into the most out-of-the-way dump and to put up a statue in the filthiest square. While the roads—the arteries of life—we never thought about them, and even now do not think much about them. . . ."

He continued to pursue this subject angrily and heatedly, and the longer he spoke, the more reserved, more distant, abstracted, and detached became Leonty Sergeyevich's face—a large, serious face with a high forehead. Leonty Sergeyevich had so obviously withdrawn himself from the conversation that when he got up and went outside, it did not even seem rude.

"Did I say something insulting to your friend?" the man asked, surprised. "He wouldn't be a road builder, by any chance?"

"No," I answered with a shrug. Of course I did not try to explain to this chance hunting acquaintance that my companion, so confident and reliable in the world of nature, was a permanently frightened man. Even in scholarship he had chosen a field infinitely remote from real life: he was making a study of ancient Khazar ornamentation. At times I had a feeling that he himself bitterly regretted this state of being "frightened," but he could do nothing to overcome it.

When Leonty Sergeyevich returned, the man, pencil in hand, was demonstrating to me that the losses caused by the lack of roads far exceeded the cost of building new roads. I like angry people. Not cold sneerers, not petty fault-finders, but people who are angry, even embittered, but angry just because they really care for what is good, right, and needed in life. The stranger fumed and cursed with pain in his heart, and I felt immediately disposed toward him.

But Leonty Sergeyevich was of a different mind. When we had lain down to sleep, he whispered in my ear:

"Let's start a little earlier. . . . We don't need anybody else along. . . ."

But the stranger had no intention of waiting for us. Though we got up very early, he was ahead of us; his bed was made and he had vanished into thin air.

However, we were destined to meet him again, and on the very same morning.

The tiny brook Stulkolka, across which we used to wade instead of using the rickety wooden bridge, had overflowed its banks, swept away the bridge, and become as wide as the Volga. The nearest ferry was some six kilometers away. We reluctantly started out to walk along the shore when we saw a dory among the reeds and an old fisherman trying to net carps. He agreed to take us across for ten rubles. We moved slowly through the small but hard and springy waves. The water was so deep that the old man's long pole sank almost to the tip. The waves clapped noisily against the bottom of the boat; it felt as if some vicious and obstinate person were trying to direct us from below. We were already nearing the shore when we saw a dark line in the water and near it what looked like two humps.

"So they capsized, I see," the old fisherman observed calmly. "How could they try it in a dugout!" He shook his head and added, with a shade of condescending admiration: "The daredevils! . . ."

Coming closer, we saw two men, waist deep in water, pushing a dugout before them.

"Hey you, in the boat!" The slightly hoarse voice sounded familiar. "Save our souls!" The voice was that of our last night's companion. I stared with some surprise at this medium-sized, middle-aged man, slender but wiry in build, his face eternally burned to a brick-red color, with light hair hanging in strands down his forehead and sticking up in a crest on the top of his head. At night, under the light of a small lamp, he had seemed bigger, older, more imposing.

"We lost our oar," said the man when we had drawn alongside. His ferryman, a stout, thick-lipped lad, emitted an embarrassed noise. We took the passengers on board and took the dugout in tow with a chain. Sitting on the bottom of the boat, the man took out a handkerchief and, leaning out over the water, blew his nose noisily and carefully. Then he began to sneeze. He sneezed steadily for about two minutes with the crest of hair on the top of his head jumping in a funny way.

Subsiding at last, he said: "The Volkhov front," and added mockingly: "Eighteen months of swamp living do wonders for one's health!"

He took some powder from his pocket, poured it into his mouth, and, scooping up a handful of water, washed down the medicine.

"This will ruin your hunting trip," Leonty Sergeyevich sympathized.

"It can't be helped." The man shrugged. "You can't buy yourself a new organism: I'll have to get along with this one."

In the watchman's shack by the lake, where we stopped, the man took off his boots and climbed immediately onto the stove shelf. The watchman told us that there were two ways to get to Podsvyatye; the nearest was by water, and the other, a detour by land. Our old path along the bank of the river was flooded.

"We've had enough of the water," I said, and couldn't help glancing toward the stove, where our ailing companion had curled up. "Let's rather take the long way around."

"It's all right with me," Leonty Sergeyevich said.

He laid out on the table the supply of medicines he always took along when hunting, although he himself was never sick, tore a sheet out of his notebook, and printed on it in large letters: "Two tablets three times a day." He placed the paper on end in a crack of the table, and we went out.

We hadn't even made ten kilometers when darkness caught us just outside a village that, we learned later, was called Konkovo.

"Let's spend the night here," Leonty Sergeyevich said, "and tomorrow we'll make the final push."

As usual, we stopped at the very first cottage. There was a light burning inside; so the people were not yet asleep.

A tall, broad-shouldered, hairy, and slightly tipsy old man opened the door.

"Come in, come in," he said with the usual local hospitality, which, in his case, had been made warmer by liquor. "Another one of your calling is already here." He nodded at the stove shelf whence, from behind a calico curtain, came the sound of the regular, damply hoarse breathing of a sleeping man.

"We won't be in the way?" Leonty Sergeyevich asked, placing his gun and knapsack in a corner.

The old man knew perfectly well that he had asked the question merely to be polite, but he thought it necessary to give a detailed account of the situation.

"In whose way? My son is on the lake, my daughter-in-law went to town, only my grandson and I are home. And this one," he nodded toward the shelf, "is almost out cold. It's true what they say: when you want something badly enough, you won't care about the difficulties. He came in here burning with fever, his breath hot. I gave him dried raspberry tea and put him on the stove shelf with two fur coats over him. Perhaps he will sweat it out."

Leonty Sergeyevich and I glanced at each other. It looked as if the man on the stove was our former companion. So the dip in the Stulkolka had made no impression on him; he could have got ahead of us only by going over water.

"And only look what he brought along to hunt with," the old man said, beckoning to us with a mysterious and mocking expression. "Did you see this?" He took off the wall a single-barreled gun of the type sold in stores for fifty rubles apiece at the height of the hunting season. "Some of our hunters here have pretty shabby guns, but I have never seen anything like this one. And look at his ammunition—not even a dozen cartridges. I asked him what he had with him for hunting. And he says: 'Can't I get any cartridges here?' He's an odd one. His cartridges are twelve-caliber. The only one in fashion here is sixteen-caliber."

The old man spoke loudly; he was not afraid that the man on the stove might hear.

I must confess that I too was surprised by our friend's combination of unusual perseverance in travel with complete disregard for the quality of his hunting equipment. Leonty Sergeyevich probably had the same thought, but he only shrugged: the ethics of the hunt barred him from criticizing a fellow hunter.

We sat down to supper, inviting the old man to share it with us. The Meshchera peasants do not drink, or rather, they do drink, but only seldom and not much. They have to keep a steady hand and a keen eye at all times. But if a Meshchera man does break his fast, he wants to get all the pleasure he can. At such times he is no longer a reserved, pensive, and laconic man, but becomes sociable, noisy, and garrulous. As a rule, he talks only about Meshchera, which is like nothing else, different, unique. With a somewhat pugnacious arrogance, which is nevertheless not offensive to outsiders, Meshchera and everything in it are praised above all countries, towns, and villages. Our old man was no exception, and only waited for an opening to embark on his favorite topic.

Leonty Sergeyevich soon provided him with a suitable opening. The old man's grandson, a boy of about ten or eleven, was hanging around the table.

"Here is some candy for you," Leonty Sergeyevich said in a kindly voice, and stroked the boy's matted brown hair. "What grade are you in?"

"He's done with studies," his grandfather answered for him while the boy licked the chocolate, soft from being in Leonty Sergeyevich's pockets, off its wrapping. "He's already twelve years old."

"That seems a bit early for him to be through with school," Leonty Sergeyevich said, puzzled.

"Hereabouts only the girls go to school beyond the third grade," the old man explained with dignity.

"Why so?"

"What else? When a lad gets to be eleven, he is given a gun. Well, that's an end to his studies. In spring and in autumn there are ducks; in winter, hares."

"But what about universal compulsory education?" Leonty Sergeyevich said sternly.

"We are a people apart!" the old man stated with relish. "Meshchera!"

The old man drank up the vodka in his glass, shook his shaggy head, and said enigmatically and weightily, his eyes sparkling with joy: "Meshchera has to be understood!" He jabbed his thumb toward the black square of the window. "The fishermen from across the river fish with rods, and with nets, and with special rods for pike. Some have even bought reels. But we look down on all that. We catch fish only once a year, as we did in the old times, but then we get two hundred and fifty or three hundred kilograms in one catch."

"How do you do that?" I asked.

"Very simply," the old man explained as before, addressing Leonty Sergeyevich, who had earned his particular respect. "Did you see the canals? I mean the ditches between the lakes? In winter our river Pra freezes solid, almost to the bottom, and the fish simply suffocate there, you may say. Then we take scoops and drive clean water along the canals to the Pra. The fish smell this water and every last one makes for the canal. To make room for more of them we widen the mouth of the canal. They crowd in there in enormous numbers and all we have to do is to scoop them out."

"Who authorized you to do this?"

"What do you mean 'authorized'?" the old man asked proudly, looking past me at my companion. "We work under an agreement with the Fishing Administration."

"Ah-ah." Leonty Sergeyevich sighed with obvious relief.

"What else should we do? A fisherman makes an agreement to deliver two hundred or two hundred and fifty kilograms. He actually delivers some thirty kilograms and then takes the rest to the free market. It's very easy!"

"But that is cheating!" Leonty Sergeyevich said, screwing up his face as if he had a toothache.

"As the saying goes, if you don't cheat, you don't sell! We also hunt the year around. We couldn't do without it. This is Meshchera!"

"What kind of a password is that you have: Meshchera, Meshchera!" came a hoarse voice from behind the calico curtain on the stove.

At these words the old man gave a start, like a war horse hearing a bugle, but he remained silent. He did not care to converse with a curtain, considering this beneath his dignity, just as he did not care to talk to me: the difference in our ages was too great. He wanted to talk to Leonty Sergeyevich, an imposing man past forty, who looked like a family man with a great deal of experience.

"Meshchera! Meshchera!" said the man on the stove between fits of coughing. "You like to think that you're baked from different dough than we are!"

The grandfather looked hopefully at Leonty Sergeyevich. He probably wanted him to say something in support of this heretical idea. Then the old man would have been overjoyed to argue against it. But Leonty Sergeyevich's face became veiled by the familiar impenetrable cloud, his eyes fixed on some remote void where there existed neither the cottage that had given us shelter, nor the sociable and persistent oldster, nor the angry and sharp man on the stove shelf, nor any doubtful conversations into which people were trying to involve him.

After a considerable silence the old man tried a ruse. "What did you say?" he asked Leonty Sergeyevich. "I don't believe I understood."

"I did not say anything," Leonty Sergeyevich sullenly replied.

"You said something about us being sort of different. . . ."

"I did not say anything," Leonty Sergeyevich repeated, looking out of the corner of his eye at the stove and exclaiming in a high-pitched, irritated voice: "And I don't want to talk about anything—is that clear?"

There was an uncomfortable pause. In an effort to make

up for Leonty Sergeyevich's unpleasant outburst and to give it a different meaning, I said:

"You really do have some strange ideas, old fellow. You live right next to the capital, but your notions . . ." I could not find the word to describe his notions, and only shook my head.

The old man, somewhat disconcerted by Leonty Sergeyevich's incomprehensible outburst, was glad to respond to my remark.

"Whether or not we are right next to the capital depends on how you look at it. True, we live right on the border between Moscow and Ryazan lands, but how long do you think it takes a letter to get from here to Moscow?"

"I don't know: it should get there in a day. . . ."

"It should, that's right. And it gets there in a day if you send it through the Moscow mails, on the other side of the Pra. But if you mail it here, you're lucky if it gets there in eight or nine days. It's the same with letters coming to us: figure on their taking about ten days . . . So—how can I explain it to you?—" The old man continued, no longer cockily, as before, but rather pensively, "it seems that everything comes to us in a roundabout way, and late."

"You can say that again!" came from the stove shelf. "But the mails could have been straightened out."

"How would you go about it? My son wrote to the rayon newspaper, his letter was printed, he even got paid for it—six rubles. But the deliveries of mail stopped completely. And since then the village people call us 'journalists.' That's all we got out of it." The old man spat on the floor, rubbed the spittle with his foot, and continued:

"Right next to Moscow . . . And just try and find out how many of us have been in Moscow. About the women you don't even need to ask, and of the men—maybe you'll find two or three. Let alone Moscow, few have even been in Ryazan! Here I am in my sixties and the only town I have ever seen is Spas-Klepiki. Of course, the ones who served in the army naturally saw a lot of the world. . . . No, our way of life cannot be compared to anyone else's. There's only one word for it—Meshchera!" the old man concluded, having recovered his cockiness.

"Don't think you can speak for the whole of Meshchera,"

was heard from the stove. The calico curtain jerked and slid to one side. We saw the face of our traveling companion; it was no longer brick-red, but scarlet from fever. For some reason his hair had grown darker, and it fell in ringlets on his forehead as if it had been curled.

"Thank you for the medicine," he said to Leonty Sergeyevich, "thank you very much. . . . Listen, old fellow," he said, addressing the old man, "perhaps the whole trouble is just that you people are so different. You ought to try living the way other people do right here in Meshchera. Not everybody around here is a fool."

"And what would you be hinting at?" The old man addressed him for the first time.

"Hunting and fishing are all right in their place, but for a villager the basis of life is still the kolkhoz."

"Wha-a-at?" The old man screwed up his eyes and looked at Leonty Sergeyevich as though expecting him to confirm the statement. "The kolkho-o-oz?"

"Of course," Leonty Sergeyevich said in an official voice. "The kolkhoz is the foundation. . . ."

"Naturally," the old man said jubilantly, as if he had foreseen the turn the conversation would take. "We have a kolkhoz, and Dun'ka is the chairman."

"Who is she, this Dun'ka?" I asked.

"She's Dun'ka, that's who she is! This kolkhoz of ours was amalgamated, but the amalgamation is only on paper. Podsvyatye is cut off from us for almost half the year, and you can't get to Bolotnaya even in the summer if the weather isn't right. And what was the use of this amalgamation, anyway? We've never seen a combine in our lives here, they can't get through to us, and we don't care. The fields are small and broken up, it's mostly forest and marsh, but we still made a living out of it—the kolkhoz, that is. But after the amalgamation everything went to pieces. It's not even possible to get people together for a meeting."

"Wait a minute, Granddad, you were going to tell us about Dun'ka," said the man on the stove.

"I'm just coming to her. Our kolkhoz is now in such straits that we don't even get back what we plant. Sometimes when calves get into the kolkhoz buckwheat fields, people say: 'It's a good thing: the peasant gains, and the kolkhoz profits too—no need to harvest the buckwheat!'

That's how far things have gone. Obviously nobody wants
to be chairman of such a kolkhoz. The rayon assigned us a
man who used to run the communications office. He balked
—not under any conditions! 'Either you accept the chair-
manship,' they told him, 'or else turn in your Party card.'
He thought a while and decided: rather than kill himself
with work first and then lose his Party membership anyway,
he would get it over with right away. And he handed in
his card. Then they got after another man who had recently moved to the rayon from Moscow. They used the
same technique on him. So he said: 'This is just the kind
of business that drove me from Moscow. I've had enough
of it!' And then this Dun'ka turned up. She had worked
as a charwoman in a military sanitarium, but she comes
from here, from Podsvyatino. And who would have
guessed it—she was a candidate for the Party. She said:
'If you guarantee me four hundred rubles salary, I'll take
on the kolkhoz.' They were delighted in the town, and
put the deal through. . . ."

"Well, and what is she like?"

"What is she like? Dun'ka is just Dun'ka. She gets her
salary."

"But why did you elect her?"

"How's that?" The old man did not understand. "And
why shouldn't we elect her? Otherwise they would have
palmed off someone even worse on us."

"You sure know a lot about what goes on in town!"
said the man on the stove in a meaningful tone.

"We do know a lot, all right, but the town doesn't
know much about us. Our life is drab, dear comrades,
very drab!" said the old man sternly and sadly. "Everyone is moving somewhere, while only we seem to be stuck
in a morass and not to move either forward or backward. Is
the river Pra so very wide? With a tail wind it takes only
half an hour to cross it, and look how people across the
river live compared to how we live! They have electric
lights, and radios, and movies, they have a ten-year school,
a club, and they say that even actors from Moscow come
there. And we have kerosene lamps, and out of all three
of our villages only Anatoly Ivanovich in Podsvyatino—
you may have heard of him—has a radio. But, to save
his batteries, he doesn't listen to anything except the news.

We have become savages here, in the wilds, there is no denying it."

"But what's the trouble, what's the reason for it?" asked Leonty Sergeyevich, suddenly returning from his infinitely far-off haven. "That isn't right!"

"The trouble, dear friend, is that the authorities have forgotten about us."

"The authorities are one thing," said the man on the stove loudly, "but they're not the only cause of this. It's you who've got used to living badly, that's the real trouble."

The old fellow couldn't think of any answer to this and only shook his head, perhaps in agreement with the man, or perhaps in response to some thoughts of his own.

"So nobody from the rayon ever comes to see you?" I asked.

"Once in a while some instructors from the rayon committee come here, but what times they pick to do it! One will turn up at the height of the hunting season—another when the fish are running and naturally everyone is away. They gab with the chairman and then make tracks for home!"

"And what about the secretary of the rayon committee?"

"For about six years the chief secretary was a woman. How could she travel to this God-forsaken place? Later they put in a man, but people say he made it a rule never to set foot outside the town. Afterward there was another man, and he did come here once. He came right to us, to the most remote place, and at the most suitable time—in March!" The old man laughed for a long time, almost to the point of tears. It seemed that he never would stop laughing—he was so delighted with the secretary's trip.

"Well, and what came of it?"

"That's just it, nothing came of it," replied the old man, who had at last stopped laughing. "That year the roads were about as bad as they are now. The secretary was a brave man—he started out straight across Velikoye. Naturally the poor soul got drenched; he came ashore more dead than alive. He went into a cottage and immediately asked for vodka. The peasants were naturally overjoyed: nothing encourages a heart-to-heart talk like half a liter of vodka. They rigged up a sail on a boat and rushed off to Faleyevka, twelve kilometers away. They almost drowned, but they got a bottle. Then what did that secretary do but use it on his outsides instead of his insides: he rubbed himself with it from head to foot. Then he asked for horses, and was off for home. I heard that he has now been removed because of several affairs. . . . That is how the authorities take care of us!"

"That's a hell of a mess!" Leonty Sergeyevich suddenly burst out. With a short, excited, indignant gesture of his hand he seemed to reveal, as if for the first time, that his heart, which he had kept locked up and sealed with seven seals, was still there, still alive. "It's like a story out of Gogol! And living people are entrusted to dead souls like those!"

"Be patient, you can't have everything at once," the man on the stove said mockingly, tossing Leonty Sergeyevich's words back at him. "We have built so much!"

Evidently the man was far from being a simpleton and was much more observant than I had thought. Leonty Sergeyevich raised his eyebrows in surprise, and a deep red color spread slowly over his face.

"I understand your irony," he said softly, "but you will agree that this is worse than impassable roads."

"They're all links in the same chain," the man flung out sharply. "Houses with pillars that do not support anything; and a complete absence of roads side by side with superhighways; and what this old fellow has just told us. Now all this is more clear than ever before! But there still are some people around"—the man looked fixedly at Leonty Sergeyevich as if he were aiming a gun at him—"who are so used to misery, to memories of misery—well, it's just the way an invalid gets used to his illness. For so many years, even though they didn't want to, they have locked up inside themselves everything living, sincere, and bold that even now they can't make up their minds to live in the open. It's not hard to understand, but it's sad. . . ."

Leonty Sergeyevich was painfully embarrassed. All his features, his eyes, and his lashes moved jerkily.

"So that's how things are, Granddad," said the man in his usual voice, taking his eyes off Leonty Sergeyevich. "So you, too, realize that things can't go on this way!"

"What gave you that idea?" the old man said. "Nobody is complaining. We are a people apart! As long as there are fish to be caught and ducks to be shot, we are not dependent on anyone."

"And what if hunting were to be forbidden?" came the voice from the stove.

"What do you mean, 'forbidden'?"

"Just that—forbidden. All over Central Russia."

"Maybe they will forbid it in some places," said the old man confidently, "but not here in Meshchera!"

But apparently the thought had stung him, because he asked immediately, with a note of alarm: "What about it? Has there been some talk of it?"

"Not only talk, but a resolution has been prepared," the man replied firmly. "As regards next spring—it is a fact. And perhaps even for the entire year, or two years. The cold has moved farther south, the birds are being frozen out of their wintering places; they are dying from lack of food. Take the swans—they are hardy birds, and even they are dying out. . . ."

"That's too bad!" the old man said with sincere sorrow. "It is right to forbid hunting so the birds can replenish themselves. But this wouldn't concern us; we will go on shooting as we've always done."

"Don't the laws apply to you?"

"They don't, dear comrade. Hunting is not a sport for us, it is our livelihood."

"Poaching causes as much damage as the frosts in the south. . . ."

"You wouldn't, by chance, be a game warden, would you?" asked the old man suspiciously.

"In a manner of speaking, yes," said the man, with just a trace of a smile.

"Then I'll tell you something: you don't know Meshchera. Even when others have nothing, we have plenty. Meshchera will never run out of game."

"Is that what you think, old man?" asked the man almost sadly. "And where is the Meshchera beaver now?"

"You have something there," the old man agreed willingly; "we did kill off the beavers."

"And how many elks do you have left?"

"We overdid things a bit with the elks, too."

"And what became of the otters?"

"We cleaned out the otters completely," rejoined the old man animatedly with satisfaction, as if he, at last, had got the better of his opponent. "Otters eat fish. We have a rule: when you go to the river, take your gun along, and show them no mercy, the vermin. So don't you worry about otters. . . ."

"Say, old man, you haven't noticed that in recent years there have been less fish?" the man asked, still softly, but with a kind of hypnotic insistence.

Perhaps sensing this insistence, I suddenly realized that the man on the stove was not talking idly, to kill time, or to get the better of an argument, like a person who simply likes to talk. No, it looked as if he had an ulterior purpose, that he had had it before he took command of the conversation. I saw that Leonty Sergeyevich was also listening keenly to the discussion.

"There are plenty of fish!" said the old fellow light-heartedly, but right away he corrected himself with the honesty of an old man. "Of course, there aren't as many as there used to be, but there are still enough to live on."

"Eh, you queer old man." The man shook his head reprovingly. "It is just because you destroyed the otters that there are fewer fish. The otters eat only weak, sickly fish; they cannot catch the strong, healthy ones. Once the otters are gone, sickness spreads among the fish. . . ."

"Maybe so," the old man agreed softly. "It is true that there is a balance in nature." He was now listening very attentively to what the man was saying, but was still reluctant to give in. "Meshchera has plenty of birds. . . ."

"And where are the wood-grouse, Granddad? And the black grouse, the woodcock, the curlew?"

"We do not have any pine-forest game here. I am in my sixties, and I have never seen any wood-grouse or black grouse hereabouts. And this—what do you call it?—curlew . . . I have never even heard the name!"

"Is that so!" said the man, and dug his hand into the breast pocket of his blouse. He took out a wad of tightly folded worn papers and separated from it a thin sheet of paper on which there was something printed. "Here, listen to what was written in *The Hunting Magazine* seventy-five years ago: '. . . The wooded shores of the river Pra have long been famous for their breeding grounds for wood-grouse and black grouse. Unfortunately, as a result of the violation of hunting regulations and hunting seasons and the killing of hens in the breeding grounds, these valuable birds are now disappearing!' What do you say, old man? And in about fifty years people will say: 'Ducks? But there have never been any ducks here, in Meshchera . . .' "

"Wait a minute." The old man suddenly jumped up from the bench and ran into the passage; the outside door slammed softly, letting in a smell of dampness.

The old man did not return alone; he brought back four neighbors with him. They came in as people do when they are late for a meeting, stepping carefully, keeping their eyes straight ahead, not saying hello to anyone, holding their caps in their hands. They sat down close together on the bench nearest the door.

"Our peasants," the old man said. "They are also curious about what concerns Meshchera. Won't you repeat it?"

"Surely," the man promptly agreed, and jumped down from the stove.

With his back pressed against the warm stove, he stood up in front of everyone in his worn military breeches and woolen socks with reinforced heels, his face red from fever and his head wet with sweat—not tall, but wiry, compact, and sharp. Interrupting himself with his hollow cough, he told about the beavers, and the elks, and the otters, and about the pine-forest game, and read again the clipping from the magazine. One of the newcomers, a husky fellow with a ruddy face surrounded by a bristly, long, unshaven, coal-black beard, slapped his knee with his palm and said loudly:

"Right!"

Apparently this coincided with some private thoughts and observations he had never voiced before, and it seemed to me that after his corroboration our old host and the other Meshchera men gave up any further doubts about the truth of what the stranger was saying.

"All this may be so, but the game will last for our lifetime," the old man said with his former cockiness, breaking a long and uneasy silence.

"Of course, it will last your lifetime, all right—you already have one foot in the grave," said the red-cheeked hunter viciously. "Perhaps it will even last my lifetime, but what'll be left for my children? No, I don't agree to that! . . ."

The other three men expressed their approval by shuffling their feet, clearing their throats, and sighing.

The old man looked with childish, helpless resentment

at the man by the stove. "What did you have to come here for?" he said heatedly. "All you've done is make us all feel bad."

"If you are afraid of the truth . . ." The other shrugged.

"You don't have to worry: you came, said your say, and now you'll go off. But we have to go on living here."

"That's just what I want to talk to you about."

"What's the use of talking to you?" the old man said with a wry smile. "One would think you were the rayon secretary himself!"

"Right, old fellow, I am the secretary," came the calm reply. "I was elected two weeks ago." Hunting makes a man resourceful and self-possessed; the old man's stupefaction lasted only a second.

"I sure showed you up nicely!" said the old man, looking around at everyone with laughing eyes. "Do you imagine that if I had not figured you out right away, I would have gabbed with you like that? I knew who you were by your gun. As if anyone would go hunting with such a piece of junk! So now let's introduce ourselves formally, comrade first secretary of the rayon committee. . . ."

I glanced at Leonty Sergeyevich. Some sort of subtle change had taken place in his appearance; his eyes were quite different. Yet not entirely different—he had probably had eyes like that before it had ever occurred to him to give up all the strength of his living soul to the study of Khazar ornaments.

[Daniil Granin (born 1919) is a Leningrad novelist and short-story writer whose reputation has been growing in recent years. His novel *Those Who Seek* (1954) was widely praised, and despite the "slips" he committed in 1956 he has gone on to new success with *After the Wedding* (1958).

"One's Own Opinion," from *Novy Mir,* No. 8 (August 1956), is an interesting attempt to provide an internal, psychological view of the pressures that tend to corrupt Soviet officials—the power of high position, influence, and "pull," the fear of changes that might upset someone's applecart, the ruthless treatment meted out to "troublemakers." But according to one critic, at least, Granin's chief mistake in this story was not so much in depicting these things, which admittedly exist, but in failing to straighten things out at the end. The note of melancholy and defeat is especially reprehensible and un-Soviet, for it may "instill in the hearts of readers, especially young ones without much real experience of life, an unwarranted pessimistic attitude toward their surroundings . . . [at a time when] international reaction is trying desperately to shake the foundations of the Soviet state. . . ." [V. Baksakov: *"O smelosti podlinnoi i mnimoi (On True Boldness and Pseudo-Boldness),"* *Oktiabr'*, No. 1 (January 1957), p. 199.]

ONE'S OWN OPINION

D. Granin

The arrogant stubbornness of the young engineer exasperated Minayev and at the same time strangely attracted him. Olkhovsky had not agreed to a single one of Minayev's requests. With his thin, nervous fingers he kept reaching for the cap to Minayev's inkwell and pushing it around the glass top of the desk. The unpleasant piercing squeak blended with the unpleasant significance of what Olkhovsky was saying and the impression made by his article, which had that same unpleasant sharpness. Actually, the main reason the article was annoying was that it was irrefutably right: Olkhovsky had conclusively proved that the new engines designed by academician Stroyev were uneconomical. Minayev could not allow such an article to be published. There was no use explaining to this young upstart that criticism of academician Stroyev would only cause a lot of trouble, both for the Institute and for Minayev himself, whose position as director had yet to be confirmed.

"I am asking you as a friend: throw out all this stuff about Stroyev," Minayev said softly. "And you ought to tone down the critical part here. That way it will be easier to get it published."

Olkhovsky jumped up. His pale face turned red and his small hands were clenched into fists.

"What would be the point of my article then? There wouldn't be any point at all!" he exclaimed in his thin voice. "Don't you see this will cause thousands of tons of fuel to be wasted? How can you——" His level eyebrows were raised in perplexity. "No. No changes. Not for anything. Why, it's dishonorable."

A fine fellow, Minayev thought. Something in Olkhovsky's bearing was startlingly familiar. Suddenly Minayev saw before him an old, long-forgotten scene, when he, Minayev, in this same way, had clenched his fists and shouted in his ringing, cracked voice. He too had once had the same tousled hair, the same Komsomol button in the lapel of a threadbare jacket. The recollection was a moving one, but there was no sign of emotion now in Minayev's faded, heavy-lidded eyes, half closed in weariness. In the corners of his mouth his heavy, energetic face kept a permanently indefinite expression that could be interpreted to mean anything.

"You all like to toss that word 'honor' around," Minayev said coldly. "But try to put it into practice. Yes, comrade Olkhovsky," he repeated with malicious satisfaction. "Don't just make proclamations. Try to carry them out. That is when certain things have to be sacrificed."

Olkhovsky leaned over the desk. His black eyes looked contemptuously at Minayev from under his tousled hair.

"What about you, Vladimir Pakhomovich? Have you earned the right to be a man of honor yet?"

The boyish insolence of the question angered Minayev. But, smiling that benevolent, friendly smile that always came to his rescue in difficult moments, he said indulgently: "Be careful. You'll upset the inkwell."

Olkhovsky blushed and moved back.

"Now you see," Minayev continued: "it's important to stop at the right time."

The conversation left Minayev with an oppressive feeling. Never mind; the most important thing now was the order confirming him as director. Then he would be able to help Olkhovsky; then he would have nothing to fear even from Stroyev. He could maintain his own opinion against anyone at all. It wasn't enough just to have opinions. You had to be in a position to do something about them. Such thoughts usually soothed Minayev. They always appeared obligingly whenever events took an unpleasant turn.

Soon afterward Minayev received an inquiry about Olkhovsky's article, signed by Loktev, the instructor of the City Party Committee. Attached to the inquiry was a letter written by Olkhovsky himself. The letter made Minayev angry. "Minayev's cowardly policy is strengthening Stroyev's Arakcheyevism. . . . It is time that Minayev, in his position, allowed himself the luxury of defending his own opinions. . . ." Why, the puppy! The insolent whelp! He's a little too smart for his own good.

Minayev wrote the reply himself. It was concise and polite, yet at the same time murderously venomous. He played to the very limit on Loktev's suspicious nature, which he knew only too well. Olkhovsky was represented as a squabbler, an intriguer, a person who habitually wasted everybody's time with his importunities. His article was simply absurd and libelous. In places Minayev's letter sounded unsubstantiated, but Minayev knew that the more unsubstantiated it was, the more convincing it became. As he was signing the paper, his pen scratched awkwardly, and he scowled at the scraping noise. Well, what else could he do? He couldn't risk everything, just when all his hopes were about to be realized, because of the obstinacy of this young rascal. It was Olkhovsky himself who had forced him to write this way. Never mind, never mind; he'd make it all up later. Olkhovsky's case was added to the long list of matters that had been put aside until after Minayev's appointment went through.

Minayev deeply respected Petrishchev, the deputy minister, and it was probably for this reason that he felt annoyed when Petrishchev arrived at the Institute. In Petrishchev's presence Minayev always experienced an obscure and constraining feeling of undefined guilt. Of course this quite useless feeling did not in the least hinder Minayev from smiling and joking; at times he was even astonished at the way his voice, his hands, and the muscles of his face operated with such well-trained independence.

Minayev took Petrishchev through the laboratories, informed him about the kind of work they were doing, and listened to his critical observations. Although Minayev himself had made these same criticisms to his subordinates, he asked his assistant to make a note of them, believing that this kind of attention was pleasing to Petrishchev.

While demonstrating an oscillator in one of the laboratories, Minayev saw Olkhovsky shoulder his way toward

the deputy minister. He was paler than usual. His sharp
chin was trembling. His wide-open black eyes looked
out with a mixture of fear and hope. Every moment that
Olkhovsky waited added to his indecision, and Minayev,
understanding this, switched on the apparatus. A roaring
noise rose to the ceiling like a geyser and showered down
into the room, filling it solidly with sound. Minayev looked
threateningly at Olkhovsky, trying to stop him, to show
him how inopportunely he had come thrusting himself
forward with his petition. After all, there was only about
a week or so left to wait. Olkhovsky's self-centeredness
exasperated him, but when the latter at last began to
speak, Minayev grew calm.

Instead of coming to the point right away, Olkhovsky
got tangled up in a long prepared introduction, talking
about the causes of old-fogyism and about the system
of accountability. Nobody could make out what he wanted.
Minayev discerned sympathetic attention in the expression
of the deputy minister and suddenly felt embarrassed for
Olkhovsky. Well, what is he driving at, the blockhead?
What sniveling theory is he going to spin now? Minayev
cursed inwardly. What a muddlehead! He'll be interrupted
before he knows it.

"Excuse me," said Petrishchev. "But what exactly do
you want?"

Olkhovsky lapsed into embarrassed silence, still moving
his dry lips soundlessly. Minayev lowered his eyes. Lord,
what an inept young idiot! Olkhovsky groped in his pocket,
jerked out a manuscript, all dog-eared along the folds, and
thrust it at Petrishchev. The deputy minister smoothed out
the curled-up papers. Inside, there was a crumpled-up ruble
and some tobacco crumbs. Someone snickered. The deputy
minister, unable to contain himself, handed the ruble to
Olkhovsky and burst out laughing. Immediately everyone
around began laughing too. There was nothing offensive
in this laughter. In a case like this the victim ought to
laugh along with the others, make a joke out of it. But
Olkhovsky blushed painfully, and his face twisted into
an awkward, embarrassed smile. It looked as if at any
moment he might burst into tears.

"Please look into this yourself," Olkhovsky said quickly,
with that desperation that comes when nothing matters
any more—you have only a minute left, and you might as

well say what you mean. "Or you can send it—I tried—
Vladimir Pakhomovich—"

"We will certainly look into it," the deputy minister
said unhurriedly, with accentuated calm.

When they returned to Minayev's office, Petrishchev
asked about the manuscript the young engineer had given
him.

Feeling it would be unwise to disclose his fears regarding Stroyev, Minayev began: "The manuscript . . ."
Then he paused. "I think perhaps the chief of the division
where Olkhovsky works might be able to evaluate it better
than I can."

There's nothing else I can do, he thought in self-defense,
picturing in advance everything that would happen.

The division chief noted Olkhovsky's interesting methods
of calculation and immediately added that a careful check
was needed, but without all this mutineering, uproar, complaints, and letters. He was trying not to injure Minayev
in any way and at the same time to preserve complete
objectivity toward Olkhovsky.

"I never dreamed he was such a malcontent," Petrishchev said with surprise.

"We studied at the same university," said Minayev's
consultant. "He was always a little bit . . ." The consultant twirled his finger in front of his temple.

Minayev knew that his assistant had said this because
he thought he, Minayev, wanted him to say it, but all
the same he had gone too far.

"We do have such people, of course," said the deputy
minister. "They scribble letters, demand investigation com-
missions, push their way through like battering rams. And
then it turns out to be utter gibberish. There are people,
on the other hand, who are falsely accused of being mere
troublemakers." He frowned, evidently at some recollection
of his own.

"Anyway, whatever may be the matter with him, the
problem itself deserves looking into," said Minayev quickly,
with that gruff independence that Petrishchev liked.

Petrishchev agreed, as though entrusting the fate of
Olkhovsky's manuscript to him. And although Minayev
was pleased at this trust, it aroused in him a vague feeling
of guilt. Minayev consoled himself: he was not morally
indebted to Petrishchev in any way. Petrishchev had been

obliged to agree; he couldn't express lack of confidence in the person he intended to confirm as director. There was nothing you could do about such things: sometimes you made people do what you wanted, but sometimes they made you do what they wanted. That's just the way things were at the present.

Now that the problem was settled, he suddenly felt sorry for Olkhovsky. Essentially they had convinced Petrishchev that Olkhovsky was a malcontent and a harmful eccentric. That was bad. To ruin a fellow simply because he was clumsy about defending the truth as he saw it—that was wrong.

What a pleasure it would be to send to the devil all these considerations and calculations and say everything he really thought! But Minayev's lips remained firmly pressed together. He sat in his chair listening to the deputy minister's comments, and his heavy face expressed only imperturbable attentiveness.

Once he became director, Minayev forgot about Olkhovsky in the rush of new business, and only a letter from the main administration reminded him of the affair. Again there was a letter by Olkhovsky attached to the inquiry. Bitterly and ineptly, he was still carrying on his hopeless campaign. In his simpleheartedness Olkhovsky scorned the typewriter, and for this reason even the outward appearance of his letters, written in a round, childish hand on pages torn from a school tablet, did not dispose the reader to take them seriously.

The first paragraphs were written out carefully. Later the letters became more and more askew, the lines bent hurriedly at the ends, and Minayev was certain that no one but himself had ever read the letter through.

With naïve ferocity Olkhovsky attacked the system of publishing scientific works. "A pernicious system of evasion of responsibility has set in," he wrote. "Why print a scientific article which is caustic or controversial? You might have to answer for it, you might be rebuked for it. But if you turn the article down, no one will ever hold you responsible."

Correct observation, Minayev thought. Judging by everything, the young fellow was really trying to get to the heart of the matter. Olkhovsky was now less disturbed about the fate of his own work than he was perplexed about the nature of the dense, impenetrable barrier he had come up against for the first time in his life. His anger had made his ideas deeper and more mature. Remorsefully Minayev discerned in them faint notes of embitterment and occasional despair. He delayed sending an answer to the main administration, intending to consider at his leisure some way of helping Olkhovsky. A certain instinct which he had developed over the years held him back from a premature attack on Stroyev. He needed to consolidate his position. These thoughts surprised Minayev. Here he was, director at last, and it turned out that nothing had changed.

At a Party meeting, Olkhovsky criticized Loktev, the instructor of the City Party Committee, for complete lack of understanding of the nature of scientific work, for "dull indifference to vital ideas." Olkhovsky's recklessness alarmed Minayev. Everything Olkhovsky said was true, but Olkhovsky did not realize that precisely because of his own limitations, Loktev would not allow a single attack against himself to go unpunished. Sooner or later he found a convenient moment to trip you up, started whispering campaigns, spread rumors, stopped at nothing.

When he heard that Olkhovsky was fearlessly assailing such a powerful opponent, Minayev felt both pity and sympathy. He even groaned with vexation: pity was all very well, but there was no way to give him any real help. Olkhovsky had gone too far; to support him openly would mean to enter into conflict with too many influential people. In the depths of his heart Minayev keenly envied Olkhovsky's reckless daring. Here was a man who felt he had nothing to lose, and no doubt he considered prudence cowardice and patience weakness.

The day after the meeting, Minayev put the inquiry and Olkhovsky's letter into a folder marked "Consultant, for reply." That afternoon the consultant, a young man with smoothly combed hair and a yellowish, pale face, wearing glasses with frames of the same yellow color, entered the office, stepping quietly on his thick rubber soles. He gave Minayev a paper to be signed, a printed form with the Institute's attractive seal on it. The vaguely favorable tenor of the reply provided no grounds for objection and left open the possibility of postponing decision indefinitely.

From under his weary, half-closed eyelids, Minayev looked curiously at the impassive face of his consultant.

"What's your opinion of Olkhovsky? An able fellow, notwithstanding?"

"Yes," the consultant said, inclining his smoothly combed head. "He is able."

Minayev felt like asking: "And what would you write, my obliging friend, if you were sitting in my place?" But Minayev had learned something about people, and he therefore said, maintaining the same interrogative tone: "It seems simple to you now, but what if you were academician Stroyev?"

For the first time Minayev saw his assistant come to life. He scratched his head vigorously and somehow youthfully, disarraying his beautifully parted hair.

"Vladimir Pakhomovich, I would publish it without even thinking. After all, such a saving of—"

"Aha! Then why do you compose replies like this for me," Minayev asked quickly, "if it goes against your own opinion? Why do you behave like Molchalin?"

The consultant slowly and forcefully smoothed back his disheveled hair. "I write the way you want me to in order someday to be able to write the way I see fit," he said, and looked Minayev squarely in the eye.

"Oho! And you think that will happen someday?" Minayev smiled thoughtfully. Taking a thick blue pencil from the glass, he signed the letter in a bold hand.

Olkhovsky no longer made any attempt to approach Minayev. Minayev ran into him several times in the Institute corridors, but Olkhovsky walked past with his head lowered gloomily, his long arms hanging down as though they belonged to someone else. Minayev longed to stop him, to speak frankly to him, to give him a little advice. He should try to be patient. Soon he, Minayev, would be making a trip to the Collegium of the Ministry; there he would have a chance to put in a word with someone. But he felt that Olkhovsky would not understand him, and this piqued Minayev. He wanted to show that it was not his fault, that very little depended on him.

Just before his departure for the Collegium, Minayev was called to the City Party Committee. He knew that Loktev was trying to get Olkhovsky dismissed. But, after all, what is Loktev? Only the instructor in the City

Party Committee. What right had he to interfere in my affairs? If it were necessary to dismiss Olkhovsky, I would do it myself. Since when do I have to indulge the petty wounded vanity of this careerist? No, I've had enough. Loktev isn't my boss. He has no business giving me orders. It would be different if he were secretary of the City Committee, but he's only an instructor. I have grown beyond you, comrade Loktev; it's a different situation now. Yes, that's just what he, Minayev, would say: it's a different situation—that's absolutely clear. In his thoughts Minayev repeated this last phrase meaningfully, with a slight ironical smile. While riding up to the City Committee building, he mechanically passed his hand over his smoothly shaven chin, straightened his tie, and then suddenly caught himself, annoyed at this old habit of his. Enough of that. The time had come when he could allow himself some independence; he was no lower down than any other director. Especially on this occasion he could—he must—bring Loktev out into the open. Climbing up the broad staircase of the City Committee, Minayev raised his head high. In the lines of his heavy face a hard decisiveness appeared in place of the usual reserve.

He came out of the Party Committee an hour later. It was beginning to rain. Small droplets covered the asphalt with a rash. Minayev stood for a long time beside his automobile. Innumerable moist speckles broke out on the gray asphalt. Drops were falling on Minayev's topcoat; he felt them like gentle pellets on his shoulders.

"Get in, Vladimir Pakhomovich," said the driver. Minayev raised his head and looked at the driver in surprise.

"Drive on without me," he said, and slammed the car door shut.

The Zim drove away, leaving a sharp outline on the street of the place where it had been parked. Minayev watched the raindrops spotting the bright, dry rectangle.

"Drive on," he repeated, listening to the sound of his own voice.

He started walking forward. Whichever way he went, it would be considered forward. He could walk to the square; he could turn into the river embankment. The one thing he could not do was to return to the City Committee. No matter what he told himself, no matter how hard he tried to convince himself. There had been few occasions in his life when he had been forced to take a good look at himself. No, that wasn't it; he thought of himself often enough, tried to anticipate every action he might take so as to keep control over his tongue. But to think about why he had done one thing and not another—that was something he had no time for. That's where this bothersome psychology business began. The practiced adroitness with which he was now steering himself away from dangerous thoughts began to amuse him. "And what happened in the City Committee?" he suddenly asked himself point-blank. Loktev had openly and crudely proposed that Olkhovsky be transferred to the experimental station at Nikolayev. Listening to Loktev, Minayev had asked himself by what right did this colorless ignoramus, this obtuse functionary, with his lifeless face that somehow looked as if it were left over from last year, who had never created anything and was incapable of creating anything—by what right did he sit here and decide the fate of people like Olkhovsky? And about the crux of the whole problem, the Stroyev engines, Loktev had not asked a single question, even for the sake of appearances. He didn't give a damn about that! He had been quite certain that Minayev would do what he, Loktev, wanted. Where did he get this vile assurance?

The last ice was moving thickly down the river. In places the river was quite white, as though still frozen over. The big heaps of ice which had piled up on the granite stanchions of the bridge were cracking softly. Jagged chunks, whirling, vanished beneath the spans. Bending over the rail, Minayev looked down. The bridge seemed to be moving while the ice stood still. Cold radiated from the black water; the long glittering crystals of ice tinkled as they broke against the granite and sank sparkling beneath the water. Minayev, getting hold of himself, pushed away from the rail. Something seemed to pierce his chest, and he suddenly felt hot. Taking off his hat, he wiped the sweat away with his sleeve. The cold raindrops seemed to burn his hot skin.

He felt old and permanently weary. Suddenly he saw himself as if he were someone else: a bald, flabby man, with a swollen face, walking along the bridge, clenching his hat in his hand. God, how quickly he had grown old!

When had it happened? He, Volodya Minayev, soloist in the school chorus, secretary of the Party cell in his university department. He suddenly felt scared: was he really an old man already?

With startling clarity Volodya Minayev appeared before him, bright-eyed, with a thin neck like a chicken's, the way he had been when he arrived at Selkhomazh. He remembered the story of the motor-suspension rack. Perhaps it had all begun with that? The shop chief had told him: "Look, Minayev, it's a little too early for you to start shoving yourself forward. What do you think a little weakling like you can do against the chief designer? He'll fix you for good. What are you? A foreman. They swallow people like you without even chewing." He remembered his own humiliating helplessness when the chief designer, sipping tea, had listened to his impassioned oration and then said, deliberately garbling his name: "Listen, Linyayev. If you stick your nose in here once more with this nonsense, I'll kick you right out of the plant. You can go." Minayev and some friends of his had resisted nevertheless, gone running about arguing and demonstrating. All in vain. They could have wasted three, five, or ten years in this hopeless struggle and would have achieved nothing.

There had been three of them. First one had been fired from the plant, then another. It was Minayev's turn. At this point he pretended to give in. He consoled himself that it was only a temporary surrender. He had first to make his way in the world, gain some independence and authority; then he would smash these bureaucrats. So, gritting his teeth, he advanced toward his goal. He was made a deputy shop chief. He taught himself to be patient and hold his tongue. For the sake of that day when he would be able to do what was needed. He swore to himself that he would endure everything. He kowtowed to dull ignoramuses. He voted "yes" when his conscience demanded that he vote "no." He said things he did not believe. He praised things he should have censured. When situations became completely unbearable, he kept silent. Silence is the most convenient form of lying. It knows how to keep peace with the conscience; it craftily preserves your right to withhold your personal opinion on the grounds that someday you will have a chance to express it.

But not just yet. Not while you are in the position
of shop chief and not when you are only chief of the
Engineering Department and not chief engineer of the plant.
And not while you are defending your dissertation. Too
early yet. Every time it had been too early! And the list
of his moral debts had grown. Life had brought forth new
ideas and had run up against new obstacles. How many
Olkhovskys he had left behind! Tirelessly, like an ant, he
had raised up the structure of his own position, striving
to make it ever stronger. For what? What had he gained?
The higher he climbed, the less of his real life remained
and the more difficult it became for him to take risks.
What was stopping him? How did other people manage to
do this? How had Petrishchev been able to? Petrishchev
had been unjustly punished, demoted, and dismissed, but
he had always pushed his way through, followed his own
path, and won out. No, nothing was topping Minayev;
he just found life easier this way. Or so he thought. And
when Loktev, waving a copy of his reply to the Party
Committee's inquiry, had accused him of hypocrisy—"You
write one thing and say another: what do you want me to
do, report this to the secretary?"—Minayev had understood
that for Loktev there was no need to worry about scruples.
He had the right to be outspoken. And now Minayev had
to retreat; it was easier that way.

Everything that Loktev proposed was base, thoroughly
base, but something else had struck Minayev. Loktev at
any rate could say what he wanted. Loktev and Olkhovsky.
Everyone else who was mixed up in this business—every
one of them—thought one thing and said another. Everyone, starting with Minayev himself and ending with his
consultant. Each in his own way was a hypocrite and a
liar. No doubt it was for this reason that Loktev could
afford not to lie.

What a scoundrel! Minayev had thought with hatred,
looking at Loktev's empty eyes. Throw him out of the
Committee on his ear! Not just out of the Committee—
such people should be thrown out of the Party. A spiteful
nobody! If he were thrown out of here, he couldn't even
get a job as a store manager! The more hatred and contempt he felt for Loktev, the more calmly he attempted
to persuade him; but when Loktev began to insist and
threaten, Minayev requested that the question be set

aside for several days. Soberly reckoning up the unpleasant-
nesses to which Loktev had the power to subject him, he
hoped to enlist support in Moscow.

"But don't drag it out," Loktev had said in parting.
"You yourself wrote that Olkhovsky was a troublemaker.
We've got to clean up this Institute and provide a healthier
atmosphere."

What a louse you are, Minayev thought as he firmly
shook Loktev's hand.

In Moscow, at the Collegium, the Institute was taken
to task for non-fulfillment of the plan, and even though
in the majority of cases the Ministry itself was at fault,
there was no point in arguing about it, as Minayev was
considered a newcomer, and all the shortcomings were
laid at the door of the previous management. Moreover,
this tactic enabled Minayev to obtain authorizations for
procuring some scarce equipment. In this ticklish problem
of procurement, the Institute's request was supported by
academician Stroyev, and after this it would have been
embarrassing for Minayev to bring up the Olkhovsky
affair. The hustle and scurry of a business trip to Moscow
left Minayev no time to think of the Olkhovsky case,
which here in Moscow seemed somehow trivial. Only
on the train, when he was alone in a compartment of the
half-empty sleeping car, did Minayev become conscious of
it again. It was the rain, no doubt, that was responsible.
It had begun imperceptibly, covering the window with
little slanting spangles. Tiny droplets threaded their way
downward in zigzags, blended with other drops on their
path, and slid downward jerkily, but at a quickened pace.
Minayev sighed, remembering the promise he had given
to Loktev. Loktev was undoubtedly fuming with rage there
at home. There was no help for it; Olkhovsky would have
to be transferred to Nikolayev. But only temporarily, until
the storm blew over.

Against the dense black background of the night the
double window, like two mirrors, showed the reflection
of a heavy figure in striped pajamas, a swollen face with
a cigarette in the corner of a firmly closed mouth, and
beyond it still another, dimmer figure, covered with sparkles
of rain. The cigarette smoke touching the cold glass spread
out in bluish clinging tendrils. Through them, out of the
black depths of the window, that other self looked at

Minayev, that young self, with a wet cap, wearing the
worn jacket of his student days. Rivulets of water trickled
over his pale cheeks and his slender chicken's neck. *You
see, you put if off again. What a worthless person you are!
It makes me sorry just to look at you.* A person has to cope
with things as they are; it's easy to indulge in fantasies
when you don't know anything about life, but I do
know it: I've studied it. *You promised to become your
real self. Wait till they make me director, you said. Wait
till I get established, but right now . . ."* You child! As
though a director were a god. If I worked in the Ministry,
I wouldn't be dependent on Loktev. I would be able to—.
*Think. Who is Loktev? You could snap your fingers at
his threats. You should have gone to the secretary of the
City Committee, even to the Central Committee.* I honestly
did and am doing all that I can. And everything will
turn out all right with Olkhovsky. I'll bring him back.
*No, you've not only betrayed your friends, not only
Olkhovsky: you've betrayed me, your own youth. How
could I believe you now?* Those are high-sounding words.
I can't stand high-sounding words. If I am retreating now,
it's only so that later I will be able to help more people
than just Olkhovsky. I have a large Institute on my
shoulders where I can support dozens of Olkhovskys.

And there was still a third Minayev who listened to the
old Minayev trying adroitly to pacify the young one, confidently proving the inevitability of everything that had
occurred, and promising to help Olkhovsky as soon as
the proper situation presented itself. This third Minayev
knew that none of this would ever happen. He would always be trying to outmaneuver himself, playing this endless
game, not having the strength to break out of the prison
of his own duplicity. He would always find justifications.
He would always aim to become an honest man tomorrow.

The blue filaments of smoke clouded over the wet face
there behind the glass. Together with the past, it swam
away into the darkness of the night. Where do past
events go? The only thing that remained was the sense
of expectation. It seemed that all these years had been filled
with endless waiting.

Minayev was met by his consultant at the station next
morning. Dressing unhurriedly, Minayev listened to the
latest news from the Institute.

"Oh, by the way," he said, "didn't Loktev, from the City Committee, telephone me?"

"Several times."

"I see," said Minayev.

They moved slowly through the crowd on the platform, past the car in which Minayev had ridden. He glanced at the window of his compartment. The dusty panes of glass reflected nothing. All you could see through them, in the dim light inside the compartment, were an unmade bed and a dirty ash tray full of cigarette stubs.

HUGH McLEAN was born in Denver, Colorado, in 1925. After undergraduate work at Yale, Mr. McLean went to Columbia, where he received his master's degree in 1949; subsequently he was an instructor in the Department of Slavic Languages and Literatures at Harvard and, after being awarded the Ph.D. there, remained for three years as Assistant Professor. Mr. McLean now teaches Russian literature at the University of Chicago. He was a fellow of the American Council of Learned Societies and has done research at the University of London on a Fulbright fellowship. Mr. McLean is co-editor of *Russian Thought and Politics* and of *For Roman Jakobson,* and author of numerous articles published in scholarly journals, including "On Mr. Pont Kič and his Ruptured Russian, On Sur-English, Vladimir Majakovskij, the Beasts at Dinner, and Related Subjects."

WALTER VICKERY was born in London in 1921. After serving in the Royal Navy during the Second World War, Mr. Vickery received his bachelor's degree at Oxford in 1948. He remained for the next five years as lecturer at Oxford, with the exception of a British Foreign Office appointment in 1951–2 to the Soviet Union. In 1953 Mr. Vickery moved to Canada. Two years later he began working for a Ph.D. at Harvard, where he held Ford Foundation and Samuel S. Fels fellowships. He received his degree in 1958, and from that time until the present has been teaching in the Department of Slavic Languages and Literatures at Indiana University. He is the author of several articles and a forthcoming book on recent developments in Soviet literature.

The text of this book was set on the Linotype in Times Roman, designed by Stanley Morison for *The Times* (London), and first introduced by that newspaper in 1932. The book was composed, printed, and bound by THE COLONIAL PRESS INC., Clinton, Massachusetts. Cover design by PAUL BACON.

VINTAGE FICTION, POETRY, AND PLAYS

VINTAGE HISTORY AND CRITICISM
OF LITERATURE, MUSIC, AND ART

A free catalogue of VINTAGE BOOKS will be sent to you at your request. Write to Vintage Books, Inc., 457 Madison Avenue, New York 22, New York.

VINTAGE WORKS OF SCIENCE
AND PSYCHOLOGY

VINTAGE POLITICAL SCIENCE
AND SOCIAL CRITICISM

VINTAGE HISTORY
EUROPEAN

A free catalogue of VINTAGE BOOKS will be sent to you at your request. Write to Vintage Books, Inc., 457 Madison Avenue, New York 22, New York.

VINTAGE HISTORY
AMERICAN

A free catalogue of VINTAGE BOOKS will be sent to you at your request. Write to *Vintage Books, Inc., 457 Madison Avenue, New York 22, New York.*

VINTAGE RUSSIAN LIBRARY